SCHOLASTIC

National Curriculum
MATHS

Teacher's
PLANNING &
ASSESSMENT
GUIDE

Years 5–6

Key Stage 2

Scholastic Education, an imprint of Scholastic Ltd
Book End, Range Road, Witney, Oxfordshire, OX29 0YD
Registered office: Westfield Road, Southam,
Warwickshire CV47 0RA
www.scholastic.co.uk

123456789 6789012345

British Library Cataloguing-in-Publication Data
A catalogue record for this book is available from the British Library.

ISBN 978-1-407-16027-6

Printed and bound by Ashford Colour Press

Due to the nature of the web we cannot guarantee the content or links of any site mentioned. We strongly recommend that teachers check websites before using them in the classroom.

Every effort has been made to trace copyright holders for the works reproduced in this book, and the publishers apologise for any inadvertent omissions.

Extracts from National Curriculum for England, Maths Programme of Study © Crown Copyright. Reproduced under the terms of the Open Government Licence (OGL). www.nationalarchives.gov.uk/doc/open-government-licence/version/3/

Author Paul Hollin
Editorial Rachel Morgan, Jenny Wilcox, Mary Nathan, Red Door Media
Cover and Series Design Neil Salt and Nicolle Thomas
Layout Neil Salt
CD-ROM Development Hannah Barnett, Phil Crothers and MWA Technologies Private Ltd

Table of Contents Year 5

About the Planning and Assessment Guides......5

About the Textbooks 6

Tracking progress................................7

Year 5 curriculum links........................8

Number and place value

Numbers up to 1,000,000 12

Counting in steps up to 1,000,000 14

Positive and negative numbers 16

Rounding numbers...18

Roman numerals 20

Calculations

Mental methods for adding and subtracting.............21

Adding large numbers 22

Subtracting large numbers 24

Multiples and factors 26

Prime numbers 28

Multiplying large numbers 30

Dividing large numbers 32

Mental methods for multiplying and dividing.............34

Square and cube numbers 35

Multiplying and dividing by 10, 100 and 1000 36

Scaling and rates..38

Using all four operations 40

Fractions, decimals and percentages

Comparing and ordering fractions............................42

Tricky fractions..44

Adding and subtracting fractions 46

Multiplying fractions and whole numbers 48

Converting simple decimals and fractions.................50

Decimal fractions...52

Numbers with three decimal places 54

Rounding decimals...56

Simple percentages..58

Measurement

Length and distance...60

Perimeter...62

Area 64

Mass, capacity and volume 66

Time...68

Money 70

Geometry

Angle facts 72

Rotating angles 74

2D shapes..76

3D shapes..78

Reflecting and translating shapes 80

Statistics

Line graphs 82

Tables and timetables..84

Year 5 answers 168

Table of Contents Year 6

About the Planning and Assessment Guides......5

About the Textbooks 6

Tracking progress..............................7

Year 6 curriculum links..........................10

Number and place value

The number system.................................86

Numbers to 10,000,000 88

Estimation and rounding..........................90

Negative numbers 92

Calculations

Addition and subtraction..........................94

Multiplication and division facts and skills.................96

Written methods for long multiplication 98

Written methods for short division...........................100

Written methods for long division............................102

Ordering operations....................................104

Factors, multiples and prime numbers.....................106

Fractions, decimals and percentages

Simplifying fractions................................108

Comparing and ordering fractions............................110

Adding and subtracting fractions 112

Multiplying fractions 114

Dividing fractions 116

Decimal equivalents......................................118

Decimal places 120

Multiplying decimals 122

Dividing decimals.....................................124

Percentage equivalents.................................125

Ratio and proportion

Ratio and proportion: numbers 126

Ratio and proportion: percentages 128

Scale factors 130

Algebra

Using simple formulae 132

Missing numbers 134

Equations with two unknowns 136

Measurement

Converting units 138

Using measures.......................................140

Perimeter and area 142

Calculating area......................................144

Calculating volume 146

Geometry

Angles 148

Properties of 2D shapes 150

Drawing 2D shapes 152

3D shapes...154

Circles 156

Positive and negative coordinates...........................158

Reflecting and translating shapes 160

Statistics

Pie charts 162

Line graphs 164

Averages 166

Year 6 answers 172

About the Planning and Assessment Guides

Scholastic National Curriculum Mathematics scheme provides schools and teachers with a flexible scheme of work to meet all of your needs for the mathematics curriculum, allowing you to keep control of what you teach, and when, while saving precious teacher time.

The scheme consists of four components:
- Teacher's *Planning and Assessment Guide*
- Children's *Textbook*
- *100 Maths Lessons* resource books and CD-ROMs
- Children's *Maths Practice Book*

The main benefits of the programme include:
- Accessible content geared towards the demands of the National Curriculum.
- Flexibility to fit into the way you already teach using the award-winning *100 Maths Lessons* teacher's books.
- Detailed support in the *Textbooks* to build secure foundations and deep understanding of key concepts.
- A bank of well-structured exercises in the practice books linked to clear explanations, which parents can understand and use to help their children.

Using the Planning and Assessment Guide

This book provides guidance on how to introduce topics (including how quickly) and how to support and extend the content in the *Textbook*. It references the accompanying *100 Maths Lessons* and *Practice Books* so you can use this material to further support learning. Each teaching notes page uses the same heading structure:

- **Prior learning:** details what the children should already know prior to introducing this content.
- **Curriculum objectives and Success criteria:** provides information about which National Curriculum objectives the section covers and the specific success criteria which will come from it.
- **Learn:** relates to the 'Learn' heading in the *Textbook*, but it also goes beyond this and helps you to introduce the learning appropriately.
- **Talk maths:** relates the the 'Talk maths' heading in the *Textbook* but will often extend ideas for these activities to provide plenty of opportunity for speaking and listening.
- **Activities and Problems:** gives pointers for those activities in the *Textbook*, as well as giving ideas to extend or support the learning.
- *100 Maths Lessons* and *Practice Book* links: these detail related lessons and activities that you can use to enhance and further develop the teaching and learning of the subject area.

Planning and Assessment CD-ROM

The accompanying CD-ROM contains planning and assessment tools, the majority of these have been supplied as a word document so you can edit them to meet your needs. They can be used as effective tools for monitoring performance, identifying areas of weakness and communicating to parents.

Tracking progress

- **Maths progression overview:** gives an overview of the whole maths curriculum across Years 1–6.
- **Teacher tracking:** breaks down an individual year group into three stages of progress 'working towards', 'working at expected level' and 'working at greater depth'.
- **Child progress chart:** 'I can' statements related to the *Textbook*. The children tick to show whether they are 'not sure', are 'getting there' or 'have got' a concept.
- **I can statements:** a cut out format of the 'I can' statements from the child progress chart.

Planning and reporting templates

For templates – see the template menu on the CD-ROM.
- **Yearly, Termly and Weekly planning:** plan your teaching – templates and completed samples.
- **Termly report:** feed back to parents – templates and completed samples.

Other resources

- **Assessment framework for maths:** printable DfE Interim Teacher Assessment frameworks for mathematics
- **Curriculum links:** printable version of the curriculum links found on pages 8–11 of this book.
- **Glossary:** printable version of a child-friendly and age-appropriate mathematics glossary

Planning with Scholastic Maths

Although the series is arranged in line with the National Curriculum, teachers will need to plan a varied scheme of work for mathematics that provides opportunities to revisit objectives, in particular arithmetic, as well as allowing room for periodic assessment.

Most schools plan their mathematics curriculum with an emphasis on number and calculation, with thematic focuses planned on a weekly, fortnightly or termly basis, usually with flexibility to allow for extended or enriching topics, recapping difficult areas, repeated practice of key arithmetic skills, and focused assessments.

The table on pages 8–11 of this book provides the curriculum objectives with page references to the *Textbook*, *100 Maths Lessons* and *Practice Book* to assist your planning.

About the Textbooks

Using the Textbooks

The *Textbook* and *Planning and Assessment Guide* are arranged thematically and are completely in line with the National Curriculum, allowing teachers and Mathematics subject leaders to create long- and medium-term plans best suited to the school's needs. Each section of the *Textbook* presents the 'core' learning for that curriculum area, with the relevant pages in the *Planning and Assessment Guide* providing further advice and links to additional lessons and resources, in particular to *100 Maths Lessons* and *Maths Practice Book*.

Textbook structure

Each section has a similar structure (although single-page topics may not have Tips or Maths talk guidance).

- **Learn:** examples and facts specific to the objective in question.
- **Tips:** short and simple advice to aid understanding.
- **Talk maths:** focused activities to encourage verbal practice.
- **Activities:** a focused range of questions, with answers provided in the *Planning and Assessment Guide*.
- **Problems:** word problems requiring mathematics to be used in context. The problems are often pitched at two different levels enabling you to identify whether children can apply key mathematical concepts or skills.

Remember that the *Planning and Assessment Guide* provides advice and links for extending learning and practice in each of these areas.

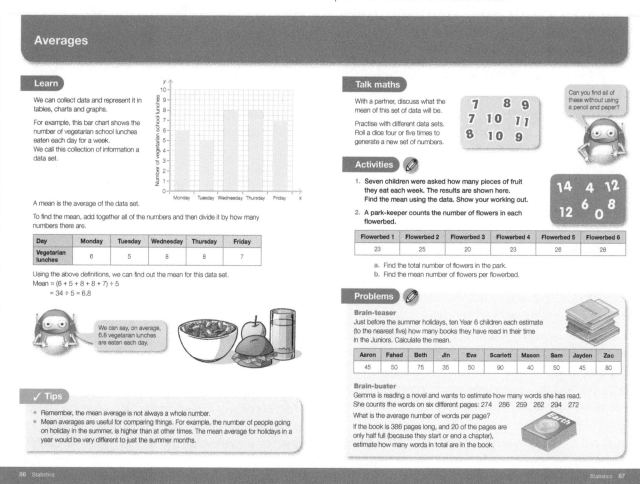

Averages

Learn

We can collect data and represent it in tables, charts and graphs.

For example, this bar chart shows the number of vegetarian school lunches eaten each day for a week.
We call this collection of information a data set.

A mean is the average of the data set.

To find the mean, add together all of the numbers and then divide it by how many numbers there are.

Day	Monday	Tuesday	Wednesday	Thursday	Friday
Vegetarian lunches	6	5	8	8	7

Using the above definitions, we can find out the mean for this data set.

Mean = (6 + 5 + 8 + 8 + 7) ÷ 5

= 34 ÷ 5 = 6.8

We can say, on average, 6.8 vegetarian lunches are eaten each day.

✓ Tips

- Remember, the mean average is not always a whole number.
- Mean averages are useful for comparing things. For example, the number of people going on holiday in the summer, is higher than at other times. The mean average for holidays in a year would be very different to just the summer months.

Talk maths

With a partner, discuss what the mean of this set of data will be.

Practise with different data sets. Roll a dice four or five times to generate a new set of numbers.

7 8 9
7 10 11
8 10 9

Can you find all of these without using a pencil and paper?

Activities

1. Seven children were asked how many pieces of fruit they eat each week. The results are shown here. Find the mean using the data. Show your working out.

14 4 12
12 6 0 8

2. A park-keeper counts the number of flowers in each flowerbed.

Flowerbed 1	Flowerbed 2	Flowerbed 3	Flowerbed 4	Flowerbed 5	Flowerbed 6
23	25	20	23	26	28

a. Find the total number of flowers in the park.
b. Find the mean number of flowers per flowerbed.

Problems

Brain-teaser

Just before the summer holidays, ten Year 6 children each estimate (to the nearest five) how many books they have read in their time in the Juniors. Calculate the mean.

Aaron	Fahad	Beth	Jin	Eva	Scarlett	Mason	Sam	Jayden	Zac
45	50	75	35	50	90	40	50	45	80

Brain-buster

Gemma is reading a novel and wants to estimate how many words she has read. She counts the words on six different pages: 274 286 259 262 294 272

What is the average number of words per page?
If the book is 386 pages long, and 20 of the pages are only half full (because they start or end a chapter), estimate how many words in total are in the book.

Assessment is always an ongoing process – formative assessments provide feedback to teacher and child for next steps; summative assessment provides snapshots of a child's current competence.

There is a self-assessment chart for children on the CD-ROM (Child progress chart). This is intended as a method of engaging children in considering their own achievement; it might also be referenced by teachers in making their own judgements. Each 'I can' statement is a generalisation for each section in the *Textbook*. These statements are also provided in a cut out and stick format.

The CD-ROM also provides a progression overview document – summarising the progress between year groups and a teacher tracking grid that allows you to track more detailed progress within a year group. The teacher tracking grid breaks each curriculum objective down into working towards the expected standard, working at the expected standard or working with greater depth. Each of these terms is explained below.

Working towards the expected standard

At this stage, children are able to access the objective at a simple level, or with some kind of support, whether from an adult, a peer or via some form of supportive resource. For example, children might be able to count in steps of two, but only using counting cubes or a number line. If questioned further they will not necessarily be able to explain the processes involved. Children requiring support to complete work may:

- correctly use skills with apparatus.
- solve simple problems.
- have difficulty correcting mistakes.
- talk about the concepts to some extent, with limited mathematical vocabulary.

Working at the expected standard

Children working at the expected level on a mathematical objective will be able to fulfil the essence of the objective independently. So, for counting in twos, they will be able to do this unsupported by person or resource, and will demonstrate a clear understanding of the process and their work. In talking about their work they will show an awareness of the mathematics involved, and may be able to apply it to solve problems in other contexts. Indications that children are working at the expected standard for a particular objective include:

- consistently apply skills correctly within the specified content.
- correctly use facts and procedures to solve straightforward problems.
- correct their own mistakes in work marked by others.
- provide straightforward explanations of their work and the concepts involved.

Working at greater depth

This category suggests that children have mastered the objective involved. They can recall facts easily, talk about them and use them in different contexts. Indicators that children are working at greater depth include:

- rapid application of the skills using different numbers.
- creative use of facts and procedures to solve unfamiliar, complex and multi-step problems.
- spot errors and self-correct them.
- reason about and clearly explain concepts, freely using correct mathematical terminology.

DFE interim guidance (2015) on Mathematics assessment is available on the CD-ROM.

Scholastic Maths and Mastery

There are many definitions of 'mastery' in maths. As well as judging how much a child has learned, it is important to assess how well they apply their learning. The National Curriculum includes the requirement for children to be able to apply their learning in different contexts, thereby deepening their knowledge, before moving onto new learning. The level to which they can make connections and apply their learning is one such definition of mastery.

Scholastic National Curriculum Mathematics offers many opportunities for children to demonstrate a skill or recall a number fact using the *100 Maths Lessons* content. To deepen or embed these skills the *Maths Practice Books* and *Textbooks* offer a range of well-structured practice exercises. Children can then go on to apply these skills using the range of problems in the *Textbooks* or the 'assess and review' content in *100 Maths Lessons*. The range of opportunities within the programme to embed or apply maths skills therefore should provide teachers with sufficient evidence to track how secure maths concepts are and whether they have truly been mastered by each child.

An individual report template has been provided on the CD-ROM to feed back to parents how well their child can apply their skills that they have learned. This might be done termly or at other times when children have attained a secure level of mastery in a particular area.

Curriculum objectives	Year 5 Textbook	100 Maths Lessons Year 5	Year 5 Practice Book
Number and place value			
Read, write, order and compare numbers to at least 1,000,000 and determine the value of each digit.	Pages: 6–7	Pages: 8–13, 42, 172–177	Pages: 9, 10, 13
Count forwards or backwards in steps of powers of 10 for any given number up to 1,000,000.	Pages: 8–9	Pages: 8–13	Pages: 6
Interpret negative numbers in context, count forwards and backwards with positive and negative whole numbers, including through zero.	Pages: 10–11	Pages: 90–95, 172–177	Pages: 7, 8, 16, 17
Round any number up to 1,000,000 to the nearest 10, 100, 1000, 10,000 and 100,000.	Pages: 12–13	Pages: 54, 172–177, 207	Pages: 14, 15
Solve number problems and practical problems that involve all of the above.		Pages: 90–95, 172–177	Pages: 8, 15, 16, 17
Read Roman numerals to 1000 (M) and recognise years written in Roman numerals.	Pages: 14	Pages: 172–177	Pages: 11, 12
Addition and subtraction			
Add and subtract whole numbers with more than four digits, including using formal written methods (columnar addition and subtraction).	Pages: 16–17, 18–19	Pages: 14–19, 96–101, 178–183, 213–218	Pages: 24, 25, 27, 28, 29, 30, 31
Add and subtract numbers mentally with increasingly large numbers.	Pages: 15	Pages: 14–19, 96–101, 131–136, 178–183, 213–218	Pages: 18, 19, 20, 22, 23
Use rounding to check answers to calculations and determine, in the context of a problem, levels of accuracy.	Pages: 34–35	Pages: 96–101, 131–136, 178–183	Pages: 32, 33
Solve addition and subtraction multi-step problems in contexts, deciding which operations and methods to use and why.		Pages: 14–19, 96–101, 125, 131–136, 178–183, 206, 213–218	Pages: 26, 27, 28, 29
Multiplication and division			
Identify multiples and factors, including finding all factor pairs of a number, and common factors of two numbers.	Pages: 20–21	Pages: 20–25	Pages: 35, 36, 38, 39, 40
Know and use the vocabulary of prime numbers, prime factors and composite (non-prime) numbers.	Pages: 22–23	Pages: 20–25	Pages: 42, 43
Establish whether a number up to 100 is prime and recall prime numbers up to 19.	Pages: 22–23	Pages: 20–25	Pages: 42, 43
Multiply numbers up to four digits by a 1- or 2-digit number using a formal written method, including long multiplication for 2-digit numbers.	Pages: 24–25	Pages: 49–54, 102–107, 137–142, 184–189, 219–224	Pages: 48, 49
Multiply and divide numbers mentally drawing upon known facts.	Pages: 28	Pages: 26–31, 219–224	Pages: 44, 45, 46, 47, 63
Divide numbers up to four digits by a 1-digit number using the formal written method of short division and interpret remainders appropriately for the context.	Pages: 26–27	Pages: 55–60, 137–142, 184–189	Pages: 50, 51
Multiply and divide whole numbers and those involving decimals by 10, 100 and 1000.	Pages: 30–31	Pages: 26–31, 49–54, 137–142	Pages: 52–53
Recognise and use square numbers and cube numbers, and the notation for squared (^{2}) and cubed (^{3}).	Pages: 29	Pages: 102–107	Pages: 54, 55, 56, 57
Solve problems involving multiplication and division including using their knowledge of factors and multiples, squares and cubes.	Pages: 20–21	Pages: 20–25	Pages: 35, 36, 38, 39, 40
Solve problems involving addition, subtraction, multiplication and division and a combination of these, including understanding the meaning of the equals sign.	Pages: 34–35	Pages: 137–142, 184–189, 219–224	Pages: 58, 59, 60, 61, 62, 63, 64, 65
Solve problems involving multiplication and division, including scaling by simple fractions and problems involving simple rates.	Pages: 32–33	Pages: 102–107	Pages: 66, 67
Fractions, decimals and percentages			
Compare and order fractions whose denominators are all multiples of the same number.	Pages: 36–37	Pages: 61–66	Pages: 68, 69
Identify, name and write equivalent fractions of a given fraction, represented visually, including tenths and hundredths.	Pages: 36–37	Pages: 61–66	Pages: 68, 69
Recognise mixed numbers and improper fractions and convert from one form to the other and write mathematical statements > 1 as a mixed number.	Pages: 38–39	Pages: 108–113, 143–148, 190–195	Pages: 71, 72, 73
Add and subtract fractions with the same denominator and denominators that are multiples of the same number.	Pages: 40–41	Pages: 190–195	Pages: 74, 75, 76, 77

Curriculum objectives	Year 5 Textbook	100 Maths Lessons Year 5	Year 5 Practice Book
Fractions, decimals and percentages (continued)			
Multiply proper fractions and mixed numbers by whole numbers, supported by materials and diagrams.	Pages: 42–43	Pages: 108–113, 143–148	Pages: 78, 79, 88
Read and write decimal numbers as fractions.	Pages: 44–45	Pages: 61–66, 67–72, 225–230	Pages: 70, 85
Recognise and use thousandths and relate them to tenths, hundredths and decimal equivalents.	Pages: 46–47	Pages: 67–72, 225–230	Pages: 80
Round decimals with two decimal places to the nearest whole number and to one decimal place.	Pages: 50–51	Pages: 67–72	Pages: 82
Read, write, order and compare numbers with up to three decimal places.	Pages: 48–49	Pages: 67–72, 225–230	Pages: 81, 83, 84
Solve problems involving number up to three decimal places.	Pages: 48–49	Pages: 67–72, 225–230	Pages: 81, 83, 84
Recognise the per cent symbol (%) and understand that per cent relates to 'number of parts per hundred', and write percentages as a fraction with denominator 100, and as a decimal.	Pages: 52–53	Pages: 149–154, 231–236	Pages: 86, 87, 89
Solve problems which require knowing percentage and decimal equivalents of ½, ¼, ⅕, ⅖, ⅘ and those fractions with a denominator of a multiple of 10 or 25.	Pages: 52–53	Pages: 149–154, 231–236	Pages: 86, 87, 89
Measurement			
Convert between different units of metric measure (for example, kilometre and metre; centimetre and metre; centimetre and millimetre; gram and kilogram; litre and millilitre).	Pages: 54–55, 60–61	Pages: 37–41, 119–123, 155–159, 201–205	Pages: 90, 92, 104, 107
Understand and use approximate equivalences between metric units and common imperial units such as inches, pounds and pints.	Pages: 54–55, 60–61	Pages: 37–41, 119–123, 155–159, 201–205	Pages: 90, 91, 92, 93, 94, 95, 104, 107
Measure and calculate the perimeter of composite rectilinear shapes in centimetres and metres	Pages: 56–57	Pages: 37–41	Pages: 96
Calculate and compare the area of rectangles (including squares), and including using standard units, square centimetres (cm²) and square metres (m²) and estimate the area of irregular shapes.	Pages: 58–59	Pages: 37–41	Pages: 97, 98, 99
Estimate volume and capacity.	Pages: 60–61	Pages: 155–159, 201–205	Pages: 94, 100, 101, 107
Solve problems involving converting between units of time.	Pages: 62–63	Pages: 201–205	Pages: 102, 103, 105
Use all four operations to solve problems involving measure using decimal notation, including scaling.	Pages: 54–55, 56–57, 58–59, 60–61, 62–63, 64–65	Pages: 37–41, 96–101, 119–123, 155–159, 201–205, 219–224	Pages: 90, 92, 96, 97, 98, 99, 104, 105, 106, 107
Geometry			
Identify 3D shapes, including cubes and other cuboids, from 2D representations.	Pages: 72–73	Pages: 73–77	Pages: 114
Know angles are measured in degrees: estimate and compare acute, obtuse and reflex angles.	Pages: 66–67	Pages: 32–36, 196–200	Pages: 108, 109, 110
Draw given angles, and measure them in degrees (°).	Pages: 66–67	Pages: 32–36, 196–200	Pages: 108, 109, 110
Identify: angles at a point and one whole turn (total 360°); angles at a point on a straight line and ½ a turn (total 180°); other multiples of 90°.	Pages: 68–69	Pages: 32–36, 196–200	Pages: 111, 112
Use the properties of rectangles to deduce related facts and find missing lengths and angles.	Pages: 70–71	Pages: 73–77, 196–200	Pages: 113, 115, 116, 117
Distinguish between regular and irregular polygons based on reasoning about equal sides and angles.	Pages: 70–71	Pages: 73–77, 196–200	Pages: 113, 115, 116, 117
Identify, describe and represent the position of a shape following a reflection or translation, using the appropriate language, and know that the shape has not changed.	Pages: 74–75	Pages: 114–118	Pages: 118, 119
Statistics			
Solve comparison, sum and difference problems using information presented in a line graph.	Pages: 76–77	Pages: 160–164, 242–246	Pages: 120, 121, 124, 125
Complete, read and interpret information in tables, including timetables.	Pages: 78–79	Pages: 78–82, 242–246	Pages: 122–123

Curriculum objectives	Year 6 Textbook	100 Maths Lessons Year 6	Year 6 Practice Book
Number and place value			
Read, write, order and compare numbers up to 10,000,000 and determine the value of each digit.	Pages: 6–7, 8–9	Pages: 8–13, 90–95, 172–176	Pages: 6–7, 8, 13
Round any whole number to a required degree of accuracy.	Pages: 10–11	Pages: 8–13, 172–176	Pages: 9, 14, 48, 51, 55
Use negative numbers in context, and calculate intervals across zero.	Pages: 12–13	Pages: 90–95	Pages: 10, 11, 16, 17
Solve number and practical problems that involve all of the above.	Pages: 10–11, 12–13	Pages: 8–13, 90–95, 172–176	Pages: 6–7, 8, 9, 10, 11, 13, 14, 16, 17, 48, 51, 55
Calculation			
Multiply multi-digit numbers up to four digits by a 2-digit whole number using the formal written method of long multiplication.	Pages: 18–19	Pages: 26–31, 49–54, 182–186	Pages: 24–25, 26, 27, 50, 57
Divide numbers up to four digits by a 2-digit whole number using the formal written method of long division, and interpret remainders as whole number remainders, fractions, or by rounding, as appropriate for the context.	Pages: 22–23	Pages: 26–31, 49–54, 131–135, 182–186	Pages: 30, 32–33, 34, 35
Divide numbers up to four digits by a 2-digit number using the formal written method of short division where appropriate, interpreting remainders according to the context.	Pages: 20–21	Pages: 49–54	Pages: 23, 28–29, 31, 39
Perform mental calculations, including with mixed operations and large numbers.	Pages: 14–15, 16–17, 24–25	Pages: 14–19, 20–25, 26–31, 66–71, 101–106, 131–135, 177–181, 213–217	Pages: 22, 23, 36, 37, 38, 39, 40, 41, 42–45, 46, 47, 49, 51, 53, 54, 56
Identify common factors, common multiples and prime numbers.	Pages: 26–27	Pages: 20–25	Pages: 18, 19, 20, 21
Use their knowledge of the order of operations to carry out calculations involving the four operations.	Pages: 24–25	Pages: 66–71, 131–135, 213–217	Pages: 40, 41, 42–45, 47, 53, 54
Solve addition and subtraction multi-step problems in contexts, deciding which operations and methods to use and why.	Pages: 24–25	Pages: 66–71, 131–135, 213–217	Pages: 40, 41, 42–45, 47, 53, 54
Solve problems involving addition, subtraction, multiplication and division.	Pages: 14–15, 16–17, 18–19, 20–21, 22–23	Pages: 14–19, 26–31, 49–54, 131–135, 177–181, 182–186	Pages: 22, 23, 24–25, 26, 27, 28–29, 30, 31, 32–33, 34, 35, 36, 37, 38, 39, 46, 49, 50, 51, 56, 57
Use estimation to check answers to calculations and determine, in the context of a problem, an appropriate degree of accuracy.	Pages: 18–19, 22–23	Pages: 26–31, 49–54, 131–135, 182–186	Pages: 24–25, 26, 27, 30, 32–33, 34, 35, 50, 57
Fractions, decimals and percentages			
Use common factors to simplify fractions; use common multiples to express fractions in the same denomination.	Pages: 28–29	Pages: 55–60	Pages: 60–61
Compare and order fractions, including fractions > 1.	Pages: 30–31	Pages: 55–60	Pages: 62, 63
Add and subtract fractions with different denominators and mixed numbers, using the concept of equivalent fractions.	Pages: 32–33	Pages: 55–60, 107–112, 187–192, 223–227	Pages: 64, 65
Multiply simple pairs of proper fractions, writing the answer in its simplest form.	Pages: 34–35	Pages: 107–112, 187–192, 223–227	Pages: 66–67, 73
Divide proper fractions by whole numbers.	Pages: 36–37	Pages: 107–112, 187–192, 223–227	Pages: 68
Associate a fraction with division and calculate decimal fraction equivalents for a simple fraction.	Pages: 38–39	Pages: 55–60, 107–112	Pages: 71
Identify the value of each digit in numbers given to three decimal places and multiply and divide numbers by 10, 100 and 1000 giving answers up to three decimal places.	Pages: 40–41	Pages: 61–65, 96–100	Pages: 15, 76, 77
Multiply 1-digit numbers with up to two decimal places by whole numbers.	Pages: 42–43	Pages: 136–140	Pages: 52
Use written division methods in cases where the answer has up to two decimal places.	Pages: 44	Pages: 136–140	
Solve problems which require answers to be rounded to specified degrees of accuracy.	Pages: 42–43, 44	Pages: 136–140	Pages: 52
Recall and use equivalences between simple fractions, decimals and percentages, including in different contexts.	Pages: 45	Pages: 141–145, 193–197, 223–227	Pages: 58, 59, 70, 72, 74, 75

Curriculum objectives	Year 6 Textbook	100 Maths Lessons Year 6	Year 6 Practice Book
Ratio and proportion			
Solve problems involving the relative sizes of two quantities where missing values can be found by using integer multiplication and division facts.	Pages: 46–47	Pages: 198–202	Pages: 78, 80
Solve problems involving the calculation of percentages and the use of percentages for comparison.	Pages: 48–49	Pages: 193–197, 223–227	Pages: 79, 83
Solve problems involving similar shapes where the scale factor is known or can be found.	Pages: 50–51	Pages: 198–202	Pages: 81, 82
Solve problems involving unequal sharing and grouping using knowledge of fractions and multiples.	Pages: 46–47, 48–49, 50–51	Pages: 193–197, 198–202, 223–227	Pages: 78, 79, 80, 81, 82, 83
Algebra			
Use simple formulae.	Pages: 52–53	Pages: 146–151, 218–222	Pages: 85, 90
Generate and describe linear number sequences.	Pages: 52–53	Pages: 218–222	Pages: 91, 92, 93
Express missing number problems algebraically.	Pages: 54–55	Pages: 146–151, 218–222	Pages: 87, 89
Find pairs of numbers that satisfy an equation with two unknowns.	Pages: 56–57	Pages: 146–151, 218–222	Pages: 86, 87, 88
Enumerate possibilities of combinations of two variables.	Pages: 56–57	Pages: 218–222	Pages: 86, 87, 88
Measurement			
Solve problems involving the calculation and conversion of units of measure, using decimal notation up to three decimal places where appropriate.	Pages: 60–62	Pages: 37–41, 152–156, 234–238	Pages: 94, 96, 97, 101, 102, 103
Use, read, write and convert between standard units, converting measurements of length, mass, volume and time from a smaller unit of measure to a larger unit, and vice versa, using decimal notation to up to three decimal places.	Pages: 58–59	Pages: 37–41, 152–156, 234–238	Pages: 95, 98, 99, 100
Convert between miles and kilometres.	Pages: 60–61	Pages: 37–41	Pages: 103
Recognise that shapes with the same areas can have different perimeters and vice versa.	Pages: 62–63	Pages: 118–122	Pages: 104
Recognise when it is possible to use formulae for area and volume of shapes.	Pages: 62–63, 64–65, 66–67	Pages: 118–122, 152–156	Pages: 104, 105, 106, 107
Calculate the area of parallelograms and triangles.	Pages: 64–65	Pages: 118–122, 152–156	Pages: 107
Calculate, estimate and compare volume of cubes and cuboids using standard units, including cubic centimetres (cm^3) and cubic metres (m^3), and extending to other units.	Pages: 66–67	Pages: 118–122	Pages: 108–109
Geometry			
Draw 2D shapes using given dimensions and angles.	Pages: 72–73	Pages: 72–76, 228–233	Pages: 115
Recognise, describe and build simple 3D shapes, including making nets.	Pages: 74–75	Pages: 72–76, 228–233	Pages: 116, 117
Compare and classify geometric shapes based on their properties and sizes and find unknown angles in any triangles, quadrilaterals, and regular polygons.	Pages: 70–71	Pages: 72–76, 228–233	Pages: 114
Illustrate and name parts of circles, including radius, diameter and circumference and know that the diameter is twice the radius.	Pages: 76–77	Pages: 32–36, 228–233	Pages: 110–111
Recognise angles where they meet at a point, are on a straight line, or are vertically opposite, and find missing angles.	Pages: 68–69	Pages: 32–36, 228–233	Pages: 112, 113
Describe positions on the full coordinate grid (all four quadrants).	Pages: 78–79	Pages: 113–117	Pages: 118
Draw and translate simple shapes on the coordinate plane, and reflect them in the axes.	Pages: 80–81	Pages: 113–117	Pages: 119
Statistics			
Interpret and construct pie charts and line graphs and use these to solve problems.	Pages: 82–83, 84–85	Pages: 77–81, 157–161, 239–243	Pages: 103, 120, 121, 122, 123
Calculate and interpret the mean as an average.	Pages: 86–87	Pages: 239–243	Pages: 124, 125

Numbers up to 1,000,000

Prior learning

- Can read and write numbers to 100,000 in numerals and words.
- Understand the relationship and value of each digit in a number to 100,000.
- Order whole numbers up to 100,000.

Learn

- Draw or display the table at the top of page 6 in the textbook to check children's understanding of place value in numbers up to 100,000.
- Check for children who inaccurately read the place value of each digit, or who do not use the appropriate number of place-holding zeros when giving the value of each digit.

- *100 Maths Lessons Year 5, Autumn 1, Week 1* covers place value to 1,000,000 and includes revision of numbers to 10,000 and 100,000 initially. Check children's knowledge is secure before moving on to 5-digit numbers.
- Play 'Human number cards'. Give children cards showing 5-digit numbers and ask them to position themselves in the correct order. Mix up the numbers again, and ask children with 'greater than' and 'less than' cards to move to the correct positions between the numbers.
- If children get mixed up with < and > symbols, tell them to think of the symbols as the mouth of a crocodile – the crocodile always eats the bigger number!

Curriculum objectives

- To read, write, order and compare numbers to at least 1,000,000 and determine the value of each digit.

Success criteria

- I can read numbers to 1,000,000 in numerals and words.
- I can order and compare numbers to 1,000,000 and know the value of each digit.

Numbers up to 1,000,000

Learn

23,471 in words is twenty-three thousand, four hundred and seventy-one.

10,000s	1000s	100s	10s	1s
2	3	4	7	1

What do the other digits represent?

The **place value** of the 3 digit represents **3000**, the **4** represents **400**.

1,000,000s	100,000s	10,000s	1000s	100s	10s	1s
	3	4	0	2	6	1

This number is three hundred and forty thousand, two hundred and sixty-one.

Now read these statements aloud. They are both true.
For this symbol: > say *is bigger than* and for this symbol: < say *is smaller than*.

999,999 > 703,374 > 12,029 > 7698

6418 < 30,206 < 163,192 < 1,000,000

What number does each of the digits represent?

✓ Tips

- Write the place-value headings in columns above numbers if you're stuck.
- Use commas in numbers over a million (1,000,000), numbers over a hundred thousand (100,000) and numbers over ten thousand (10,000).
- If you get mixed up with the > and < symbols, just think of the symbol as the mouth of a crocodile – the crocodile always eats the bigger number!

Hey there! Follow my tips and you'll soon find big numbers are not a big problem!

876,457 292,345

- Ask the children to take turns reading the numbers to a partner. Ask each child to write their own numbers or number sentences for their partner to read.

- In pairs or individually, ask the children to complete questions 1–5. Check children understand the place value of the numbers in each question and that they can accurately compare numbers.
- The activities in *Year 5 Practice Book* provide further practice.

- Review answers to the problems and check children's reasoning. Set the Brain-teaser only for less confident learners.

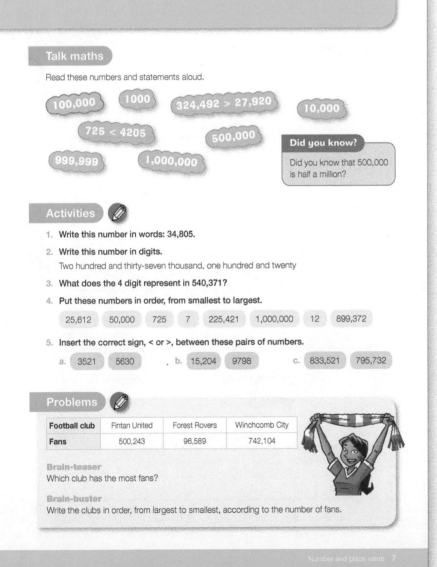

Talk maths

Read these numbers and statements aloud.

100,000   1000   324,492 > 27,920   10,000

725 < 4205   500,000

999,999   1,000,000

Did you know?
Did you know that 500,000 is half a million?

Activities

1. Write this number in words: 34,805.
2. Write this number in digits.
   Two hundred and thirty-seven thousand, one hundred and twenty
3. What does the 4 digit represent in 540,371?
4. Put these numbers in order, from smallest to largest.

   25,612   50,000   725   7   225,421   1,000,000   12   899,372

5. Insert the correct sign, < or >, between these pairs of numbers.

   a. 3521   5630   b. 15,204   9798   c. 833,521   795,732

Problems

Football club	Fintan United	Forest Rovers	Winchcomb City
Fans	500,243	96,589	742,104

Brain-teaser
Which club has the most fans?

Brain-buster
Write the clubs in order, from largest to smallest, according to the number of fans.

Number and place value   7

100 Maths Lessons Year 5 links:

- Autumn 1, Week 1 (pages 8–13): explain what each digit represents and partition numbers to 1,000,000
- Summer 1, Week 1 (pages 172–177): place value to 1,000,000; relate numbers to position on the number line
- Autumn 1, Assess and review (page 42): assess children's understanding, using a game and place value arrow cards

Year 5 Practice Book links:

- (page 9): Reading and writing large numbers
- (page 10): Place value in large numbers
- (page 13): Ordering hundreds and thousands

Counting in steps up to 1,000,000

Prior learning

- Can count from any given number in whole-number steps.
- Identify number patterns in steps of 10, 100 and 1000.

Learn

- Draw or display the two number lines at the top of page 8 in the textbook and ask individual children to count on or back from the given numbers. Extend to higher numbers using empty number lines on an interactive whiteboard. Check for children who inaccurately read the numbers aloud. Establish the rules when counting in different steps and make sure that children can apply these rules correctly from different starting numbers (backwards and forwards).

- *100 Maths Lessons Year 5, Autumn 1, Week 1* covers counting forwards and backwards in different steps up to 100,000.
- Make sure that children understand that powers of 10 are numbers made by multiplying 10 by itself a number of times. Show the pattern of powers of 10 on page 8 of the textbook, and demonstrate counting in steps of 100 and 10,000 using the examples. Demonstrate how the numbers increase in size with each step, by writing the digits of the numbers in the columns of a place-value table.

Curriculum objectives

- To count forwards or backwards in steps of powers of 10 for any given number up to 1,000,000.

Success criteria

- I can count forwards and backwards in 10s, 100s and 1000s from any given number.

Counting in steps up to 1,000,000

Can you count on from 0 in 5s? Can you count back from 100 in 10s?

Learn

When we count in steps, we add or subtract the same number each time.

Powers of 10 are numbers that are made by multiplying 10 by 10 a number of times:

- 100 is 10 × 10 or 10 to the power of 2 (10^2)
- 1000 is 10 × 10 × 10 or 10 to the power of 3 (10^3)
- 10,000 is 10 × 10 × 10 × 10 or 10 to the power of 4 (10^4)

We can count on or back in steps for any power of 10.

This number line goes up to 1000. Starting at 45, we count in steps of 100.

Can you continue the count?

This number line goes up to 60,000. Starting at 1362, we count in steps of 10,000.

Can you count back in ten thousands? Try starting at 51,362.

✓ Tips

- Write the place values in columns above numbers if you're stuck.
- Remember which power of 10 you are adding each time.
- Choose a number less than 1000, then try counting on in 100,000s.

8   Number and place value

- Ask the children to take turns with partners in counting aloud in steps of different powers of 10, using the examples in the textbook. Extend by supplying them with blank number lines. Ask them to divide the line in jumps of 100,000 from to 1,000,000. Give the children 0–9 digit cards to make 6-digit numbers. Ask them to write one of these numbers on the number line, and then to count up and back in 100,000s.

- In pairs or individually, ask the children to complete questions 1–4. Check children understand the place value of the numbers in each question. To check their sequences are correct, ask them to write the place value of each digit of the numbers in their answers in the columns of a place-value table.
- The activities in *Year 5 Practice Book* provide further practice.

- Review answers to the problems and check children's reasoning. Set the Brain-teaser only for less confident learners.

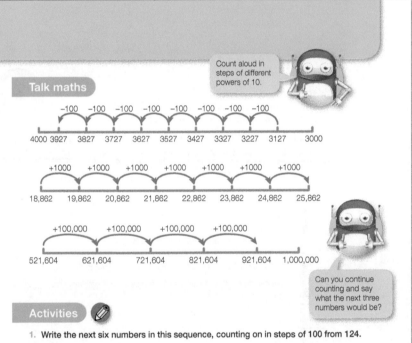

Talk maths

Count aloud in steps of different powers of 10.

Activities

1. Write the next six numbers in this sequence, counting on in steps of 100 from 124.

2. Write the next six numbers in this sequence, counting back in steps of 1000 from 12,906.

3. Write the next six numbers in this sequence, counting on in steps of 100,000 from 320,435.

4. Write the next six numbers in this sequence, counting back in steps of 10,000 from 243,000.

Problems

Brain-teaser
Evie's mum is saving for a family holiday. She has already saved £746 and will continue to save £100 a month. How many more months of saving will it take before she has over £2000?

Brain-buster
There are 123,456 people at a football match. At the end of the match 10,000 people leave every ten minutes. How many people will still be in the stadium 50 minutes after the match has finished?

Number and place value · 9

100 Maths Lessons Year 5 links:

- Autumn 1, Week 1 (pages 8–13): count from any given number in whole number steps of 10, 100, 1000

Year 5 Practice Book links:

- (page 6): Counting in 10s, 100s and 1000s

Positive and negative numbers

Prior learning

- Use positive and negative numbers in practical contexts and position them on a number line.

Learn

- Discuss how we cannot have a negative number of objects. If there are three pencils, you cannot take away five. Consider when numbers in real life might be positive and negative, such as temperature.

- Ensure that children understand the differences and links between positive and negative numbers, and the operations of addition and subtraction. For example, adding −5 to +8 is equivalent to subtracting 5 from 8.

- *100 Maths Lessons Year 5, Spring 1, Week 1* covers negative numbers in context and counting backwards and forwards through zero.

- Draw or display a number line from −5 to +5 and ask individual children to count on or back from five given numbers. Extend this to a −10 to +10 line, with only zero marked and other numbers indicated by a point on the line. Point to a dot and ask children to identify the number represented, focusing on children who are not secure in counting below zero.

- Consolidate knowledge by presenting a real, virtual (there is an interactive thermometer on the *100 Maths Lessons Year 5* CD-ROM) or drawn thermometer with clearly visible scales above and below zero, referencing the examples on page 10 of the textbook if desired.

- More confident learners might be challenged to start applying mental calculation skills for adding and subtracting in both directions across zero.

Curriculum objectives

- To interpret negative numbers in context, count forwards and backwards with positive and negative whole numbers, including through zero.

Success criteria

- I can count with positive and negative whole numbers.

Positive and negative numbers

Learn

Numbers less than zero are called negative numbers; numbers more than zero are called positive numbers.

Start at 5 and count back 6. Where do you stop?

> On a number line, when we add numbers we move to the right; when we take away numbers we move to the left.

Temperature is a great way to practise using positive and negative numbers.

- If you start at +5 and count back 5 you stop at 0.
- If you start at −8 and count on 6 you stop at −2.
- If you start at −3 and count on 4 you stop at +1.
- If you start at +2 and count back 10 you stop at −8.

We can do simple calculations with positive and negative numbers.
For example, $2 - 3 = -1$ Or, $-3 + 2 = -1$

Think of a few of your own.

✓ Tips

- Remember that adding, or counting on, moves up a thermometer, or to the right on a number line.

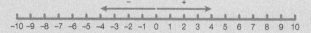

- Use your finger to count on and back from different numbers. Each time say your calculation out loud, such as *minus four add seven equals plus three*.

10 Number and place value

Talk maths

- Cover the vocabulary presented in the textbook, and then arrange children in pairs or small groups to practise with each other. Give each group a small number line and ask them challenge each other to count on or back from given numbers, checking each other's vocabulary as they go.

Activities

- Ask the children to complete questions 1–4 individually. In particular, check that they understand counting in steps of 2 (question 2) and that they are counting across zero correctly in all questions.
- The activities in *Year 5 Practice Book* provide further practice.

Problems

- Review answers to the problems and check children's reasoning. Set the Brain-teaser only for less confident learners. More confident learners might set each other further temperature-related problems.

Talk maths

Make sure you understand the different vocabulary for talking about positive and negative numbers. Read these statements aloud.

We say count on, plus or add.

We say count back, minus or subtract.

We say minus three to subtract three, but we also say minus three to talk about the number –3. We also say negative 3 to talk about the number –3.

We can say positive or plus for numbers greater than zero, but usually we just say the number.

We always say negative or minus for numbers less than zero.

We say plus five to add five, but we also say plus five to talk about the number 5.

Activities

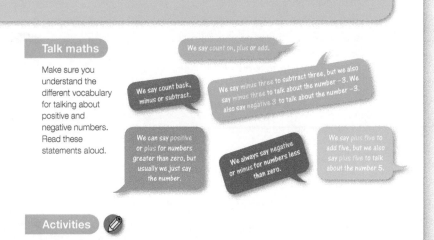

```
-10 -9 -8 -7 -6 -5 -4 -3 -2 -1  0  1  2  3  4  5  6  7  8  9  10
```

1. Copy and complete these calculations.
   - a. $-5 + 5$
   - b. $5 - 5$
   - c. $-2 - 7$
   - d. $3 - 7$

2. Count on from −6 to +6 in steps of 2. Write down each number.

3. Copy these number sentences and insert the missing signs, + or −.
   - a. $-4 \underline{\quad} 4 = 0$
   - b. $-5 \underline{\quad} 6 = 1$
   - c. $2 \underline{\quad} 7 = 9$
   - d. $2 \underline{\quad} 8 = -6$

4. Copy these number sentences and insert the missing numbers.
   - a. $-3 + \underline{\quad} = 1$
   - b. $1 - \underline{\quad} = -2$
   - c. $\underline{\quad} - 7 = 2$
   - d. $\underline{\quad} - 10 = -8$

Problems

Brain-teaser
The temperature at dusk is 4 degrees Celsius (4°C). If the temperature drops 6°C by midnight, what will the temperature be?

Brain-buster
In January, the temperature at 11am in Montreal, Canada, was −9°C and in Sydney, Australia, it was 27°C. What was the difference in temperature?

Number and place value   11

---

100 Maths Lessons Year 5 links:

- Spring 1, Week 1 (pages 90–95): order and compare positive and negative numbers
- Summer 1, Week 1 (pages 172–177) count forwards and backwards through zero; understand negative numbers in real-life contexts

Year 5 Practice Book links:

- (page 7): Counting with negative numbers
- (page 8): Negative temperatures
- (page 16): Number problems (1)
- (page 17): Number problems (2)

Rounding numbers

Prior learning

- Order whole numbers up to 100,000.
- Round any number up to 100,000 to the nearest 10, 100 or 1000.

Learn

- Use a selection of number-line fragments, like those at the top of page 12 in the textbook to reinforce children's understanding of place value in small and large numbers.
- Remind children that rounding is a method of approximating that allows us to estimate and visualise numbers more easily.
- *100 Maths Lessons Year 5, Summer 1, Week 1* covers rounding and place value. Check children's knowledge is secure before moving on.
- On A3 paper or card, write two large numbers such as 300 and 400, 6000 and 7000, 50,000 and 60,000, and so on. Ask two children to hold these numbers for everyone to see, and then assign further numbers that lie between these two numbers (for example, 340, 6750). Other children should then take these new numbers and, with class consensus, position themselves between the two original numbers. Finally, have the children agree and then place the 'halfway' number (for example, 350, 6500) and then round up or down each number to a specified power of 10. Look at and discuss the two groups that emerge, remembering that the 'halfway' number always rounds up.
- This can be repeated for rounding for different powers of 10 as appropriate.

Curriculum objectives

- To round any number up to 1,000,000 to the nearest 10, 100, 1000, 10,000 and 100,000.

Success criteria

- I can round any number to the nearest power of 10.

Rounding numbers

Learn

To round a number to the nearest 10 we can look at its position on the number line.

Don't forget, 34 and below round down to 30, 35 and above round up to 40.

We then look for the nearest 10.
32 rounds down to 30   37 rounds up to 40

We can do the same with 100s and 1000s.
355 rounds up to 400   1268 rounds down to 1000

Don't forget (again!), 50 and 500 round up, 49 and 499 round down.

We often round numbers to the nearest power of 10 (that's 10, 100, 1000, 10,000, 100,000, and so on).

Rounding to the nearest 10,000: 4235 rounds down to zero and 6249 rounds up to 10,000.

Rounding to the nearest 100,000: 344,235 rounds down to 300,000 and 689,249 rounds up to 700,000.

✓ Tips

- Always think carefully about what you want to round to: nearest 10, 100, 1000 and so on, and then think about the part of the number line the number is on. So:
  635,850 rounds to the nearest 10 as 635,850
  635,850 rounds to the nearest 100 as 635,900
  635,850 rounds to the nearest 1000 as 636,000
  635,850 rounds to the nearest 10,000 as 640,000
  635,850 rounds to the nearest 100,000 as 600,000

It isn't hard, you just need to think about where they are on the number line.

12   Number and place value

Talk maths

- Start the activity with smaller numbers and gradually increase them, encouraging the children to identify which power of 10 they are rounding to and to use appropriate vocabulary. Identify good examples and using these to model language to the whole class.

Activities

- Ask the children to copy the chart into their exercise books, and check that they understand how numbers change depending on which power of 10 they are rounded to.
- The activities in *Year 5 Practice Book* provide further practice.

Problems

- Review answers to the Brain-teaser and discuss what the answers would be if rounded to different powers of 10.
- The Brain-buster helps reveal children's appreciation of gains and losses when rounding in real-life situations. This question can be simplified or extended as appropriate.

Talk maths

Write six different numbers between 0 and 1,000,000. Read aloud each number to a partner and challenge them to round it to each power of 10 from 10 to 10,000.

347,248 rounded to the nearest 1000 is 347,000.

What is 54,250 rounded to the nearest 100?

Activities

Copy and complete the table. Make sure it is large enough to write all the numbers in.

	Rounded to nearest 10	Rounded to nearest 100	Rounded to nearest 1000	Rounded to nearest 10,000	Rounded to nearest 100,000
67					
145					
3320					
78,249					
381,082					
555,555					

Problems

Brain-teaser
54,527 people watch a football match. What is this rounded to the nearest 10,000?

Brain-buster
A famous footballer normally gets paid £346,000 per match! If he scores a goal his pay is rounded up to the next 100,000. If he doesn't score a goal it is rounded down to the nearest 100,000. How much does he lose if he doesn't score, and how much does he gain if he does?

100 Maths Lessons Year 5 links:

- Summer 1, Week 1 (pages 172–177): round any number up to 1,000,000 to the nearest 10, 100, 1000, 10,000 and 100,000
- Summer 1, Oral and mental starter 54 (page 208): round and estimate
- Summer 1, Assess and review (page 207): assess children's understanding using number cards

Year 5 Practice Book links:

- (page 14): Rounding to the nearest 10 and 100
- (page 15): Rounding to the nearest 1000, 10,000 and 100,000

Roman numerals

Prior learning

- Can read Roman numerals to 100 (I to C).

Learn

- Examine the Roman numerals for 1–12 on a clock. Spend time considering how each number is formed and look for patterns. Extend this by creating a chart or number line for 1 to 30. Also point out that the Romans did not have a symbol for zero.

- Using the chart on page 14 of the textbook, introduce the symbols for 50 and 100. Look at how the rules for making smaller numbers (for example, IV for 4) extend to larger numbers (for example, XC for 90).

- Use the 'Roman numerals game cards' photocopiable sheet (on the *100s Maths Lessons Year 5*

Curriculum objectives

- To read Roman numerals to 1000 (M) and recognise years written in Roman numerals.

Success criteria

- I can read Roman numerals up to 1000.

100 Maths Lessons Year 5 links:

- Summer 1, Week 1 (pages 172–177): read and use Roman numerals to 1000; recognise years written as Roman numerals

Year 5 Practice Book links:

- (page 11): Roman numerals
- (page 12): Years in Roman numerals

CD-ROM) to play recognition and reinforcement games such as 'Snap' and 'Pelmanism'.

- Call out numbers and challenge the children to write them in Roman numerals. Then writing down Roman numerals and asking the children to convert them to numbers.

Talk maths

- Ask the children to write an explanation of the way Roman numerals work, and then practise it together.

Activities

- Children should complete the questions in pairs or individually. Challenge the more confident to repeat the questions, but adding 17 each time.

Problems

- Review answers to the problem and check children's reasoning. Develop this further by writing their family's ages and birth years in Roman numerals.

Roman numerals

Learn

Look at the clock and check that you know the Roman numerals for numbers 1–12.

What are the rules for making 4 and 9 with Roman numerals?

Number	1	2	3	4	5	6	7	8	9	10
Roman numeral	I	II	III	IV	V	VI	VII	VIII	IX	X
Number	11	12	13	14	15	16	17	18	19	20
Roman numeral	XI	XII	XIII	XIV	XV	XVI	XVII	XVIII	IXX	XX
Number	30	40	50	60	70	80	90	100	500	1000
Roman numeral	XXX	XL	L	LX	LXX	LXXX	XC	C	D	M

With a bit of brain power, you can use this chart to find out any Roman numeral up to 1000!

Activities

1. Write these Roman numerals in numbers.
   - a. VIII
   - b. XXII
   - c. CCC
   - d. XCV
   - e. CIV
   - f. CXL
   - g. DCX
   - h. CM

2. Write these numbers in their Roman numeral equivalent.
   - a. 23
   - b. 41
   - c. 55
   - d. 93
   - e. 112
   - f. 160
   - g. 212
   - h. 965

Problems

Brain-buster
The Romans left Britain in the year AD410, 465 years after they first arrived. Use Roman numerals to write the date they left, and the number of years they spent in Britain.

14   Number and place value

Mental methods for adding and subtracting

Prior learning

- Can add and subtract mentally, using and applying their number bonds knowledge to extend to pairs that make 10, 100 and 1000.

Learn

- Recap mental methods that the children have encountered for adding and subtracting numbers, such as using known number bonds, partitioning and use of place value. Cover simple tricks too, such as to add 99, just add 100 and then subtract 1.

- Consider a wider range of 'mentally accessible' problems. Encourage the children to list ten calculations that they are certain they can do mentally.

Talk maths

- Arrange the children in small groups. Give them a small selection of calculations appropriate to their level. Ask them to agree on the mental method to use for each calculation.

Activities

- Check that the children understand the mental method required for each question.

Problems

- Review answers to the problems and check children's reasoning.

Curriculum objectives

- To add and subtract numbers mentally with increasingly large numbers.

Success criteria

- I can choose and use mental methods to add and subtract some large numbers.

100 Maths Lessons Year 5 links:

- Autumn 1, Week 2 (pages 14–19): add and subtract mentally using large numbers
- Spring 1, Week 2 (pages 96–101): add and subtract mentally using knowledge of number patterns
- Spring 2, Week 1 (pages 131–136): use mental methods
- Summer 1, Week 2 (pages 178–183): use mental methods
- Summer 2, Week 1 (pages 213–218): add and subtract money mentally

Year 5 Practice Book links:

- (page 18): Pairs and doubles
- (page 19): Adding order
- (page 20): Near doubles and trebles
- (page 22): Bridging and adjusting
- (page 23): Mental addition and subtraction

Mental methods for adding and subtracting

Learn

You will probably know several ways of doing mental calculations.

You must know your number bonds: $7 + 8 = 15$ $15 - 8 = 7$ $15 - 7 = 8$
Partitioning numbers is important too: $25 + 12 = 37$

Mental methods can work just as well for larger numbers, but you need to be confident and know your limits!

$45{,}356 + 12{,}103$ ✓ There is no carrying necessary; just add each column.

$123{,}729 + 943{,}509$ ✗ Too much carrying!

$34{,}302 - 8753$ ✗ Too much exchanging!

$16{,}583 - 8000$ ✓ The 100s, 10s and 1s stay exactly the same!

Remember, adding 99 is easy: add 100 and take away 1!

Activities

1. Add these numbers using mental methods.
   - a. $46 + 50$
   - b. $127 + 99$
   - c. $3274 + 2002$
   - d. $2500 + 7454$
   - e. $120{,}000 + 10{,}320$

2. Subtract these numbers using mental methods.
   - a. $80 - 46$
   - b. $160 - 65$
   - c. $345 - 99$
   - d. $4000 - 2500$
   - e. $275{,}675 - 10{,}000$

Problems

Brain-teaser
Jason has read 123 pages of his book. If he reads another 150 pages he will finish it. How many pages does the book have altogether?

Brain-buster
Armchairs cost £299 and sofas cost £499. How much would two armchairs and one sofa cost altogether?

Adding large numbers

Prior learning

- Can use a written method for addition for whole numbers, either an informal, expanded method or columnar addition.

Learn

- Revise written methods taught to children in previous years, spending time modelling the language needed: columns, place value, powers of 10, and so on.

- Point out that mental methods, in particular secure number bonds up to 20, are essential in ensuring that written methods are correct.

- Start by presenting two 1-digit numbers that add up to less than 9 in a column addition. Complete this, then write two 2-digit numbers, again with each column totalling 9 or less, and perform the column addition. Continue this until you are working with the children to add two 6-digit numbers, all with no carrying. Write down the column titles (for example, thousands).

- Repeat this exercise using multi-digit numbers that do have some carrying, such as the example 664,572 + 153,054 in the textbook, carefully modelling the carrying of numbers.

- *100 Maths Lessons Year 5, Autumn 1, Week 2* provides opportunities to review written and mental addition and subtraction.

Talk maths

- Talking aloud though a calculation provides excellent reinforcement. Using the example in the textbook as a starting point, have children work in pairs to explain completed calculations to each other as well as talking through additions as they perform them.

Curriculum objectives

- To add and subtract whole numbers with more than four digits, including using formal written methods (columnar addition and subtraction).

Success criteria

- I can add large numbers using formal written methods.

Adding large numbers

Learn

There are formal written methods for adding numbers. You may have been taught methods a bit different to this one. You should use whichever method you are comfortable with – as long as you get the right answer!

```
    2  7  2
+   5  1  4
    7  8  6
```

We can arrange numbers in their place-value columns.

We know that the place-value columns continue for 1000s, 10,000s, 100,000s and so on.

We can use formal written methods using these columns.

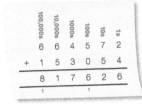

Don't forget, you can add as many numbers as you like in the columns!

✓ Tips

- Lay out your work neatly, showing the + sign and carefully exchanging the numbers between columns.

- When adding two or more numbers some people prefer to write the larger number in the top row of the calculation, but it really doesn't matter which way round you arrange them – the answer will always be the same!

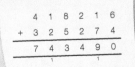

If in doubt, work it out!

16 Calculations

- Notice that the questions progress in difficulty and will quickly show which children are having difficulties. If children are experiencing problems, allow time for them to complete further calculations at a level they are comfortable with – preferably allowing them to set these calculations themselves to help raise their awareness. For children who are still struggling, apparatus may be beneficial to visualise the carrying process.

- Note that the Brain-buster problem involves multiple steps. This provides a good opportunity to help children to develop their appreciation of the importance of methodical working and good layout.

- For those children progressing well, the links to *100 Maths Lessons Year 5* will provide further practice, particularly in applying these skills in context. (Note that these may also involve formal methods for subtraction.)

100 Maths Lessons Year 5 links:

- Autumn 1, Week 2 (pages 14–19): add large numbers using formal written methods (columnar addition)
- Spring 1, Week 2 (pages 96–101): add numbers and money using formal written methods
- Summer 1, Week 2 (pages 178–183): add whole numbers with up to five digits
- Summer 2, Week 1 (pages 213–218): add money using formal methods

Year 5 Practice Book links:

- (page 24): Written addition and subtraction (choose appropriate questions)
- (page 25): Add it!
- (page 27): Adding and subtracting practice (1) (choose appropriate questions)
- (page 28): Adding and subtracting practice (2) (choose appropriate questions)
- (page 29): Adding and subtracting practice (3) (choose appropriate questions)
- (page 30): Spot the deliberate mistake (choose appropriate questions)
- (page 31): You're the teacher

Talk maths

Look at the addition below and talk it through aloud, explaining how each stage was done. Make sure you work in the correct order.

```
    2  3  7  1  6  2
+   4  8  4  7  5  3
─────────────────────
    7  2  1  9  1  5
    1  1        1
```

Use estimation to quickly see if your answers are *about right*.

2435 + 809 is around 2500 + 1000, so the answer will be around 3500.

In fact, 2435 + 809 = 3244 so my estimate was close!

Activities

1. Copy and complete these additions.
   a. 2435 + 809
   b. 7432 + 4877
   c. 24,357 + 45,823
   d. 245,020 + 376,209

2. Use squared paper to write and complete each of these additions.
   a. 2459 + 3507
   b. 23,417 + 46,219
   c. 124,467 + 89,458
   d. 231,472 + 238,419 + 121,615 + 67,424

Problems

Brain-teaser

City	Bim	Bam	Bom
Population	236,325	143,544	367,269

Are the combined populations of Bim and Bam larger than the population of Bom?

Brain-buster

If the population of each city increased by 50,000 people, would the total population of the three cities be more than one million people?

Calculations   17

Subtracting large numbers

Prior learning

- Can use a written method for subtraction for whole numbers, either an informal, expanded method or columnar subtraction.

Learn

- Revise written methods for subtraction taught in previous years, spending time modelling the language needed: columns, place value, powers of 10, exchanging, and so on.

- As with addition, point out that mental methods, in particular secure number bonds up to 20, are essential in ensuring that written methods are correct.

- Start by presenting two 1-digit numbers in a column subtraction. Complete this, and then write two 2-digit numbers in a column subtraction, with no exchanging. Continue this until you are working with the children to subtract two 6-digit numbers, all with no exchanging. Write down the column titles (for example, thousands).

- Repeat this exercise using multi-digit numbers in combinations that do involve some exchanging, such as the 6-digit examples on page 18 of the textbook, carefully modelling the processes and methods.

- *100 Maths Lessons Year 5, Autumn 1, Week 2* provides opportunities to subtract large numbers using formal written methods (columnar addition and subtraction).

Talk maths

- As with written addition, talking aloud through a subtraction provides excellent reinforcement. Using the example in the textbook as a starting point, have children work in pairs to explain completed subtractions to each other as well as talking through calculations as they perform them.

Curriculum objectives

- To add and subtract whole numbers with more than four digits, including using formal written methods (columnar addition and subtraction).

Success criteria

- I can subtract large numbers using formal written methods.

Subtracting large numbers

Learn

There are formal written methods for subtracting numbers. You may have been taught methods a bit different to this one. You should use whichever method you are comfortable with – as long as you get the right answers!

Notice how we exchange one 100 for ten 10s.

Just like with addition, we can use the place-value columns to help us subtract larger numbers.

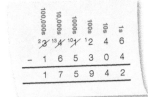

Look at what you must do if you want to exchange ten of one number for a larger number but the next column has a zero.

You need to be very careful at each stage of a written subtraction. Look at this one:

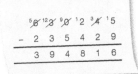

Here are some useful subtraction hints.

✓ Tips

- Remember, you can check your subtractions by adding your answer to the number you took away.
  243 – 175 = 68   checking...   68 + 175 = 243   correct!
- If you have a method you like, stick to it, practise it, and always check your answers.

Activities

- Notice that the questions progress in difficulty and will quickly show which children are having difficulties. If children are having difficulties, allow time for them to complete further calculations at a level they are comfortable with – preferably allowing them to set these calculations themselves to help raise their awareness. For children who are still struggling, apparatus may be beneficial to visualise the exchanging process.

Problems

- The Brain-buster requires children to use the relationship between addition and subtraction.
- For those progressing well, the links to *100 Maths Lessons Year 5* and the *Year 5 Practice Book* will provide further practice, particularly in applying these skills in context.

100 Maths Lessons Year 5 links:

- Autumn 1, Week 2 (pages 14–19): subtract large numbers using formal written methods (columnar subtraction)
- Spring 1, Week 2 (pages 96–101): subtract numbers and money using formal written methods
- Summer 1, Week 2 (pages 178–183): subtract whole numbers with up to five digits
- Summer 2, Week 1 (pages 213–218): subtract money using formal methods

Year 5 Practice Book links:

- (page 24): Written addition and subtraction (choose appropriate questions)
- (page 26): Take it away!
- (page 27): Adding and subtracting practice (1) (choose appropriate questions)
- (page 28): Adding and subtracting practice (2) (choose appropriate questions)
- (page 29): Adding and subtracting practice (3) (choose appropriate questions)
- (page 30): Spot the deliberate mistake (choose appropriate questions)

Talk maths

Look at the subtraction below and talk it through aloud, explaining how each stage was done. Make sure you work in the correct order.

$$\begin{array}{r} {}^{3}\cancel{4}\ {}^{1}3\ \ 5\ \ 5\ \ {}^{5}\cancel{6}\ {}^{1}2 \\ -\ \ 2\ \ 4\ \ 5\ \ 4\ \ 2\ \ 6 \\ \hline 1\ \ 9\ \ 0\ \ 1\ \ 3\ \ 6 \end{array}$$

Use estimation to quickly see if your answers are *about right*.

1405 – 950 is around 1400 – 900, so the answer will be around 500.

In fact, 1405 – 950 = 455, so my estimate was close!

Activities

1. Copy and complete these subtractions.
   a. 374 – 235   b. 7428 – 3265   c. 432,625 – 243,206

2. Use squared paper to write and complete each of these subtractions.
   a. 235 – 116   b. 4823 – 2550   c. 13,274 – 9306
   d. 10,206 – 6345   e. 240,231 – 123,308

Problems

Brain-teaser

City	Bim	Bam	Bom
Population	236,325	143,544	367,269

Which is bigger, the difference between the populations of Bim and Bam, or the difference between the populations of Bim and Bom?

Brain-buster
There is a fourth city called Bem. It has a population that is 154,289 less than Bom. What is the population of Bem?

Calculations   19

Multiples and factors

Prior learning

- Can recall times-tables facts to 12 × 12.
- Understand the place value of whole numbers and the effect of multiplying and dividing by 10.

- Display a large times-tables square and recap how this can be used for identifying relationships in both multiplication (for example, 4 × 5 = 20, 5 × 4 = 20) as well as division (20 ÷ 5 = 4, 20 ÷ 4 = 5).

- Spend some time looking at number patterns for the 2-, 3- and 5-times tables. Consider how we can know whether a number is a multiple of 2, 3 or 5.
- Point out that 2, 3 and 5 only have themselves and 1 as factors – because of this, they are called prime numbers.
- Still using the multiplication square, focus on how we can find pairs of factors. Use the number 12 to show that a number may have more than one pair of factors. Remind the children that this number (12) is a multiple of each of its factors.
- Touch on prime factors, limiting this to the prime numbers 2, 3 and 5.
- *100 Maths Lessons Year 5, Autumn 1, Week 3* provides ample opportunity to practise finding and identifying factors and multiples.

Curriculum objectives

- To identify multiples and factors, including finding all factor pairs of a number, and common factors of two numbers.
- Solve problems involving multiplication and division including using their knowledge of factors and multiples, squares and cubes.

Success criteria

- I can find and identify multiples, factor pairs and common factors.

Multiples and factors

Learn

A **multiple** is a number that is made by multiplying two numbers.

$$4 \times 3 = 12$$

12 is a **multiple** of 3, and it is also a **multiple** of 4.

We can also say that 3 and 4 are **factors** of 12.

Factors are the numbers that we multiply together to get multiples.

Factors are easiest to find as pairs.

$$12 = (1 \times 12), (2 \times 6) \text{ or } (3 \times 4)$$

So the factors of 12 are 1, 2, 3, 4, 6 and 12.

$$15 = (1 \times 15) \text{ or } (3 \times 5)$$

So the factors of 15 are 1, 3, 5 and 15.

Remember, we can also say that 12 is a multiple of 1, 2, 3, 4 and 6.

Sometimes two different numbers will share the same factor. We call this a **common factor**.

3 is a common factor of 12 and 15.

We can also say that 12 and 15 are common multiples of 3.

✓ Tips

- Remember, factors divide into multiples. 3 is a factor of 12, and 12 is a multiple of 3.
- Some numbers have lots of factors; some only have 2.
- All prime numbers only have themselves and 1 as factors.
- A factor that is *also* a prime number is called, a *prime factor*!

Here's some help with multiples and factors.

20   Calculations

- Arrange children in small groups and give each group a set of around ten numbers written on paper. These should be a mix of factors, common factors, prime factors and multiples (for example, 2, 3, 6, 9, 24). If these are different for each group, you can rotate the sets of numbers for further practice.

- Next, ask the children to make at least one statement, or more if possible, for each number. Such as:
  - *4 is a factor of 12.*
  - *4 is a multiple of 2.*
- This can be extended to relating numbers, such as:
  - *3 and 5 are factor pairs of 15.*
  - *3 is a common factor of 9 and 12.*

Activities

- Children who competently complete this section might try to find factors and multiples for larger numbers, perhaps over 100.

- The activities in *Year 5 Practice Book* provide further practice.

Problems

- You may wish to challenge more confident learners to start investigating patterns and rules for assessing whether a number is divisible by 2, 3, 4, 5, 6, 7, 8 and 9.

Talk maths

Close this book, and then explain to someone what a factor is and what a multiple is. Use examples to help you.

Then open the book and check how you did.

Did you know?

Did you know that multiples go on forever? Don't try it out, just trust me!

Activities

1. Write down all the factors of 6.
2. Write down five multiples of 4.
3. Write all the factor pairs for each of these numbers.
   a. 15   b. 27   c. 24   d. 30
4. Find the common factors of these numbers.
   a. 12 and 16   b. 15 and 20   c. 28 and 40   d. 50 and 100

Problems

Brain-teaser
Selina has 24 small chocolates and she wants to share them equally with some of her friends. Copy and complete the chart to show how many children she **could** share them equally between, and how many chocolates each person would get.

Children	1	2							
Chocolates	24	12							

What would happen if Selina tried to share her chocolates between five friends?

Brain-buster
Everyone knows there are 365 days in a year, and 7 days in a week. Are there exactly 52 weeks in a year? Explain your answer.

100 Maths Lessons Year 5 links:

- Autumn 1, Week 3 (pages 20–25): find pairs of factors to at least 50

Year 5 Practice Book links:

- (page 35): Multiples
- (page 36): Know your multiples
- (page 38): Divisibility tests
- (page 39): Factor trees
- (page 40): Identify common factors

Prime numbers

Prior learning

• Can recall multiples to 12 × 12.

Learn

• Bring six children to the front of the class and ask them to arrange themselves into equal groups. Depending on whether they create pairs or threes, next challenge them to create the other. Ask one child to sit down, and then ask the remaining five to arrange themselves into equal groups. They will soon discover this is not possible.

• Discuss with the children and then explain that a prime number is one that can only be divided exactly by itself and 1, with no remainder.

• Tell the children that 1 is not a prime number. In discussion, look at prime numbers between 1 and 10. Can children see what is special about the prime number '2'?

• Display a large 100-square and work with the children to eliminate numbers that are not prime (composite numbers), modelling the language involved, such as: *All even numbers are divisible by 2, so all even numbers are not prime.*

• Explain that this method is sometimes called the sieve of Eratosthenes, after the Greek mathematician who created it.

• *100 Maths Lessons Year 5, Autumn 1, Week 3* provides ample opportunity to practise finding and identifying prime numbers.

Curriculum objectives

• To know and use the vocabulary of prime numbers, prime factors and composite (non-prime) numbers.

• To establish whether a number up to 100 is prime and recall prime numbers up to 19.

Success criteria

• I can recall all prime numbers up to 19.

• I can find out if any number up to 99 is a prime.

Prime numbers

Learn

A number that can only be divided by itself or 1, with no remainder, is called a prime number. For example, 2, 3 and 5 are all prime numbers.

1 is not counted as a prime number.

2 is the only even prime number. All other even numbers can be divided by 2 as well as 1 and themselves.

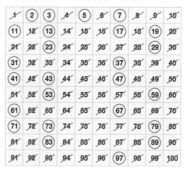

Look at the numbers 1 to 10. We can circle 2 as a prime number. We know that all even numbers can be divided by 2, so we can delete all other even numbers because we know that none of these can be prime numbers.

We can also circle 3, and then delete 9. We know from the times tables that 9 can be divided by 3, so it cannot be a prime number.

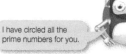

I have circled all the prime numbers for you.

✓ Tips

• There are rules that can help you decide if any number is a prime or not.

• A number that is even can be divided by 2, so no even numbers are prime numbers, except 2 itself of course!

• Add the digits of the number together. If the sum can be divided by 3, so can the number, and so it is not a prime number, for example 207: 2 + 0 + 7 = 9, 9 can be divided by 3, so 207 is not a prime number!

• If a number ends in 0 or 5 it can be divided by 5, so it is not a prime number, for example 115 is not a prime number.

Warning! These rules only *help* you to decide, you may still need to check for other prime factors!

Talk maths

- The textbook outlines a game called 'Prime Time', which requires children to challenge each other to identify prime numbers. It is important to model this first so that children can see the importance of using explanations to justify their answers.

Activities

- In addition to the given questions, ideally all children should complete a 'sieved' 100-square of their own.
- The activities in *Year 5 Practice Book* provide further practice.

Problems

- Any children who complete the problems should be encouraged to create a Brain-teaser and Brain-buster of their own.

Talk maths

Challenge an adult or a friend to a game of *Prime Time*. You need something to time minutes on, such as a stopwatch. You will also need a pencil and paper, for keeping scores and remembering which numbers have been used.

Take it in turns to say a number and challenge the other player to decide whether it is a prime number or not, and record how long it took to answer the question. If challenged, a player must prove why their answer is yes or no, with a sensible explanation.

Play *Prime Time*!

Did you know?

Mathematicians are still discovering new prime numbers. Imagine how enormous those numbers must be!

Activities

1. What is a prime number?

2. Write all the prime numbers between 1 and 20 (there are eight altogether).

3. Say which of these numbers are prime, and explain each of your answers.

   a. 25   b. 71   c. 87

4. Can you think of a prime number greater than 100?

Problems

Brain-teaser
77 cannot be divided by 2, 3 or 5. Does this make it a prime number? Explain your answer.

Brain-buster
Mohammed says that 7 is a prime number, and so is 17, so 27 must also be a prime number. Explain why he is wrong.

Calculations   23

100 Maths Lessons Year 5 links:

- Autumn 1, Week 3 (pages 20–25): establish whether a number up to 100 is prime and recall prime numbers up to 19

Year 5 Practice Book links:

- (page 42): Prime numbers and composite numbers
- (page 43): Prime factors

Multiplying large numbers

Prior learning

- Can recall multiplication facts up to 12 × 12.
- Can multiply using arrays, groups of, multiplying by 10 and partitioning.
- Can use informal written methods for multiplication.

Learn

- Using three or four simple multiplications (of a 2-digit number by a 1-digit number), present and discuss the methods and vocabulary that are standard to your school, focusing on carrying 10s and 100s forward and showing how they are included in the final answer.
- Progress to multiplying 3- and 4-digit numbers by a single digit, using smaller numbers to maintain a focus on the process.
- Allow the children time to practise before moving on to formal methods for long multiplication, which are best introduced in a separate session.
- Using a similar approach, work through the procedure for long multiplication, carefully focusing on each step. If your school has a standard method that everyone should learn, try writing the steps involved next to a large example and displaying it in the classroom.
- *100 Maths Lessons Year 5, Spring 1, Week 3* provides good introductory activities for long multiplication.

Curriculum objectives

- To multiply numbers up to four digits by a 1- or 2-digit number using a formal written method, including long multiplication for 2-digit numbers.

Success criteria

- I can use formal written methods for multiplying larger numbers.

Multiplying large numbers

Learn

There are formal written methods for multiplying numbers. You may have been taught methods a bit different to this one. You should use whichever method you are comfortable with – as long as you get the right answers!

	6	3
×		7
4	4	1
		2

	3	2	5
×			6
1	9	5	0
	1	3	

	4	6	2	5
×				5
2	3	1	2	5
	3	1	2	

Remember, the numbers are arranged in their place-value columns.

We know that the place-value columns continue for thousands, ten-thousands, hundred-thousands and so on. We can use formal written methods using these columns.

When multiplying two numbers larger than 10, multiply each digit on the top by each digit on the bottom, carrying numbers to the next column along, when necessary.

You can multiply first by the 10s, or the 1s; the answer will still be the same.

	4	6
×	1	5
2	3³	0
4	6	0	+
6	9	0

Answer: 690

We call this **long multiplication**.

✓ Tips

- Most people find it easier to put the larger number on the top, although it doesn't really matter which way round you arrange them – the answer will still be the same.
- Remember, the 1 digit in 14 is 10.
- It doesn't matter if you start with the 10s or the 1s.

		3	2	
	×	1	4	
(32 × 4)	1	2	8	
(32 × 10)	3	2	0	+
	4	4	8	

OR

		3	2	
	×	1	4	
(32 × 10)	3	2	0	
(32 × 4)	1	2	8	+
	4	4	8	

- The textbook provides a selection of examples for children to investigate and discuss with one another. This can be extended to considering the standard steps for long multiplication and writing these for each example. The discussion might be extended further to calculations of the children's own choosing.

Activities

- Children's answers to this section should provide enough information to enable you to assess which children have understood the procedures. Look out in particular for problems in dealing with multiplying by 10s, and correct presentation of the written method.

Problems

- Variations on both the Brain-teaser and the Brain-buster, easier or harder, can easily be presented by tweaking the numbers involved.

- Further problems are available in the links to *100 Maths Lessons Year 5* and *Year 5 Practice Book*.

100 Maths Lessons Year 5 links:

- Autumn 2, Week 1 (pages 49–54): multiply 3-digit numbers by a 1-digit number or 2-digit numbers by 2-digit numbers using a formal written method

- Spring 1, Week 3 (pages 102–107): multiply numbers with up to three digits by a 1- or 2-digit number, using a formal written method, including long multiplication for 2-digit numbers

- Spring 2, Week 2 (pages 137–142): multiply numbers with up to four digits and decimals by a 1- or 2-digit number, using a formal written method, including long multiplication

- Summer 1, Week 3 (pages 184–189): long multiplication with numbers with up to four digits and decimals by a 1-digit number

- Summer 2, Week 2 (pages 219–224): use multiplication in money problems

Year 5 Practice Book links:

- (page 48): Written multiplication strategies

- (page 49): Written multiplication practice

Talk maths

Look at the long multiplications below and talk them through aloud, saying how each stage was done.

Remember that zeros still have to be multiplied, and anything times zero is zero!

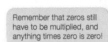

Activities

1. Copy and complete each of these long multiplications.
   - a. 21 × 13
   - b. 23 × 24
   - c. 45 × 31
   - d. 63 × 56

2. On squared paper, write out and complete each of these long multiplications.
   - a. 15 × 21
   - b. 26 × 32
   - c. 53 × 15
   - d. 33 × 40

Problems

Brain-teaser
A school's tuck shop sells cartons of fruit juice. Each carton cost 15p. If 43 cartons are sold, how much money will be collected?

Brain-buster
There are 475 children in a school. The school is raising money for charity with a sponsored walk, and they hope to raise £6000. If each child raises £13 will they hit their target? Explain your answer.

Calculations 25

Dividing large numbers

Prior learning

- Can recall multiplication facts up to 12 × 12.
- Can use informal written methods for division, for example the 'chunking' method.

Learn

- Display a multiplication square and spend time discussing the relationship between multiplication and division, practising different tables from a division perspective (such as 12 ÷ 4 = 3, 20 ÷ 4 = 5, 32 ÷ 4 = 8 for the 4-times table).
- Work through a number of small, simple short divisions with the children, modelling layout and vocabulary, and look at how the remainder is presented. Also, look at how remainders change by altering numbers slightly. For example, compare 12 ÷ 4, 13 ÷ 4, 14 ÷ 4, 15 ÷ 4 and 16 ÷ 4.
- *100 Maths Lessons Year 5, Autumn 2, Week 2* provides lots of advice and examples on short division.

Curriculum objectives

- To divide numbers up to four digits by a 1-digit number using the formal written method of short division and interpret remainders appropriately for the context.

Success criteria

- I can use written formal methods for dividing larger numbers.
- I can present remainders correctly.

Dividing large numbers

Learn

There are formal written methods for dividing numbers. You may have been taught methods a bit different to this one. You should use whichever method you are comfortable with – as long as you get the right answers!

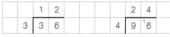

		1	2			2	4	
3	3	6			4	9	¹6	

For 36 ÷ 3 = 12 we say 36 divided *by* 3 equals 12.

Remember what divide means. It tells you how many times one number *goes into* another number.

In short division we move forward remainders. Sometimes there is a remainder at the end.

		1	2	r1			2	4	r3
3	3	7				4	9	¹9	

There is also a method called long division. You don't have to use that method yet, but if you know how to use it no one is going to stop you!

We can still use short division when we are dividing by 2-digit numbers. We just need to look for the first whole number that the 2-digit number can divide into, the rest is the same.

			0	2	1	r3			0	3	2	r11
1	2	2	²5	¹5			1	5	4	⁴9	⁴1	

✓ Tips

- Lay out your work carefully. Use squared paper to help you.
- You can always check your answer by multiplying the answer by the number you divided by, and then add the remainder.

Talk maths

- Provide pairs of children with a selection of short-division examples. Tell them to talk them through and develop a step-by-step set of instruction for each stage, asking for volunteers to explain their steps to the class and noting good use of language with correct procedure.

Activities

- If children struggle with these calculations, allow them to try simpler problems. In particular, questions 1d and 2d are only there to challenge those who are comfortable with single-digit divisions. Note that long division is not expected of most children in this age group.

- The activities in *Year 5 Practice Book* provide further practice.

Problems

- The problems allow children the opportunity to interpret remainders in context.

- The Brain-buster involves long multiplication, and so is most suitable for more confident learners. By tweaking the numbers, show how the whole number in the answer might remain the same, but the remainder is altered (for example, 510 staples, 245 pieces of popcorn).

Talk maths

Look at this division and talk it through aloud, saying how each stage was done.

	1	2	4	r3
4	4	9	¹9	

Remember that zero divided by anything is zero.

Activities

1. Complete each of these divisions.

   a. 95 ÷ 5   b. 68 ÷ 6   c. 234 ÷ 5   d. 482 ÷ 15

2. Write out and complete each of these divisions.

   a. 98 ÷ 7   b. 125 ÷ 5   c. 522 ÷ 8   d. 318 ÷ 15

Problems

Brain-teaser
There are 500 staples in a box. If the teacher's staple gun holds 40 staples, how many times can she refill her staple gun?

Brain-buster
Mako makes a large bowl of popcorn for her class party. If there are 246 pieces of popcorn, and there are 21 children in the class, how many pieces of popcorn will each child get if it is divided equally? Mako's teacher eats any remaining pieces. How many pieces does he get?

100 Maths Lessons Year 5 links:

- Autumn 2, Week 2 (pages 55–60): divide numbers with up to four digits by a 1-digit number, using short division, and interpreting remainders appropriately for the context

- Spring 2, Week 2 (pages 137–142): use short division and express remainders as fractions

- Summer 1, Week 3 (pages 184–189): use short division to solve problems and express remainders as decimals or fractions

Year 5 Practice Book links:

- (page 50): Divided up

- (page 51): Written division (with remainders)

Calculations   27

Mental methods for multiplying and dividing

Prior learning

- Can recall multiples to 12 × 12.
- Understand the place value of whole numbers and the effect of multiplying and dividing by 10.

Learn

- Use a large multiplication square for regular, brief sessions to consolidate knowledge and recap the inverse relationship between multiplication and division.
- Working through the examples in the textbook, model how to analyse calculations with larger numbers. Emphasise how to break the calculations down into parts.

Curriculum objectives

- To multiply and divide numbers mentally drawing upon known facts.

Success criteria

- I can recall my times tables.
- I can use my times tables to carry out harder multiplication and division calculations.

100 Maths Lessons Year 5 links:

- Autumn 1, Week 4 (pages 26–31): factors and adjusting
- Summer 2, Week 2 (pages 219–224): use mental methods

Year 5 Practice Book links:

- (page 44): Calculation patterns
- (page 45): Using related multiplication and division facts
- (page 46): Partitioning when multiplying mentally
- (page 47): Division with remainders
- (page 63): Lots of division

- Move on to identifying factors, primes and square numbers as a method of breaking down larger numbers. For example:
$15 × 16 = 3 × 5 × 2 × 8 = 5 × 2 × 3 × 8 = 10 × 24 = 240$.

Talk maths

- Ask the children to write down five calculations (focusing on multiplication, division and mixed calculations) to work out mentally. Then ask them to challenge each other to complete their calculations and explain their approaches.

Activities

- The questions in this section will provide information about children's basic understanding and confidence in using mental methods.

Problems

- If possible, provide the children with a variety of both simple and complex word problems focusing on the mental skills covered so far.

Mental methods for multiplying and dividing

Learn

You know how to use a multiplication square.

Multiplication squares help to show us that division is the *inverse* of multiplication.

So, we can say

$6 × 7 = 42$ $7 × 6 = 42$

$42 ÷ 6 = 7$ $42 ÷ 7 = 6$

You can use your times tables to help you with harder mental calculations.

$4 × 30 = 120$ (We know that $4 × 3 = 12$, so $4 × 30 = 120$)

$520 × 6 = 3120$ (We know that $5 × 6 = 30$, so $500 × 6 = 3000$, and $20 × 6 = 120$)

$123 ÷ 3 = 41$ (We know that $12 ÷ 3 = 4$, so $120 ÷ 3 = 40$, and $3 ÷ 3 = 1$)

$2816 ÷ 4 = 704$ (We know that $28 ÷ 4 = 7$, so $2800 ÷ 4 = 700$, and $16 ÷ 4 = 4$)

×	1	2	3	4	5	6	7	8	9	10
1	1	2	3	4	5	6	7	8	9	10
2	2	4	6	8	10	12	14	16	18	20
3	3	6	9	12	15	18	21	24	27	30
4	4	8	12	16	20	24	28	32	36	40
5	5	10	15	20	25	30	35	40	45	50
6	6	12	18	24	30	36	(42)	48	54	60
7	7	14	21	28	35	42	49	56	63	70
8	8	16	24	32	40	48	56	64	72	80
9	9	18	27	36	45	54	63	72	81	90
10	10	20	30	40	50	60	70	80	90	100

Too tricky? If in doubt, write it out!

Activities

1. Solve these multiplications mentally.
   - a. $4 × 50$
   - b. $320 × 3$
   - c. $2 × 4444$
   - d. $5 × 6000$
   - e. $7 × 2050$

2. Now try these divisions using mental methods.
   - a. $300 ÷ 6$
   - b. $129 ÷ 3$
   - c. $5005 ÷ 5$
   - d. $3608 ÷ 4$
   - e. $2828 ÷ 7$

Problems

Brain-buster
Six people share a lottery ticket that wins £12,300. If they share the winning amount equally, how much will they each receive?

Square numbers and cube numbers

Prior learning

- Can recall quickly multiplication facts up to 12 × 12.

Learn

- On a large squared grid, draw squares of side lengths 1 unit, 2 units and 3 units to demonstrate the concept of square numbers.

- Provide children with squared paper and ask them to draw different-sized squares. Allow children time to count the number of squares contained by the squares of different length sides, stressing that the focus is not on the actual length of the sides but simply the number of side lengths. (This is especially important if the children are using squared paper with squares of 0.5cm length sides.)

- Displaying a multiplication square, look in turn at each number multiplied by itself, introducing the terminology of a superscript 2, for example $5^2 = 5 \times 5 = 25$, saying *five squared equals twenty-five*.

- Move on to explaining cubed and demonstrating.

Talk maths

- If possible, provide children with a pile of 1cm cubes and ask them to investigate cube numbers individually or in pairs or groups.

- Ask the children to compare the growth of cube numbers compared to squares.

Activities

- For an extension, ask children to use their chart to investigate inverses, for example $125 \div 5 = 25$.

Problems

- This can be extended by asking children to create their own problems.

Square numbers and cube numbers

Learn

A square number is a number multiplied by itself, for example, 2 squared is $2 \times 2 = 4$

A cube number is a number multiplied by itself, and then by itself again, for example,

2 cubed is $2 \times 2 \times 2 = 8$ ($2 \times 2 = 4$, then $4 \times 2 = 8$)

We use special numbers, called **powers**, to show square and cube numbers.

For 5 squared, instead of 5×5 we say $5^2 = 25$

For 4 cubed, instead of $4 \times 4 \times 4$ we say $4^3 = 64$

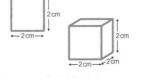

Five squared equals twenty-five.

Four cubed equals sixty-four.

Activities

Copy and complete this chart, then use it to practise and learn square and cube numbers.

1	2	3	4	5	6	7	8	9	10
1^2	2^2								
1×1	2×2								
1	4								
1^3	2^3								
$1 \times 1 \times 1$	$2 \times 2 \times 2$								
1	8								

Problems

Brain-teaser
Some children organise a five-a-side football match. Each player in Sanjay's team scored five goals. How many goals did his team score altogether?

Brain-buster
A farmer stores apples in boxes. Each box holds nine layers of apples; each layer is nine apples wide and nine apples long. How many apples are there in each box?

Calculations 29

Curriculum objectives

- To recognise and use square numbers and cube numbers, and the notation for squared (^{2}) and cubed (^{3}).

Success criteria

- I can recognise and calculate square and cube numbers.

100 Maths Lessons Year 5 links:

- Spring 1, Week 3 (pages 102–107): understand and use square numbers

Year 5 Practice Book links:

- (page 54): Square numbers
- (page 55): Square numbers and notation
- (page 56): Cube numbers
- (page 57): Cube numbers and notation

Multiplying and dividing by 10, 100 and 1000

Prior learning

- Can recall multiplication facts up to 12 × 12.
- Understand the place value of whole numbers and the effect of multiplying and dividing by 10.

Learn

- Drawing columns on your whiteboard, focus children's attention on the powers of 10. Looking at simple calculations (for example, 6 × 10, 4 × 100), consider how digits move columns according to the power of 10 they are multiplied by. Reminding the children that division is the inverse of multiplication, show how dividing numbers by powers of 10 has the reverse effect (for example, 420 ÷ 10).

- Next, include a decimal point and tenths, hundredths and thousandths columns. Focus on applying the rules of multiplying and dividing by powers of 10 on both sides of the decimal point.

- Using the table in the textbook as a basis, work through several examples of 1- or 2-digit numbers being multiplied and divided by different powers of 10. As these are completed, discuss the operations and model the vocabulary involved.

- *100 Maths Lessons Year 5, Autumn 1, Week 4* consolidates these concepts.

Multiplying and dividing by 10, 100 and 1000

Learn

Our number system is arranged in **powers of 10**. When we multiply a number by 10 we make each digit 10 times bigger. Each digit moves one place to the left.

Please don't say *just add a zero*. That doesn't work for decimals!

6 × 10 = 60   43 × 10 = 430   257 × 10 = 2570
0.4 × 10 = 4   0.07 × 10 = 0.7

When we divide a number by 10, we make each digit 10 times smaller. Each digit moves one place to the right.

6 ÷ 10 = 0.6   43 ÷ 10 = 4.3   257 ÷ 10 = 25.7
0.4 ÷ 10 = 0.04   0.07 ÷ 10 = 0.007

The decimal point doesn't move! It is always between the ones and tenths.

Operation	Example 1	Example 2
× 10	65 × 10 = 650	7 × 10 = 70
× 100	65 × 100 = 6500	7 × 100 = 700
× 1000	65 × 1000 = 65,000	7 × 1000 = 7000
÷ 10	65 ÷ 10 = 6.5	7 ÷ 10 = 0.7
÷ 100	65 ÷ 100 = 0.65	7 ÷ 100 = 0.07
÷ 1000	65 ÷ 1000 = 0.065	7 ÷ 1000 = 0.007

✓ Tips

- Think about the **place-value** columns:

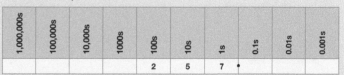

1,000,000s	100,000s	10,000s	1000s	100s	10s	1s	0.1s	0.01s	0.001s
				2	5	7			

- For any calculation, think about the number becoming bigger or smaller, moving it to the left or the right. Try this for 257 × 1000, then for 257 ÷ 1000. Then try some other numbers.

- Using the textbook as a starting point, have the children challenge each other to multiply and divide different numbers by 10, 100 or 1000. Encourage them to explain their methods to each other and say whether their answer is bigger or smaller, and by how much (for example, a hundred times smaller).

Activities

- Complete the first grid with the children and discuss the patterns in it. Children who seem insecure in their understanding should have further practice with simpler numbers.
- *100 Maths Lessons Year 5, Autumn 2, Week 1* and *Spring 2, Week 2* provide opportunities to practise multiplication skills, using 10, 100 and 1000 as part of breaking down larger multiplications.

Problems

- These problems focus only on multiplying and dividing by powers of 10, and provide an excellent route for introducing children to problems of scale. The Brain-teaser and Brain-buster can easily be adapted to provide further practice.

Talk maths

Practise using the correct vocabulary.

Now, using a pencil and paper, explain to a partner how to multiply and divide by 10, 100 and 1000.

23 times 1000 is 23,000. It is now 1000 times bigger.

3 divided by 100 is 0.03. It is now 100 times smaller.

0.06 divided by 10 is 0.006. It is now 10 times smaller.

0.023 times 100 is 2.3. It now is 100 times bigger.

Activities

Copy and complete these grids.

	× 10	× 100	× 1000
3	30	300	3000
÷ 10	0.3	3	
÷ 100	0.03		3
÷ 1000	0.003			3

	× 10	× 100	× 1000
27			
÷ 10			
÷ 100			
÷ 1000			

	× 10	× 100	× 1000
48			
÷ 10			
÷ 100			
÷ 1000			

	× 10	× 100	× 1000
317			
÷ 10			
÷ 100			
÷ 1000			

Problems

Brain-teaser
Tim says that an aeroplane flying over his house is 1000 times higher than the roof of his house. His house is 32 feet tall. How high up is the aeroplane?

Brain-buster
A new-born piglet weighs just one hundredth of its mother's weight. If its mother weighs 135.6kg, what weight will the piglet be?

Calculations   31

---

100 Maths Lessons Year 5 links:

- Autumn 1, Week 4 (pages 26–31): multiply and divide whole numbers and decimals by 10, 100 and 1000

- Autumn 2, Week 1 (pages 49–54): multiply and divide increasingly large whole numbers 10 and 100

- Spring 2, Week 2 (pages 137–142): use knowledge of place value to multiply and divide by 10, 100 and 1000

Year 5 Practice Book links:

- (pages 52–53): Multiplying and dividing by 10, 100 and 1000

Scaling and rates

Prior learning

- Can recall quickly multiplication facts up to 12 × 12.
- Can use informal or formal written methods for multiplication.
- Understand the process of multiplication, based on arrays and 'lots' or 'groups of'.

Learn

- Allow time, preferably not all in the same session, to cover the basic concepts of fractions of quantities (for example, ½ of 34 children), scale (for example, 100 times bigger than a 5cm toy) and rate (for example, eating 12 peas per minute). Via class discussion, try to collect examples of when we use fractions of quantities, scales and rates.

- Using the textbook as a starting point, consider a wide range of problems involving fractions, scales and rates. Adapt the number in the examples in the textbook if additional material is required.

- It may be preferable to tackle each of these areas in separate sessions as they can be easily confused. The textbook focuses more on fractions of quantities and on scale. The main rate that might be looked at is what can be done in a certain length of time (for example, per minute, per hour) although exchange conversion rates could also be covered.

- *100 Maths Lessons Year 5, Spring 1, Week 3* has activities and resources for using scale in context.

Curriculum objectives

- To solve problems involving multiplication and division, including scaling by simple fractions and problems involving simple rates.

Success criteria

- I can use multiplication and division to solve problems involving fractions, scales and rates.

Scaling and rates

Learn

We can easily calculate fractions of quantities.

A farmer sells half his flock of 24 sheep. $\frac{1}{2}$ of 24 sheep = 12 sheep.

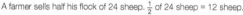

Calculate **scale**: The building is 100 times bigger than the model.

The model is 20cm tall, so the building must be 2000cm, or 20 metres tall.

We can also calculate the rate that things happen.

If I eat 25 chips in five minutes, I have eaten five chips per minute.

Here are some problems involving scales and rates.

Examples of scales:

A child is half the height of his dad. If the child is 90cm, the father must be 180cm.

A car is four times the size of a model. If the car is 5 metres long the model must be 1.25 metres.

The scale of a map is 1:100,000. This means that every centimetre on the map equals a kilometre in real life.

Examples of rates:

In a traffic survey, 12 cars drive past a school in one hour. We can estimate that in six hours 72 cars will go past the school (6 × 12 = 72 cars).

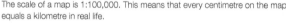

 A bathtub fills up at a rate of 10 litres per minute. If it takes 15 minutes to fill the bath, the bath must have a capacity of 150 litres (10 × 15 = 150 litres).

Ten people per minute go into a cinema. If it takes 40 minutes to fill all the seats, the cinema must hold 400 people (10 × 40 = 400 people).

✓ Tips

- When calculating scales, remember you can use the inverse too.
- If a road is 12km long then we know it will be 12cm on a map with a scale of 1 to 100,000.
- If a 10cm model is one fifth the size of an object, the object will be 50cm high.

Talk maths

- Bring a selection of simple maps, ideally with large scales, into the classroom and practise calculating the actual distances by multiplying the distances on the map by the scale.

Activities

- Check to see how children work out their answers for question 2. The areas of the rectangles in the textbook are 24 squares and 30 squares, so the answers are 12 squares and 15 squares respectively.
- The activities in *Year 5 Practice Book* provide further practice.

Problems

- The Brain-buster problem should only be used as an extension.
- The Brain-teaser problem is a 'rate' problem. If it is too difficult, ask children to find how many times Mason's heart beats in 5 minutes, then 10, and so on. This problem can be easily extended to measure the children's heart rates. Challenge them to find out how often their heart beats in a week, a month, or a year.

Talk maths

Look at this map and check that you understand the scale. Talk about it with a partner, discussing what the real-life distances will be between different features on it.

0 100m

Activities

1. Write out and calculate these fractions.

   a. $\frac{1}{2}$ of 6 cakes
   b. $\frac{1}{4}$ of 20 adults
   c. $\frac{1}{3}$ of 66 animals
   d. $\frac{3}{4}$ of 100 children

2. Draw two rectangles half the length and width of those shown.

3. A teacher makes a scale model of her classroom. She builds everything at a scale of 1 to 20. Copy and complete the chart to show the sizes of each item in her model.

Item	Room	Table	Chair	Cupboard	Waste basket
Real height	280cm	90cm	40cm	170cm	25cm
Model height					

Problems

Brain-teaser
Mason measures his heart rate. It is 60 beats per minute. How many times will his heart beat in an hour? How many times in a day?

Brain-buster
A sculptor makes a 12cm model of an athlete. The athlete is 180cm tall. What scale is the model? (Give your answer as a fraction.)

100 Maths Lessons Year 5 links:

- Spring 1, Week 3 (pages 102–107): solve problems involving multiplication and division, including scaling and problems involving simple rates

Year 5 Practice Book links:

- (page 66): Recipe problem
- (page 67): Exchange rates

Using all four operations

Prior learning

- Can recall their times tables up to 12×12.
- Can calculate using a written method and have some experience of using formal methods for multiplication and division.

Learn

Learn

- Briefly discuss with the children how in addition and multiplication it doesn't matter what order the numbers are in as the answers are the same, whereas in division and subtraction they aren't. Work though a selection of examples to demonstrate this.
- Starting with the examples in the textbook, work carefully, step-by-step, to demonstrate the correct order of operations for complex calculations. Use this as an opportunity to model good practice in laying out work neatly and working methodically.
- When developing further examples of your own, check the

answers before presenting them to the children

- Stress the importance and usefulness of estimation. Children should develop the habit of estimating the rough magnitude of what their answer should be. This could include rounding numbers for ease of mental calculation.
- *100 Maths Lessons Year 5*, Spring 2, Week 2, Lesson 5 (page 142) provides further practice in using all four operations.

Curriculum objectives

- To solve problems involving addition, subtraction, multiplication and division and a combination of these, including understanding the meaning of the equals sign.
- To use rounding to check answers to calculations and determine, in the context of a problem, levels of accuracy.

Success criteria

- I can identify and use the correct order of operations in more complex calculations.
- I can choose and use the correct operations to solve multi-step problems.

Talk maths

- Using a selection of price lists such as the one in the textbook, arrange children in pairs and have them place different orders with each other. Encourage them to set problems that involve more than one operation but are not so hard as to be too mentally challenging. This can be taken a stage further by calculating the change given for different notes tendered.

Using all four operations

Learn

$\neq$ means does **NOT** equal.

Addition and multiplication work in any order, division and subtraction do not.

| $3 + 4 = 4 + 3$ | $5 \times 6 = 6 \times 5$ | $12 - 3 \neq 3 - 12$ | $10 \div 2 \neq 2 \div 10$ |

Calculations and problems involving more than one operation are called **multi-step**. You must do one calculation at a time.

And you must do them in the right order!

The right order is division and multiplication first, followed by addition and subtraction, working from left to right.

Look at this calculation: $16 \div 4 + 2 \times 5 - 12$

Division first ($16 \div 4 = 4$)	$4 + 2 \times 5 - 12$
Multiplication next ($2 \times 5 = 10$)	$4 + 10 - 12$
Then addition ($4 + 10 = 14$)	$14 - 12$
And last subtraction ($14 - 12 = 2$)	**Answer** = 2

Now let's try this one: $24 - 3 \times 5 + 10 \div 2$

Multiplication first ($3 \times 5 = 15$)	$24 - 15 + 10 \div 2$
Division next ($10 \div 2 = 5$)	$24 - 15 + 5$
Then subtraction ($24 - 15 = 9$)	$9 + 5$
And last addition ($9 + 5 = 14$)	**Answer** = 14

✓ Tips

- When you use maths to solve problems, think about the operations you will use, and start with an estimate. A quick estimate for $12 \times 6 - 24 \div 3 + 15$ would be to do the division and multiplication $72 - 8 + 15$ then round to get $70 - 10 + 15$, giving an estimate of 75 (the answer is 79).

OK, everything seems to be in order here, so let's think about estimation.

Activities

- Use these questions to assess whether children know and can use the correct order of operations in complex calculations. In particular, look for children who can present each stage of their working clearly and who lay out their work correctly to aid understanding. Share this good practice with the children.

Problems

- Further Brain-teasers and Brain-busters can easily be developed using the price list in the textbook.
- *100 Maths Lessons Year 5, Summer 1, Week 3* provides practice in solving real-life problems and activities using four operations, and in using rounding and estimation to check their work.

- *100 Maths Lessons Year 5, Summer 2, Week 2* provides extended and complex tasks for using these skills in real-life contexts.

100 Maths Lessons Year 5 links:

- Spring 1, Week 2 (pages 96–101): round numbers and solve problems
- Spring 2, Week 1 (pages 131–136): add and subtract to solve real-life problems
- Spring 2, Week 2 (pages 137–142): solve problems involving addition, subtraction, multiplication and division
- Summer 1, Week 2 (pages 178–183): use written calculations to solve problems
- Summer 1, Week 3 (pages 184–189): solve problems involving all four operations
- Summer 2, Week 2 (pages 219–224): solve problems involving all four operations with money and measures

Year 5 Practice Book links:

- (page 32): Round, estimate, check
- (page 33): Estimate and win
- (page 58): Problem solver
- (page 59): History trip
- (page 60): Restaurant rip-off
- (page 61): Operation calculate
- (page 62): All at sea!
- (page 63): Lots of division
- (page 64): Half a bus
- (page 65): A sporting problem

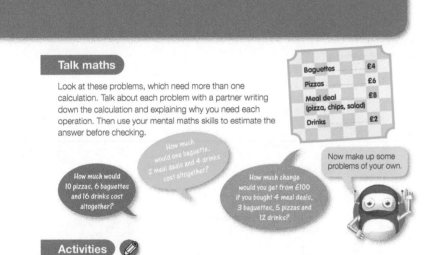

Talk maths

Look at these problems, which need more than one calculation. Talk about each problem with a partner writing down the calculation and explaining why you need each operation. Then use your mental maths skills to estimate the answer before checking.

Baguettes	£4
Pizzas	£6
Meal deal (pizza, chips, salad)	£8
Drinks	£2

How much would 10 pizzas, 6 baguettes and 16 drinks cost altogether?

How much would one baguette, 2 meal deals and 4 drinks cost altogether?

How much change would you get from £100 if you bought 4 meal deals, 3 baguettes, 5 pizzas and 12 drinks?

Now make up some problems of your own.

Activities

1. Copy and complete these calculations.
   a. $6 \times 2 - 3$
   b. $6 + 2 \times 3$
   c. $6 \div 2 + 3$
   d. $6 - 2 \times 3$

2. Decide if each of these calculations is right or wrong.
   a. $3 \times 8 + 16 \div 4 - 12 \div 6 = 26$
   b. $20 - 6 \times 2 = 28$
   c. $13 - 25 \div 5 \times 2 = 3$
   d. $12 - 6 + 3 = 3$
   e. $45 \div 5 + 4 \times 5 - 3 \times 7 = 8$
   f. $70 - 20 \times 3 + 50 \div 10 = 20$

3. Copy these calculations, adding the missing signs to make each of them true.
   a. $5 \times 5 + 12 \_\_\_ 2 - 3 \times 4 = 19$
   b. $12 \_\_\_ 3 \_\_\_ 14 \div 7 + 2 \times 4 = 10$

Problems

Brain-teaser
A customer asks for two cabbages and five onions. How much will this cost altogether?

Brain-buster
A customer requests three cabbages, four onions, one lettuce and a cucumber. How much change will she receive from a £10 note?

Grocer's price list

	Cabbages	80p
	Cucumbers	£1.20
	Lettuce	90p
	Onions	30p

Calculations 35

Comparing and ordering fractions

Prior learning

- Understand simple fractions, such as ½ and ¼, as equal parts of a whole.
- Understand fractions as parts of a shape as well as part of a number.

Learn

- Use a visual aid, whether drawn or actual, for showing how an object can be divided in to two, four then eight equal parts. Recap the use of 'numerator' and 'denominator' to indicate that a fraction is part of a whole. Also focus on the concept of one whole (for example, four quarters make one whole).

- Repeat the exercise using different shapes (circle, square, rectangle) to demonstrate that fractions show proportions of each particular whole.
- Using the visual aids and shapes, carefully examine the concept of equivalent fractions. Provide opportunities for children to cut paper circles into halves, quarters and eighths, and then investigate equivalents.

- Move on to considering how denominators can be adjusted to aid comparison of fractions, multiplying top and bottom by the same number.
- *100 Maths Lessons Year 5, Autumn 2, Week 3* provides a range of lessons and resources for developing skills for comparing and ordering fractions.

Curriculum objectives

- To compare and order fractions whose denominators are all multiples of the same number.
- To identify, name and write equivalent fractions of a given fraction, represented visually, including tenths and hundredths.

Success criteria

- I can compare and order fractions by giving them the same denominator.
- I can identify equivalent fractions.

Comparing and ordering fractions

Learn

Fractions have a numerator and a denominator.
They show us proportions of a whole.
One out of four pieces of this pizza has been eaten.

$$\text{numerator} \rightarrow \frac{1}{4} \leftarrow \text{denominator}$$

...and $\frac{3}{4}$ has not been eaten!

We can say $\frac{1}{4}$ has been eaten...

We can compare and order fractions by giving them the same denominators.

To do this we must understand **equivalent fractions**.
This pizza has been cut into eight equal pieces, or eighths.

$$\frac{2}{8} = \frac{1}{4}$$

These fractions are **equivalent** because they are **the same proportion of the whole**.
We can check this by changing either one of them:

$$\frac{2 \div 2 = 1}{8 \div 2 = 4} \qquad \frac{1 \times 2 = 2}{4 \times 2 = 8}$$

To compare and order fractions, it is easier if they all have the same denominator.

Which is bigger, $\frac{1}{3}$ or $\frac{2}{5}$? We can change both fractions into fifteenths and then compare:

$$\frac{1 \times 5 = 5}{3 \times 5 = 15} \qquad \frac{2 \times 3 = 6}{5 \times 3 = 15}$$

So, $\frac{2}{5}$ is bigger than $\frac{1}{3}$. 15 is the **common denominator**.

If you multiply or divide the numerator and denominator by the same number the fraction still has the same value.

✓ Tips

- Finding a common denominator is the same as finding a lowest common multiple.
- Remember: < means **is smaller than** and > means **is bigger than**.
  We can say $\frac{2}{5} > \frac{1}{3}$ and $\frac{1}{3} < \frac{2}{5}$.

Talk maths

- Use the fractions in the textbook, or present a suitable selection, and ask the children to work together to create a selection of statements based around the given fractions. Their statements should incorporate key vocabulary, such as 'equivalent to', 'is greater than', 'is smaller than', 'lowest common denominator'.

Activities

- If appropriate, children can avoid questions other than those focusing on ½, ⅓, ¼, ⅕ and ⅛.
- Look for children who are struggling to identify lowest common denominators, and revisit the concept of multiples with them.
- The activities in *Year 5 Practice Book* provide further practice.

Problems

- The Brain-teaser can be easily adapted and extended for a range of pizza-based problems. If appropriate, the children might devise some questions of their own.
- The Brain-buster should only be given to more confident learners.

Talk maths

Look at the fractions in the circle and make statements using < and >.

Use these phrases to help you.

The lowest common denominator of ____ and ____ is ____

____ is bigger than ____

____ is smaller than ____

____ is equivalent to ____

Can you make a statement that includes three fractions?

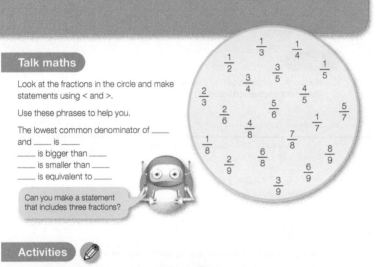

Activities

1. Change each fraction to give it a denominator of 8.
   a. $\frac{1}{2}$ b. $\frac{1}{4}$ c. $\frac{3}{4}$ d. 1 whole

2. Change each fraction to give it a denominator of 12.
   a. $\frac{1}{2}$ b. $\frac{1}{4}$ c. $\frac{2}{3}$ d. $\frac{5}{6}$

3. True or false? Copy the correct statements.
   a. $\frac{1}{3} = \frac{2}{6}$ b. $\frac{1}{2} = \frac{3}{5}$ c. $\frac{3}{4} = \frac{6}{8}$ d. $\frac{6}{9} = \frac{2}{3}$ e. $\frac{3}{4} > \frac{2}{3}$ f. $\frac{1}{3} > \frac{2}{5}$

   g. $\frac{7}{8} > \frac{8}{10}$ h. $\frac{7}{14} > \frac{1}{2}$ i. $\frac{1}{3} < \frac{2}{6}$ j. $\frac{5}{8} < \frac{6}{7}$ k. $\frac{3}{4} < \frac{8}{10}$ l. $\frac{13}{15} < \frac{2}{3}$

4. Write the fractions in order, smallest to largest.
   a. $\frac{1}{3}, \frac{1}{5}, \frac{1}{6}, \frac{1}{2}, \frac{1}{4}, \frac{1}{10}$ b. $\frac{3}{4}, \frac{3}{5}, \frac{5}{8}$ c. $\frac{2}{3}, \frac{4}{7}, \frac{7}{9}$

Problems

Brain-teaser

Jen has $\frac{1}{3}$ of a pizza. Tim has $\frac{2}{5}$. Which is the larger amount?

Brain-buster

In a football stadium, $\frac{3}{7}$ of the crowd support the blue team and $\frac{1}{3}$ support the red team. The rest don't mind who wins; they are neutral. Arrange the crowd – red, blue or neutral – in order, by fraction, starting with the smallest.

100 Maths Lessons Year 5 links:

- Autumn 2, Week 3 (pages 61–66): compare and order fractions whose denominators are all multiples of the same number

Year 5 Practice Book links:

- (page 68): Compare and order fractions

- (page 69): Fraction squeeze

Tricky fractions

Prior learning

- Can recall quickly multiplication facts up to 12 × 12 and derive corresponding division facts.
- Understand simple fractions of shapes.
- Understand that fractions relate to whole numbers and shapes divided into equal parts.

Learn

- Draw a grid of 20 dots on the whiteboard. Circle a suitable proportion and look at the equivalence of proportions (for example, 4 out of 20 = $\frac{4}{20}$ = $\frac{1}{5}$).
- If necessary, allow children time to investigate proportions of other amounts and how they can be simplified.

- Drawing four circles on the whiteboard, divide each one in half and discuss how four wholes are equivalent to eight halves. Next, remove one half of one circle, and discuss how the remainder should be represented. Move on to explain improper fractions (in this case $\frac{7}{2}$) and mixed numbers ($3\frac{1}{2}$) and that they are equivalent.

- Repeat this with a different number of wholes, all divided into quarters or thirds.
- *100 Maths Lessons Year 5, Spring 1, Week 4* provides structured approaches and activities for approaching these concepts.

Curriculum objectives

- To recognise mixed numbers and improper fractions and convert from one form to the other and write mathematical statements > 1 as a mixed number.

Success criteria

- I can convert between improper fractions and mixed numbers.

Tricky fractions

Learn

Fractions show proportions of a **whole**.
Equivalent fractions represent the **same** proportion.

$$\frac{3}{12} = \frac{1}{4}$$

To compare and order fractions they must have a common denominator.

Which fraction is bigger, $\frac{1}{3}$ or $\frac{1}{4}$?

$$\frac{1 \times 4 = 4}{3 \times 4 = 12} \qquad \frac{1 \times 3 = 3}{4 \times 3 = 12}$$

$$\frac{1}{3} > \frac{1}{4}$$

There were four cakes, but someone ate half of one of them.

There are now three and a half cakes. We write this as $3\frac{1}{2}$.
There is a whole number and a fraction. This is called a **mixed number**.

Improper fractions have a numerator that is bigger than the denominator.

Look: $\frac{7}{2}$ is an improper fraction.

Look at the cakes and think about how many halves there are. Each whole cake has two halves, so there are seven halves altogether.

$\frac{7}{2}$ is the same as saying seven divided by two... which is three and a half!

$$\frac{7}{2} = 3\frac{1}{2}$$

✓ Tips

- Remember that a fraction is a numerator divided by a denominator: $\frac{1}{2} = 1 \div 2$

  Do you know your numerators from your denominators?

- Converting improper fractions to mixed numbers is easy.

  $\frac{14}{3} = 14 \div 3 = 4 \text{ r}2$ and as a mixed number = $4\frac{2}{3}$
- Practise converting improper fractions into mixed numbers by writing down some improper fractions and, with a partner, challenge each other to make them into mixed numbers.

3 out of 12 of the dots are red. This is the same as one quarter.

2 out of 6 of the dots are red. This is the same as one third.

Talk maths

- Starting with the textbook activity, have children work in pairs to match mixed numbers with improper fractions They should make verbal statements about each pairing, using 'is equivalent to'.
- This activity can be repeated with an additional focus, for example concentrating only on quarters, fifths or tenths.

Activities

- If children struggle with the questions, encourage them to draw out the whole and fractions for each question, using circles to represent the wholes and dividing them appropriately.
- *100 Maths Lessons Year 5, Spring 2, Week 3* and *Summer 1, Week 4* provide activities and resources which will help to support and consolidate these skills.

Problems

- The pizzas can be used for a wide range of other fractions. If desired, this can be taken a stage further by setting problems involving pizza toppings, varied numbers of slices, and so on.

Talk maths

Each of these mixed numbers is equivalent (equal) to one of the improper fractions. Work with a partner to discuss which ones are equivalent, explaining your answers.

Mixed numbers

$3\frac{1}{4}$ $2\frac{1}{2}$ $4\frac{1}{3}$

$2\frac{2}{3}$

$3\frac{3}{5}$ $5\frac{1}{2}$ $1\frac{1}{5}$

$2\frac{3}{4}$

$2\frac{3}{10}$ $1\frac{8}{10}$ $4\frac{1}{10}$

Improper fractions

$\frac{6}{5}$ $\frac{41}{10}$ $\frac{13}{4}$ $\frac{18}{5}$

$\frac{11}{4}$ $\frac{11}{2}$ $\frac{13}{3}$

$\frac{18}{10}$ $\frac{5}{2}$ $\frac{8}{3}$ $\frac{23}{10}$

Activities

1. Change these mixed numbers to improper fractions.

   a. $3\frac{1}{2}$ b. $2\frac{1}{4}$ c. $4\frac{1}{5}$ d. $1\frac{1}{3}$

   e. $2\frac{2}{3}$ f. $2\frac{3}{4}$ g. $3\frac{4}{5}$ h. $8\frac{1}{2}$

2. Change these improper fractions to mixed numbers.

   a. $\frac{3}{2}$ b. $\frac{4}{3}$ c. $\frac{5}{4}$ d. $\frac{6}{5}$

   e. $\frac{11}{3}$ f. $\frac{7}{4}$ g. $\frac{15}{2}$ h. $\frac{13}{5}$

3. Copy then insert =, < or > signs between each pair of fractions.

   a. $\frac{3}{2}$ $2\frac{1}{2}$ b. $\frac{4}{3}$ $1\frac{1}{3}$ c. $\frac{7}{4}$ $1\frac{1}{4}$ d. $\frac{13}{2}$ $7\frac{1}{2}$

   e. $6\frac{1}{4}$ $\frac{25}{4}$ f. $3\frac{1}{2}$ $\frac{8}{2}$ g. $\frac{10}{3}$ $2\frac{2}{3}$ h. $3\frac{1}{5}$ $\frac{12}{5}$

Problems

Brain-teaser
A pizza shop sells pizzas as whole pizzas and in portions of half a pizza, a third of a pizza or a quarter of a pizza. Ali orders five pizza halves, and Joanne orders seven pizza thirds. Who has ordered the most pizza?

Brain-buster
The pizzeria chef has made four whole pizzas. Robin orders $\frac{13}{4}$ pizzas. How much pizza will be left over?

---

100 Maths Lessons Year 5 links:

- Spring 1, Week 4 (pages 108–113): recognise and convert between mixed numbers and improper fractions; write statements > 1 as a mixed number

- Spring 2, Week 3 (pages 143–148): recognise and convert between mixed numbers and improper fractions

- Summer 1, Week 4 (pages 190–195): use fraction skills

Year 5 Practice Book links:

- (page 71): Equivalent shape fractions

- (page 72): Improper fractions to mixed numbers

- (page 73): To convert or not?

Adding and subtracting fractions

Prior learning

- Can recall quickly multiplication facts up to 12 × 12 and derive corresponding division facts.
- Can order fractions whose denominators are the same, including mixed numbers.
- Can recognise and convert mixed numbers and improper fractions.

Learn

- Review the methods shown in the textbook for creating equivalent fractions, as well as for simplifying them, by multiplying or dividing the numerator and denominator by the same number.
- Create a large paper circle divided into equal ⅛ sections. Cut these up and place one in front of each of eight children. With the fractions displayed, ask the children to create three eighths, four eighths and one eighth. Note to the children that ⅛ + ⅛ + ⅛ = ⅜. Next, bring the three eighths and the four eighths together, noting that ⅜ + 4⁄8 = ⅞. Conclude by showing that ⅛ + ⅞ = 8⁄8 or one whole.
- Using similar cut-outs, demonstrate simple additions of fractions, such as ¼ + ¼, ½ + ½.
- This activity can be repeated to model subtraction: one whole minus two eighths = five eighths, and so on.
- Remind the children that to add or subtract fractions, just as when comparing them, they must have the same denominator.

Talk maths

- Using the textbook examples as a basis, and starting with a rule of using only questions that have a common denominator, ask the children to each write down five simple additions or subtractions, specifying the limited range of denominators allowed, and that no calculation can exceed 1 (for example, ⅖ + ⅕, ¾ – ¼).

Curriculum objectives

- To add and subtract fractions with the same denominator and denominators that are multiples of the same number.

Success criteria

- I can add and subtract fractions, changing their denominators if necessary.

Adding and subtracting fractions

Learn

We can easily compare fractions by giving them the same denominator.

$\frac{1 \times 4}{3 \times 4} = \frac{4}{12}$ $\frac{1 \times 3}{4 \times 3} = \frac{3}{12}$ so $\frac{1}{3} > \frac{1}{4}$

We can simplify fractions by dividing the top and bottom by a common factor.

$\frac{8 \div 2}{10 \div 2} = \frac{4}{5}$ $\frac{15 \div 5}{10 \div 5} = \frac{3}{2} = 1\frac{1}{2}$

To add and subtract fractions, they must have the same denominator.

To add $\frac{1}{4}$ and $\frac{3}{8}$, first find the lowest common denominator. This is 8.

Next, convert each fraction to give it a denominator of 8.

$\frac{1 \times 2}{4 \times 2} = \frac{2}{8}$ $\frac{3}{8}$ is ok

Then, add the new fractions:

$\frac{2}{8} + \frac{3}{8} = \frac{5}{8}$

You must only add the numerators!
$\frac{3}{12} + \frac{4}{12} = \frac{7}{12}$

Taking away is exactly the same – you only subtract the numerators.

$\frac{7}{10} - \frac{3}{10} = \frac{4}{10}$

$\frac{1}{2} - \frac{1}{3} = \frac{3}{6} - \frac{2}{6} = \frac{1}{6}$

✓ Tips

- When you add fractions your answer might be an improper fraction. No problem!

  For example, $\frac{2}{3} + \frac{5}{6}$ Lowest common denominator = 6.

  $\frac{2}{3} = \frac{4}{6}$ $\frac{5}{6}$ is ok $\frac{4}{6} + \frac{5}{6} = \frac{9}{6}$

  As a mixed number this is $1\frac{3}{6}$. This can be simplified to $1\frac{1}{2}$.

40 Fractions, decimals and percentages

Once children have their list of calculations and are sure they are right, arrange them in pairs to challenge each other verbally (for example, *What is ⅖ plus ⅕?*). More confident learners might extend this to fractions with different denominators, where one is a multiple of the other – typically quarters and halves, or fifths and tenths.

Note that questions 1 and 2 are quite straightforward, requiring only that numerators are added or subtracted, whereas questions 3 and 4 require that one of the fractions be converted to create equivalent denominators. These two questions will indicate how well children understand the concepts involved. Those who struggle might need equipment or drawings to support them.

100 Maths Lessons Year 5, Summer 1, Week 4 provides varied activities and resources to support and extend this learning.

Problems

Both of the problems require a first step of finding a common denominator, but the Brain-buster requires that the denominators of both fractions are adjusted.

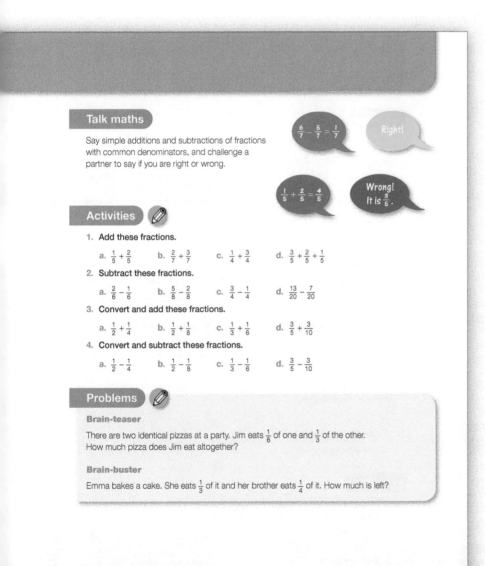

Talk maths

Say simple additions and subtractions of fractions with common denominators, and challenge a partner to say if you are right or wrong.

$\frac{6}{7} - \frac{5}{7} = \frac{1}{7}$ Right!

$\frac{1}{5} + \frac{2}{5} = \frac{4}{5}$ Wrong! It is $\frac{3}{5}$.

Activities

1. Add these fractions.

   a. $\frac{1}{5} + \frac{2}{5}$ b. $\frac{2}{7} + \frac{3}{7}$ c. $\frac{1}{4} + \frac{3}{4}$ d. $\frac{3}{5} + \frac{2}{5} + \frac{1}{5}$

2. Subtract these fractions.

   a. $\frac{2}{6} - \frac{1}{6}$ b. $\frac{5}{8} - \frac{2}{8}$ c. $\frac{3}{4} - \frac{1}{4}$ d. $\frac{13}{20} - \frac{7}{20}$

3. Convert and add these fractions.

   a. $\frac{1}{2} + \frac{1}{4}$ b. $\frac{1}{2} + \frac{1}{8}$ c. $\frac{1}{3} + \frac{1}{6}$ d. $\frac{3}{5} + \frac{3}{10}$

4. Convert and subtract these fractions.

   a. $\frac{1}{2} - \frac{1}{4}$ b. $\frac{1}{2} - \frac{1}{8}$ c. $\frac{1}{3} - \frac{1}{6}$ d. $\frac{3}{5} - \frac{3}{10}$

Problems

Brain-teaser

There are two identical pizzas at a party. Jim eats $\frac{1}{6}$ of one and $\frac{1}{3}$ of the other. How much pizza does Jim eat altogether?

Brain-buster

Emma bakes a cake. She eats $\frac{1}{3}$ of it and her brother eats $\frac{1}{4}$ of it. How much is left?

Fractions, decimals and percentages   41

100 Maths Lessons Year 5 links:

- Summer 1, Week 4 (pages 190–195): adding and subtracting fractions with the same denominator and denominators that are multiples of the same number

Year 5 Practice Book links:

- (page 74): Adding fractions with the same denominator

- (page 75): Subtracting fractions with the same denominator

- (page 76): Add and subtract fractions with related denominators

- (page 77): Fractions challenge

Multiplying fractions and whole numbers

Prior learning

- Can recall quickly multiplication facts up to 12 × 12 and derive corresponding division facts.
- Know that whole numbers and fractions may be combined and are known as mixed numbers.

Learn

- Draw several arrays of dots (for example, three rows of four, six rows of two) and ask the children to identify half of the dots. Show that this half can be grouped in any way and circle half of the dots. Continue this with appropriate sets of dots to show one quarter of, one third of, and so on.
- For each fraction of a group of dots, demonstrate how this can be shown as a multiplication, such as $\frac{1}{6}$ of 12 = 2. Remind the children that multiplications can be done in any order: $\frac{1}{6} \times 12 = 12 \times \frac{1}{6}$.
- Spend time reminding the children that multiplication is repeated addition, for example $7 + 7 + 7 = 3 \times 7$. With this established, model how this also applies to fractions (for example, $\frac{1}{3} + \frac{1}{3} + \frac{1}{3} = 3 \times \frac{1}{3} = 1$).
- Use different examples to establish that when multiplying a fraction by a whole number it is the numerator that is multiplied by the whole number.
- Next, when working through examples that create improper fractions, recap how these are converted to mixed numbers.
- Finally, demonstrate that when a mixed number is multiplied by a whole number, the whole number part and the fraction can be multiplied separately, for example $5 \times 6\frac{1}{7} = 5 \times 6 + 5 \times \frac{1}{7} = 30\frac{5}{7}$.
- Throughout, emphasise methodical working and clear layout.
- *100 Maths Lessons Year 5, Spring 1, Week 4* provides practice in manipulating mixed numbers and improper fractions.

Curriculum objectives

- To multiply proper fractions and mixed numbers by whole numbers, supported by materials and diagrams.

Success criteria

- I can multiply fractions and mixed numbers by whole numbers.

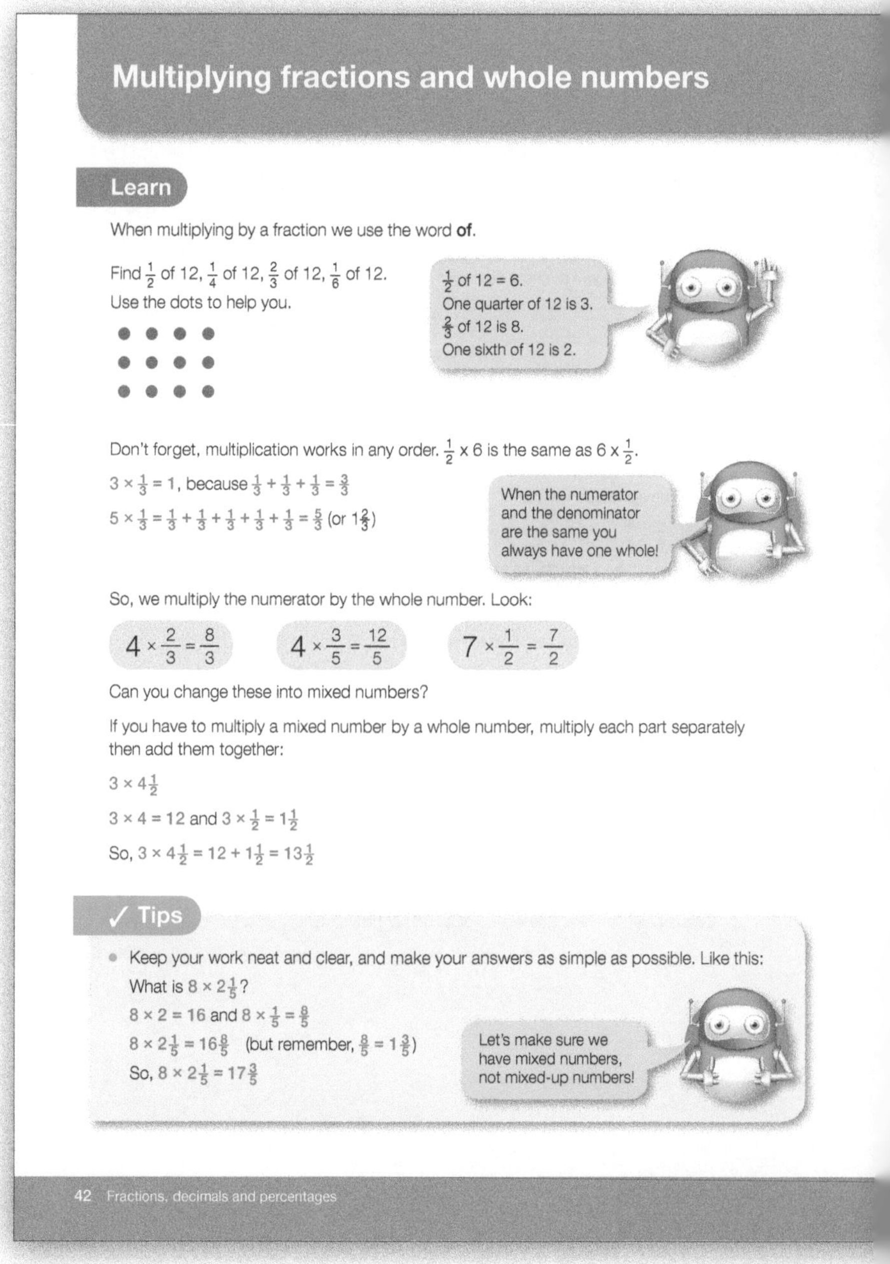

Multiplying fractions and whole numbers

Learn

When multiplying by a fraction we use the word **of**.

Find $\frac{1}{2}$ of 12, $\frac{1}{4}$ of 12, $\frac{2}{3}$ of 12, $\frac{1}{6}$ of 12.
Use the dots to help you.

$\frac{1}{2}$ of 12 = 6.
One quarter of 12 is 3.
$\frac{2}{3}$ of 12 is 8.
One sixth of 12 is 2.

Don't forget, multiplication works in any order. $\frac{1}{2} \times 6$ is the same as $6 \times \frac{1}{2}$.

$3 \times \frac{1}{3} = 1$, because $\frac{1}{3} + \frac{1}{3} + \frac{1}{3} = \frac{3}{3}$

$5 \times \frac{1}{3} = \frac{1}{3} + \frac{1}{3} + \frac{1}{3} + \frac{1}{3} + \frac{1}{3} = \frac{5}{3}$ (or $1\frac{2}{3}$)

When the numerator and the denominator are the same you always have one whole!

So, we multiply the numerator by the whole number. Look:

$4 \times \frac{2}{3} = \frac{8}{3}$ $4 \times \frac{3}{5} = \frac{12}{5}$ $7 \times \frac{1}{2} = \frac{7}{2}$

Can you change these into mixed numbers?

If you have to multiply a mixed number by a whole number, multiply each part separately then add them together:

$3 \times 4\frac{1}{2}$

$3 \times 4 = 12$ and $3 \times \frac{1}{2} = 1\frac{1}{2}$

So, $3 \times 4\frac{1}{2} = 12 + 1\frac{1}{2} = 13\frac{1}{2}$

✓ Tips

- Keep your work neat and clear, and make your answers as simple as possible. Like this:
  What is $8 \times 2\frac{1}{5}$?
  $8 \times 2 = 16$ and $8 \times \frac{1}{5} = \frac{8}{5}$
  $8 \times 2\frac{1}{5} = 16\frac{8}{5}$ (but remember, $\frac{8}{5} = 1\frac{3}{5}$)
  So, $8 \times 2\frac{1}{5} = 17\frac{3}{5}$

Let's make sure we have mixed numbers, not mixed-up numbers!

42 Fractions, decimals and percentages

- Provide a bank of examples of calculations involving simple fractions multiplied by whole numbers. You could use those in the textbook or ask children to work in pairs and develop their own. Next, request volunteers to explain each step of the calculation. Focus on correct vocabulary at each stage.
- Ensure that each calculation is presented using both '×' and 'of', for example 4 × ½ = ⁴⁄₂ = 2, and ½ of 4 = 2.

Activities

- Children's work will reveal how easily they can carry out the calculations. Also, check that they are comfortably converting to mixed numbers.
- Some children may require equipment to support them with these calculations.
- *100 Maths Lessons Year 5, Spring 2, Week 3* provides ideas and activities for extended practice.

Problems

- The Brain-teaser is easily adaptable to provide other problems of a similar level.
- Note that the Brain-buster is tricky and is easiest solved by estimating and trying out calculations with different numbers of laps.

Talk maths

Practise saying these calculations both ways:

$$4 \times \frac{1}{2} = \frac{4}{2} = 2$$

$$\frac{1}{2} \times 4 = 2$$

Four times one half equals four halves, which equals two.

Half of four equals two.

Now try saying these:

$$9 \times \frac{1}{3} = \frac{9}{3} = 3 \qquad \frac{1}{3} \times 9 = 3$$

Try this with some other numbers and fractions.

Activities

1. Complete these multiplications.

   a. $\frac{1}{2}$ of 10   b. $\frac{1}{4}$ of 8   c. $\frac{2}{3} \times 9$ d. $\frac{1}{2} \times 20$

2. Write the answers as mixed numbers.

   a. $10 \times \frac{1}{4}$ b. $3 \times \frac{1}{2}$ c. $4 \times \frac{3}{7}$ d. $20 \times \frac{1}{6}$

3. Find the answers.

   a. $2 \times 3\frac{1}{2}$ b. $3 \times 1\frac{1}{2}$ c. $2\frac{1}{6} \times 5$ d. $20 \times 1\frac{1}{3}$

Problems

Brain-teaser

A farmer chops up trees to make logs for fires. If each tree makes $6\frac{1}{2}$ logs, how many logs will she get from three trees?

Brain-buster

It takes Ben $12\frac{1}{2}$ seconds to jog once around the school hall. If he keeps up a steady speed, how many laps will he complete in 100 seconds?

100 Maths Lessons Year 5 links:

- Spring 1, Week 4 (pages 108–113): calculate fractions of numbers using multiplication
- Spring 2, Week 3 (pages 143–148): multiply proper fractions and mixed numbers by whole numbers

Year 5 Practice Book links:

- (page 78): Multiplying properly!
- (page 79): Mixed multiplying!
- (page 88): Fractions to calculate

Converting simple decimals and fractions

Prior learning

- Convert simple fractions to their decimal equivalents to one or two decimal places.
- Understand place value.

Learn

- Draw a circle divided into equal segments of one tenth. Referring to the diagram, with the children create a chart for one to ten tenths. Also show any simplified fractions such as ½, ⅖ and 1 as equivalent fractions in tenths.

- Draw a line of ten dots and demonstrate how each dot is one tenth of the line of dots. Remind the children that a fraction is the numerator divided by the denominator. Therefore, show how $\frac{1}{10} = 0.1$, $\frac{2}{10} = \frac{1}{5} = 0.2$ and so on. Remind children that numbers such as 0.7, 0.2 are called decimals.

- Repeat the activity above, using a large grid of 100 dots to represent one whole. Look at how different fractions of 100 can be converted to decimal form, such as $^{25}/_{100} = \frac{1}{4} = 0.25$.

- *100 Maths Lessons Year 5, Autumn 2, Week 4* contains a range of lessons to develop and support understanding of tenths, hundredths and thousandths.

Curriculum objectives

- To read and write decimal numbers as fractions.

Success criteria

- I can convert between simple decimals and fractions.

Converting simple decimals and fractions

Learn

A proper fraction is a proportion of one whole.

$$\frac{1}{4} \quad \frac{1}{3} \quad \frac{1}{2} \quad \frac{2}{3} \quad \frac{3}{4}$$ are all proper fractions.

Amounts less than 1 can also be represented by decimals.

0.1 is one tenth $= \frac{1}{10}$

0.2 is two tenths $= \frac{2}{10}$

0.3 is three tenths $= \frac{3}{10}$

Can you keep going?

Any fraction can be written as a decimal. These are common ones:

Fraction	$\frac{1}{2}$	$\frac{1}{4}$	$\frac{3}{4}$	$\frac{1}{5}$	$\frac{1}{10}$
Decimal	0.5	0.25	0.75	0.2	0.1

There are 100 dots here.

50 of them are circled in blue. As a fraction it is $\frac{50}{100}$ or $\frac{1}{2}$.
As a decimal it is 0.5.

Any decimal can be written as a fraction.
For example:

25 of the dots are circled in green.
As a fraction it is $\frac{25}{100}$ or $\frac{1}{4}$.
As a decimal this is 0.25.

0.25

0.5

✓ Tips

- Remember that for a decimal the first column is tenths, the second column is hundredths, and the third column is thousandths.

100s	10s	1s	0.1s	0.01s	0.01s

Time for some decimal tips!

- We read decimals aloud using numbers 0 to 9.
We say 0.5 is **zero point five**. We say 0.75 is **zero point seven five**.

44 Fractions, decimals and percentages

- Use the chart in the textbook or ask children to create their own. They can then test each other to improve their recall and knowledge of fraction and decimal equivalents.

- Check that children are saying decimals correctly, for example 0.66 is read as *zero point six six*, not *zero point sixty-six*.

Activities

- The questions here provide basic reinforcement. Question 3 will provide fractions that could be simplified. If children would benefit from further practice in converting decimals to fractions, *100 Maths Lessons Year 5, Summer 2, Week 3* has lessons that provide extended practice.

- Children who are finding the work straightforward might be challenged to investigate adding decimals and adding the equivalent fractions. Which form do they find easier to work with? They could move on to mixed numbers if appropriate.

Problems

- Further problems are available through the links to *100 Maths Lessons Year 5* and *Year 5 Practice Book*.

Talk maths

Use this chart to make you familiar with the decimal equivalents for these common fractions. Work with a partner and test each other.

Fraction	$\frac{1}{2}$	$\frac{1}{4}$	$\frac{3}{4}$	$\frac{1}{5}$	$\frac{1}{10}$	$\frac{1}{3}$	$\frac{2}{3}$
Decimal	0.5	0.25	0.75	0.2	0.1	0.33	0.66

Remember to read the decimals aloud. Try other fractions too! What will $\frac{4}{5}$ be? What will $\frac{6}{10}$ be?

Activities

1. Copy and complete these charts.

 a.

Fraction	$\frac{1}{10}$	$\frac{2}{10}$	$\frac{3}{10}$	$\frac{4}{10}$	$\frac{5}{10}$	$\frac{6}{10}$	$\frac{7}{10}$	$\frac{8}{10}$	$\frac{9}{10}$	$\frac{10}{10}$
Decimal	0.1	0.2								

 b.

Fraction	$\frac{1}{5}$	$\frac{2}{5}$	$\frac{3}{5}$	$\frac{4}{5}$	$\frac{5}{5}$				
Decimal	0.2	0.4							

2. Change these fractions to decimals.
 a. $\frac{1}{2}$ b. $\frac{3}{4}$ c. $\frac{1}{10}$

3. Change these decimals to fractions.
 a. 0.25 b. 0.7 c. 0.4

Problems

Brain-teaser

Adjith wins a competition. As his prize he can take $\frac{3}{4}$ of a bowl of sweets, or 0.7 of the sweets. Which will give him more sweets?

Brain-buster

A pizza is cut into four equal slices. Gemma eats one slice and says that she has eaten 0.2 of the pizza. Is she right? Explain your answer.

100 Maths Lessons Year 5 links:

- Autumn 2, Week 3 (pages 61–66): read and write decimal numbers as fractions

- Autumn 2, Week 4 (pages 67–72): read and write decimal numbers as fractions including thousandths

- Summer 2, Week 3 (pages 225–230): read and write decimal numbers as fractions including thousandths

Year 5 Practice Book links:

- (page 70): Equivalent fractions and decimals

- (page 85): Writing decimal numbers as fractions

Decimal fractions

Prior learning

- Know place value beyond zero.
- Begin to know simple fraction and decimal equivalents.

Learn

- Draw a place-value grid on the whiteboard to represent ones, tenths, hundredths and thousandths. Using a selection of large digits on pieces of card or paper, create a range of decimals.
- Add a permanent zero in the ones column, and then place different digits in different decimal places and practise reading the decimals with the children.

- Remember that it is difficult for children to appreciate the magnitude of decimals, especially hundredths and thousandths. It is possible using a word processor to create a page (probably landscape format) with 1000 dots in it. To do this, create a line of 100 full stops, with a space between each, and then copy it ten times. This is useful to show just what one thousandth is and how it relates to one hundredth (ten dots) and one tenth (one row of 100 dots).

- Still using the grid and digits from above, explain that a decimal fraction is one that has a denominator that is a power of 10. Write several numbers as both a decimal and its fraction equivalent.
- Spend time demonstrating that, just as with larger whole numbers, zeros are only added to the tenths and hundredths columns if they are holding the place for a number in a subsequent column.

Curriculum objectives

- To recognise and use thousandths and relate them to tenths, hundredths and decimal equivalents.

Success criteria

- I can read and write tenths, hundredths and thousandths as decimals or fractions.

Decimal fractions

Learn

Our number system uses **powers of 10**. We sometimes call this 100s, 10s and 1s.

100s	10s	1s	0.1s	0.01s	0.001s
3	4	6	1	2	5

The decimal places in this place-value chart show tenths (0.1s), hundredths (0.01s) and thousandths (0.001s).

346 is three hundred and forty-six. Between zero and 1 we use decimal fractions. **0.125 is zero point one two five**.

A decimal fraction is a way of writing a fraction that has a power of 10, such as 10, 100, 1000, as its denominator.

When we divide a number by 10, 100 or 1000, we move the numbers to the right.

Fraction name	Fraction	Decimal fraction	Decimal name
one tenth	$\frac{1}{10}$	0.1	zero point one
one hundredth	$\frac{1}{100}$	0.01	zero point zero one
one thousandth	$\frac{1}{1000}$	0.001	zero point zero zero one

Can you see how many places the digit 1 moves each time?

Here are some decimal fractions:

$$\frac{7}{10} = 0.7 \qquad \frac{31}{100} = 0.31 \qquad \frac{418}{1000} = 0.418$$

✓ Tips

- When dividing by a power of 10, move the digits one place to the right for each power of 10.

Denominator of fraction	10	100	1000
The digit 1	0.1	0.01	0.001

Talk maths

- Use a selection of decimal fractions, either from the textbook or on flashcards, to provide regular short practice sessions for children to say the equivalent fraction.

- Ask children who need additional reinforcement to copy each number in the textbook into a place-value table. Check that they've written the digits into the correct columns for tenths, hundredths and thousandths, and ask them to state the value of each digit.

Activities

- The chart provides practice in converting between fractions and decimals, and naming each correctly. Challenge early finishers to extend the table with decimal fractions of their own choosing.

- The activity in *Year 5 Practice Book* provide further practice.

Problems

- These problems are relatively straightforward, and are easily adjustable for further practice.

- Both of the links to *100 Maths Lessons Year 5* provide context-based activities for using decimal fractions, particularly with measures.

Talk maths

Practise using the correct words for decimal fractions and decimal places.

Say these numbers as fractions and also as decimal fractions.

| 0.2 | 0.32 | 0.523 | 0.204 |

| 0.8 | 0.641 | 0.09 |

$\frac{45}{100}$ is *forty-five hundredths* as a fraction.

For 0.45 as a decimal fraction we say *zero point four five*.

Activities

1. Copy and complete this chart.

Fraction name	Fraction	Decimal fraction	Decimal name
five tenths			
twenty-three hundredths			
four hundred and thirty-five thousandths			
			zero point three
			zero point eight six
	$\frac{8}{10}$		
	$\frac{132}{1000}$		
		0.39	
		0.104	

Problems

Brain-teaser
In a group of 100 children, 87 are right-handed. Write this number as a fraction and a decimal.

Brain-buster
In a group of 1000 children, 235 do not like cheese. What proportion of the children do like cheese? Write the number as a fraction and as a decimal.

Fractions, decimals and percentages   47

100 Maths Lessons Year 5 links:

- Autumn 2, Week 4 (pages 67–72): double and halve decimals

- Summer 2, Week 3 (pages 225–230): explain what each digit represents in decimals with up to three decimal places and partition, round and order these numbers

Year 5 Practice Book links:

- (page 80): Decimals: hundredths and thousandths

Numbers with three decimal places

Prior learning

- Know place value beyond zero.
- Begin to know simple fraction and decimal equivalents.

Learn

- Using a place-value table, review the meaning of decimal fractions and the place value of each digit to the right of the decimal point.
- Display a selection of fractions with denominators that are powers of 10, and then work with the children to convert them to decimals by writing them in a place-value table. Focus on the correct naming of the digit in each column.
- Use a word processor to create a page (probably landscape format) with 1000 dots in it. To do this, create a line of 100 full stops, with a space between each, and then copy it ten times. This is useful to exemplify just what one thousandth is and how it relates to one hundredth (ten dots) and

one tenth (one row of 100 dots). Display this on the interactive whiteboard to help show the relationship of one tenth to one hundredth and one thousandth, explaining that there are ten tenths in one whole, ten one hundredths in one tenth, and ten thousandths in one hundredth. With time, this should help children to see the connection between the place value of decimals and the place value of whole numbers.

- *100 Maths Lessons Year 5, Autumn 2, Week 4* provides practice in reading and ordering decimals with up to three decimal places.

Curriculum objectives

- To read, write, order and compare numbers with up to three decimal places.
- To solve problems involving numbers up to three decimal places.

Success criteria

- I can read, order and write decimals with up to three decimal places.
- I can solve problems with decimal numbers.

Numbers with three decimal places

Learn

Decimal places show the decimal fraction for numbers between zero and 1.

A decimal fraction is a way of writing a fraction that has a power of 10 such as 10, 100, 1000, as its denominator.

1s	0.1s	0.01s	0.001s
.			

$$\frac{123}{1000} = 0.123$$

We say **one hundred and twenty-three thousandths** as **zero point one two three**.

We read decimals using digit names: 0.428 is **zero point four two eight**.

Tenths are bigger than hundredths. Hundredths are bigger than thousandths. Look:

| 0.6 > 0.5 | 0.431 > 0.429 | 0.1 > 0.099 |

| 0.28 < 0.3 | 0.739 < 0.81 | 0.4 < 0.515 |

Say each statement aloud.

$$\frac{1}{10} > \frac{1}{100} > \frac{1}{1000}$$

✓ Tips

Let's try to clear up different types of decimals.

- Think about what tenths, hundredths and thousands are:
  There are ten tenths in a whole.
  There are one hundred hundredths in a whole, but ten hundredths in one tenth.
  There are one thousand thousandths in a whole, but ten thousandths in one hundredth.

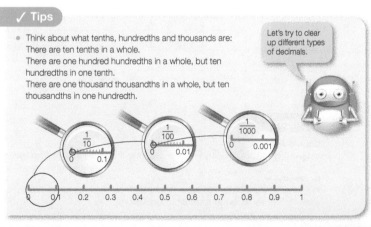

- The textbook activity requires children to create a presentation to explain the differences between tenths, hundredths and thousandths. This could be set as a task to prepare props and cue cards, with the oral element coming from the presentation itself.

- The questions provide focused practice in writing decimals in words and numerals. The final question requires children to position decimals on a number line between one and zero. This final activity is worthy of sustained and repeated practice using a wide range of decimals.

- Variations on these problems are easy to achieve by writing new problems with different sizes of bugs, or using other bugs and insects.

- *100 Maths Lessons Year 5, Summer 2, Week 3* provides additional practice in a range of contexts.

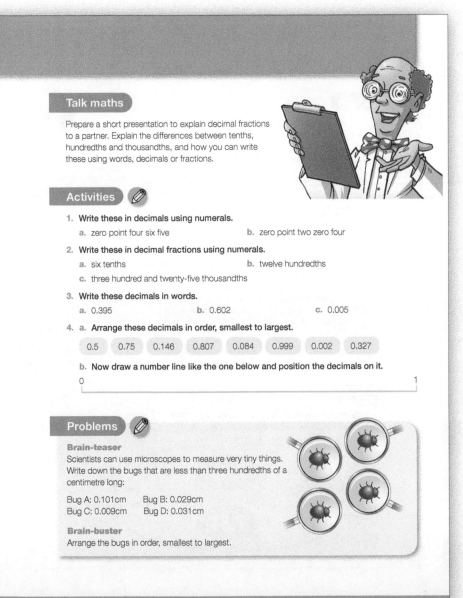

Talk maths

Prepare a short presentation to explain decimal fractions to a partner. Explain the differences between tenths, hundredths and thousandths, and how you can write these using words, decimals or fractions.

Activities

1. Write these in decimals using numerals.
   a. zero point four six five
   b. zero point two zero four

2. Write these in decimal fractions using numerals.
   a. six tenths
   b. twelve hundredths
   c. three hundred and twenty-five thousandths

3. Write these decimals in words.
   a. 0.395
   b. 0.602
   c. 0.005

4. a. Arrange these decimals in order, smallest to largest.

   | 0.5 | 0.75 | 0.146 | 0.807 | 0.084 | 0.999 | 0.002 | 0.327 |

   b. Now draw a number line like the one below and position the decimals on it.

   0 ————————————————————————————————— 1

Problems

Brain-teaser
Scientists can use microscopes to measure very tiny things. Write down the bugs that are less than three hundredths of a centimetre long:

Bug A: 0.101cm Bug B: 0.029cm
Bug C: 0.009cm Bug D: 0.031cm

Brain-buster
Arrange the bugs in order, smallest to largest.

Fractions, decimals and percentages 49

100 Maths Lessons Year 5 links:

- Autumn 2, Week 4 (pages 67–72): read, write, order and comparing numbers with up to three decimal places; solve problems involving numbers up to three decimal places

- Summer 2, Week 3 (pages 225–230): read, write, order and compare numbers with up to three decimal places

Year 5 Practice Book links:

- (page 81): Using thousandths

- (page 83): Decimal sports results

- (page 84): Three decimal places

Rounding decimals

Prior learning

- Can round whole numbers to the nearest 10, 100 or 1000.
- Understand place value beyond zero.

Learn

- Review the work done so far to demonstrate the relationships between tenths, hundredths and thousandths.
- Ask children to demonstrate how whole numbers are rounded up and down. Explain that decimals can also be rounded up and down. They can be rounded to the nearest whole number or to the nearest tenth. (They can be rounded to the nearest hundredth too of course, although this is not absolutely necessary at this stage.)

- Using a range of sample numbers, model rounding to the nearest whole number and the nearest tenth, focusing in particular on how 0.5 and 0.05 rounds upwards.
- A useful activity is to create large cards with 0.1, 0.2, 0.3 and so on, up to 1 on them. Display these at the front of the class and distribute a range of decimals (all less than 1) on pieces of paper, and ask children to take their

decimal and round themselves to the nearest tenth (including to 1). Walking to the appropriate decimal, they should check with others who have also rounded to their number if they are correct.
- Point out the Tips in the textbook: consider with the children how the same number can change, depending on how it is rounded.

Curriculum objectives

- To round decimals with two decimal places to the nearest whole number and to one decimal place.

Success criteria

- I can round decimals to the nearest tenth or whole number.

Rounding decimals

Learn

Decimals are used to shows fractions of numbers. Each decimal place shows smaller and smaller parts.

Tenths   Hundredths   Thousandths

0.235 has three decimal places: two tenths, three hundredths and five thousandths. 4.7 has one decimal place: seven tenths.

We can round decimals to the nearest whole number, it's easy: 0.5 or more, round up. Less than 0.5, round down.

0.65 rounds up to 1	2.34 rounds down to 2
0.723 rounds up to 1	8.058 rounds down to 8
4.629 rounds up to 5	0.255 rounds down to 0

Sometimes we want to be more accurate, and round numbers to one decimal place.

When rounding to the nearest tenth, you must look at the hundredths. 0.05 or more, round up. Less than 0.05, round down.

0.65 rounds up to 0.7	2.34 rounds down to 2.3
0.723 rounds down to 0.7	8.058 rounds up to 8.1
4.629 rounds down to 4.6	0.255 rounds up to 0.3

✓ Tips

- Beware! The same number can be rounded off differently, depending on whether you round it to the nearest whole number, or to one decimal place.

To the nearest whole number: **7**   **7.49**   To the nearest tenth: **7.5**

To the nearest whole number: **8**   **7.51**   To the nearest tenth: **7.5**

- This section introduces the game 'Guess My Decimal'. This can be differentiated by encouraging less confident learners to write decimals with only one or two decimal places, extending to three if appropriate.

- Note that some of the questions in this section have thousandths. Look for children who realise that these do not have an impact for rounding to one decimal place, and challenge more confident learners to say what these numbers would be if rounded to the nearest hundredth.

- Note that the Brain-buster requires that the Brain-teaser is completed first. For children who need a further challenge ask them to create a second week of takings, and ask their partner to complete their own version. If desired, ask them to round to the nearest 10p.

- *100 Maths Lessons Year 5, Autumn 2, Week 4, Lesson 3* provides further context-based practice in rounding decimals.

Talk maths

Play *Guess My Decimal*. Two or more people can play.

Take turns to think of any decimal with two or three decimal places and secretly write it down. Challenge others to ask questions about it to guess what it is. How fast can they discover your decimal?

Activities

1. Round these decimals to the nearest whole number.

   a. 0.8   b. 1.7   c. 4.5   d. 0.4
   e. 0.625 f. 7.489 g. 12.32 h. 7.08

2. Round these decimals to one decimal place.

   a. 0.83   b. 0.77   c. 0.45   d. 0.838
   e. 5.625 f. 4.089 g. 12.75 h. 7.023

3. Explain why rounding decimals is useful, but also why it might cause problems.

Problems

Brain-teaser

A shopkeeper always rounds the money he makes each day to the nearest pound. Copy and complete this chart.

Day	Monday	Tuesday	Wednesday	Thursday	Friday	Saturday
Money	£52.14	£45.61	£60.13	£46.50	£72.24	£35.51
Rounded						

Brain-buster

For the week above, can you decide if the rounded amount is more or less than the money the shopkeeper actually has? Explain your answer.

Fractions, decimals and percentages 51

100 Maths Lessons Year 5 links:

- Autumn 2, Week 4 (pages 67–72): round decimals with two decimal places to the nearest whole number and to one decimal place

Year 5 Practice Book links:

- (page 82): Rounding and ordering decimals

Simple percentages

Prior learning

- Can use decimal notation for tenths and hundredths, and partition decimals.
- Can recognise equivalent fractions and decimals.

Learn

- Remind the children about their work on decimals, in particular whole numbers divided by 100.
- Explain that per cent means parts of 100, or out of 100.
- Display a grid of 100 squares (if this is on the interactive whiteboard, so much the better). Highlight or shade different numbers of squares. Show these numbers out of 100 as decimals, fractions and percentages.

- Stress that 100% is one whole. Remind the children that sometimes the fraction equivalents can be simplified, for example 50% = $\frac{50}{100}$ = ½.
- The Tips section should help children to become increasingly familiar with the equivalence of different fractions, decimals and percentages.
- *100 Maths Lessons Year 5, Spring 2, Week 4 provides additional practice, as does Summer 2, Week 4.*

Curriculum objectives

- To recognise the per cent symbol (%) and understand that per cent relates to 'number of parts per hundred', and write percentages as a fraction with denominator 100, and as a decimal.
- Solve problems which require knowing percentage and decimal equivalents of ½, ¼, ⅕, ⅖, ⅘ and those fractions with a denominator of a multiple of 10 or 25.

Success criteria

- I can recognise and understand the per cent symbol (%) and write percentages as equivalent fractions or decimals.
- I can solve simple problems involving percentage and decimal equivalents of simple fractions.

Simple percentages

Learn

$\frac{35}{100}$ is a fraction. We can say **35 over 100** or **35 out of 100**.

Fractions with a denominator of 100 are very important. They are also called percentages.

Per cent means **parts of a hundred** or **out of 100**.

Look at the 100 grid. 65 of the 100 squares are shaded – this is 65%

As a decimal it is 0.35: *zero point three five.*

We use the words, *per cent* and use the symbol % to represent it.

$0.65 = \frac{65}{100} = 65\%$

We can also simplify fractions as percentages:

$50\% = \frac{50}{100} = \frac{1}{2}$ So, $50\% = \frac{1}{2}$

✓ Tips

- Because fractions can also be turned into decimal fractions, they can also be percentages. Here are some you should know:

Don't worry, I can help with percentages!

Fraction	$\frac{1}{2}$	$\frac{1}{4}$	$\frac{1}{10}$	$\frac{2}{10}$	$\frac{1}{5}$	$\frac{2}{5}$	$\frac{65}{100}$	$\frac{3}{4}$	$\frac{1}{1}$
Decimal	0.5	0.25	0.1	0.2	0.2	0.4	0.65	0.75	1.0
Per cent	50%	25%	10%	20%	20%	40%	65%	75%	100%

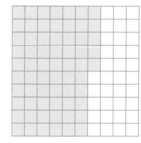

Try to learn off by heart the percentage equivalents of easy fractions.

- This activity provides practice in mental conversion between percentages, decimals and fractions. Remind children, if in doubt, to say un-simplified fractions (for example, $^{65}/_{100}$).

- The activity provides further practice in recognising equivalent percentages, fractions and decimals. This can be extended by copying each of the items onto paper and playing games such as 'Snap' and 'Pelmanism'.

- The activities in *Year 5 Practice Book* provide further practice.

- These problems involve a range of steps and conversions. Additional practice is available in *100 Maths Lessons Year 5, Spring 2, Week 4* and *Summer 2, Week 4*.

Talk maths

Look at the different fractions, decimals and percentages in the box.

$$\frac{1}{2} \quad 0.1 \quad 20\% \quad 0.3 \quad 1\% \quad \frac{3}{4}$$
$$67\% \quad \frac{1}{5} \quad 0.45 \quad 1.4 \quad 100\% \quad 0.8$$

For each one read it aloud, then say what it would also be as a decimal, percentage or fraction.

Activities

1. Carefully copy out each column and then link the correct percentage to its fraction and decimal equivalent.

10%	0.37	$\frac{1}{2}$
25%	1.0	$\frac{1}{10}$
30%	0.1	$\frac{1}{4}$
37%	0.3	$\frac{100}{100}$
50%	0.75	$\frac{3}{10}$
60%	0.25	$\frac{3}{5}$
75%	0.5	$\frac{37}{100}$
100%	0.6	$\frac{3}{4}$

Problems

Brain-teaser

There are 30 children in a class. Half of the class have school dinners and $\frac{1}{10}$ have sandwiches. The rest of the class go home for lunch. How many children have school dinners? What percentage of the class have sandwiches?

Brain-buster

In the above class, how many children go home for lunch? What percentage of the class

---

100 Maths Lessons Year 5 links:

- Spring 2, Week 4 (pages 149–154): understand percentage as the number of parts in every 100 and relate this to fractions and decimals

- Summer 2, Week 4 (pages 231–236): solve problems which require knowing percentage and decimal equivalents

Year 5 Practice Book links:

- (page 86): Fractions, decimals and percentages (1)

- (page 87): Fractions, decimals and percentages (2)

- (page 89): Percentage problems

Length and distance

Prior learning

- Can measure in centimetres and millilitres, using a ruler.
- Can convert between metric units of length: millimetres, centimetres and metres.

Learn

- List various distances and objects of different lengths. Consider the best units for measuring these. Note these on the whiteboard and write an estimated length for each unit, as in the textbook.
- Recap the number of millimetres in 1cm and the number of centimetres in 1m. Write each measurement from the brainstorm in millimetres, centimetres and metres.

- Explain the origins of imperial and metric units. (Metric are more recent, unify measurements worldwide, and are in powers of 10, which makes them easier to use.) If possible, look at a selection of rulers and maps to distinguish between the two types of unit.
- Notice also that the Tips provide key information for converting between metric units of length, as well as the factors for converting between imperial and metric units. Try to model and practise these as much as possible.
- *100 Maths Lessons Year 5, Autumn 1, Week 6, Lesson 1* has advice and an activity for developing understanding of conversion between metric and imperial units for lengths and distances.

Curriculum objectives

- To convert between different units of metric measure (for example kilometre and metre; centimetre and metre; centimetre and millimetre).
- To understand and use approximate equivalences between metric units and common imperial units, such as inches, pounds and pints.
- To use all four operations to solve problems involving measure using decimal notation, including scaling.

Success criteria

- I can convert between different units of length.
- I can make approximate conversions between metric and imperial units
- I can solve problems involving length and distance.

Length and distance

Learn

We usually measure longer distances in metres and kilometres, and shorter lengths in centimetres and millimetres.

Abbreviations:
10mm = 1cm
100cm = 1m
1000m = 1km

Did you know?

There are one million millimetres in a kilometre!

We sometimes use imperial units too:

1mm = 0.1cm
1cm = 0.01m
1m = 0.001km

Beware: when adding lengths together they must have the same units!

A six-inch ruler is around 15cm.

And a mile is around 1.61km.

✓ Tips

- Use this guide to help you convert metric units.

Conversion	Operation	Example
mm to cm	÷ 10	12mm = 1.2cm
cm to m	÷ 100	256cm = 2.56m
m to km	÷ 1000	467m = 0.467km
cm to mm	× 10	3.5cm = 35mm
m to cm	× 100	1.85m = 185cm
km to m	× 1000	4.3km = 4300m

When measuring, be sure to position the zero of your ruler properly.

- For imperial units of length, just remember these two facts:
  1 inch = 2.54cm and **1 mile = 1.61km**

- The textbook activity can be extended by asking the children to write each measurement in millimetres, centimetres and metres, as well as inches if desired. (The conversion calculation can be rather difficult, and estimation will suffice.)

- Note that it may be preferable to complete the charts in Activities before attempting this activity.

Activities

- The charts all focus on straightforward conversion. Note that the chart for imperial conversion is from imperial to metric only, as this is the main skill needed in real life.

- The activities in *Year 5 Practice Book* provide further practice.

Problems

- The problems will require children to show their workings carefully. As children move on to perimeter and area, there will be many opportunities for further use of length and distance in context.

- For a practical approach, create activities that involve measurement and scale drawings of areas around the classroom and school.

Talk maths

You will need a ruler and a tape measure.

Working with a partner, choose a selection of different-sized objects. Write them in a list and then estimate their length. Write down your estimates and then swap lists. Measure the objects using the ruler and tape measure and compare answers.

Can you measure to the nearest millimetre? Can you write all your measurements in millimetres?

Activities

1. Copy and complete these conversion charts.

a.

mm	cm
10	
25	
52	
100	
	30
	17
	6
	0.2

b.

cm	m
100	
35	
450	
1000	
	80
	9
	0.9
	0.27

c.

m	km
1000	
250	
5350	
10,000	
	6
	4.5
	1.35
	0.004

2. Copy and complete this chart to convert these imperial units to metric units. (Remember, 1 inch = 2.54cm and 1 mile = 1.61km.)

Imperial	Metric	Imperial	Metric	Imperial	Metric
1 inch		10 inches		100 miles	
5 inches		1 mile		300 miles	

Problems

Brain-teaser
The desks in a classroom are all 120cm long. How long would a line of four desks be in metres?

Brain-buster
An online map shows the length of sections of a cycle path. What is the total length of the path in km?

Path section	A–B	B–C	C–D	D–E
Distance	800m	750m	2.5km	1.3km

Measurement 55

---

100 Maths Lessons Year 5 links:

- Autumn 1, Week 6 (pages 37–41): use metric and imperial units and approximate equivalences; calculate perimeter and area

Year 5 Practice Book links:

- (page 90): Measuring and converting lengths

- (page 92): Metric and imperial length problems

- (page 104): Measurement problems (choose appropriate problems)

Perimeter

- Can measure and calculate perimeter in simple cases.

Learn

- Focusing only on rectangles and squares, review the children's knowledge of perimeter. Begin simply by counting the sides of small squares, moving on to the simple addition of the four lengths involved.

- The textbook will help to develop children's understanding of the formulae for the perimeter of a rectangle and a square. (This is also early algebra.) Consider the application of these formulae to a range of rectangles and squares.

Initially, draw these on the whiteboard, and then move on to simply providing the side lengths and asking the children to insert them in the appropriate formula.

- The Tips give an example of finding the perimeter of a composite shape. It is important to spend time on these as the formulae are often redundant in these situations, and irregular measurements need to be calculated.

- *100 Maths Lessons Year 5, Autumn 1, Week 6* has a range of lessons and activities that focus on calculating both perimeter and area. It may be preferable to cover area before the children attempt these activities.

Curriculum objectives

- To measure and calculate the perimeter of composite rectilinear shapes in centimetres and metres.

- To use all four operations to solve problems involving measure using decimal notation, including scaling.

Success criteria

- I can calculate the perimeter of rectangles and squares.

- I can calculate the perimeter of shapes made of different rectangles and squares joined together.

Perimeter

Learn

Perimeter is the distance around the outside of a shape.

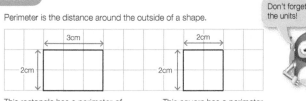

Don't forget the units!

This rectangle has a perimeter of $3 + 3 + 2 + 2 = 10$cm.
We can also say $2 \times 3 + 2 \times 2 = 10$cm.

This square has a perimeter of $4 \times 2 = 8$cm.

If all rectangles have a length and a width, then the perimeter can be calculated with a formula. In a formula, letters are used instead of numbers.

$P = 2l + 2w$ or $P = 2(l + w)$
Perimeter = $2 \times$ length + $2 \times$ width
The perimeter of this rectangle is
$P = 2 \times 4 + 2 \times 2 = 12$cm.

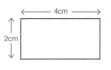

Or we can say
$P = 2(4 + 2)$, so
$P = 2 \times 6 = 12$cm

The formula for a square is easier, because all the sides are the same length.
$P = 4s$
$P = 4 \times 3 = 12$cm

✓ Tips

- **Composite** shapes are made of different shapes. Be very careful how you calculate the perimeter of this shape, which was made by joining a square and a rectangle. You might have to work out some measurements!

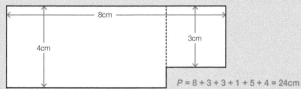

$P = 8 + 3 + 3 + 1 + 5 + 4 = 24$cm

Talk maths

- The textbook activity can be related to the practical tasks that the children have carried out in their work on length and distance.

Activities

- Note that question 4 requires manipulation of numbers in an equation. Some children may need support when tackling this.
- Should children find any particular question difficult, spend time investigating a wider range of rectangles and squares on squared paper, noting the width, length and perimeter of each one and encouraging them to spot patterns.

- More confident learners should create their own composite shapes and challenge friends to find the perimeters.

Problems

- Encourage the children to create scale drawings of each scenario. Further practice with problems can be provided by recreating the problems with different measurements, as well as in *100 Maths Lessons Year 5, Autumn 1, Week 6*.

Talk maths

Practise estimating and measuring the perimeter of different rectangles and squares around your school. Try to calculate them to check your measuring.

l = 85 cm
w = 50 cm

Explain your answers aloud.

Activities

1. Calculate the perimeter of these shapes.

   a.   b.   c.

2. Calculate the perimeter of these composite shapes.

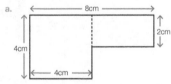

   a. 8cm, 2cm, 4cm, 4cm

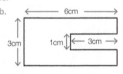

   b. 6cm, 3cm, 1cm, 3cm

3. Copy and complete this chart.

Shape	Formula	Length	Width	Perimeter
Rectangle	P =	6mm	3mm	
Square	P =	2.5mm	2.5mm	

4. Find the width of each of these shapes.

   a. $6cm + 2w = 8cm$ b. $4m + 2w = 20m$

Problems

Brain-teaser
Tina's garden is 7m long and has a perimeter of 20m. How wide is the garden?

Brain-buster
Tables in a classroom are 1m long and 0.5m wide. What would be the perimeter of three tables pushed end to end?

Measurement   57

100 Maths Lessons Year 5 links:

- Autumn 1, Week 6 (pages 37–41): understand and find perimeters

Year 5 Practice Book links:

- (page 96): Perimeter

Area

Prior learning

- Can recall multiplication facts up to 12 × 12.
- Can convert between metric units of length: millimetres, centimetres and metres.

Learn

- Draw some grids on the whiteboard and mark squares of side length 1cm, 2cm and 3cm on them. Remind the children of their knowledge of squared numbers, and verify this by counting the grid squares in each drawn square.

- Recap the use of the superscript 2 to denote squared numbers and explain that this is used for units of area, for example m^2, cm^2, mm^2.

- Introduce the formula for the area of a rectangle or square and ask the children to investigate this through drawing a range of shapes on cm^2 paper and then finding their areas by both counting squares and using the formula.

- Demonstrate how larger areas can be found by using both scale drawing and the formula, such as the field example in the textbook.

- Note that the Tips show children how to find areas of irregular shapes.

Curriculum objectives

- To calculate and compare the area of rectangles (including squares), and including using standard units, square centimetres (cm^2) and square metres (m^2) and estimate the area of irregular shapes.

- To use all four operations to solve problems involving measure using decimal notation, including scaling.

Success criteria

- I can calculate, compare and estimate the areas of rectangles and squares using cm^2 or m^2.

Area

Learn

Area is measured in **square units**.

This square is 1cm long and 1cm wide. Its area is 1cm².

We can count squares to calculate simple areas.

Area of rectangle = 8cm²

The formula for calculating the Area of rectangles and squares is the length times the width. $A = l \times w$

The area of this rectangle is $A = 5 \times 3 = 15$cm².

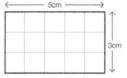

Don't forget to square the units!

For squares, the length and the width are the same. The area of this square is $A = 3 \times 3 = 9$cm².

This field is 40m long and 30m wide. The area of the field is $A = 40 \times 30 = 1200$m².

✓ Tips

- If an irregular shape is drawn on 1cm² paper we can still estimate its area. Just count the squares!

Two half squares make one whole cm².

- This activity challenges children to work backwards from given areas of rectangles and squares to consider what the widths and lengths could be. Encourage them to do all calculations mentally and use the formula when verifying each other's suggestions.

- If appropriate, this is an opportunity for reinforcing recall of square numbers between 1 and 100.

Activities

- The questions should provide enough evidence to assess difficulties or proficiency. Ensure that children can present their calculations clearly in appropriate steps.

- *100 Maths Lessons Year 5, Autumn 1, Week 6* has a range of lessons and activities that focus on calculating both perimeter and area.

Problems

- Both of the problems are tricky, requiring children to find areas and then calculate further.

- For those who encounter difficulties, the links to *100 Maths Lessons Year 5* and *Year 5 Practice Book* contain further problems that will reinforce learning.

Talk maths

Look at these areas, and then tell a partner what the lengths and widths could be. Can they draw them?

There should be more than one answer for each rectangle. How many can you find?

Shape	Rectangle	Rectangle	Rectangle	Square	Square	Square
Area	6cm²	12cm²	30cm²	9cm²	16cm²	25cm²

Activities

1. Estimate the areas of these shapes assuming each square is 1cm².

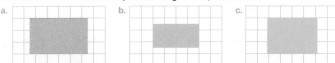

a.   b.   c.

2. Calculate the areas of these shapes.

    a. A rectangle with length 12cm and width 9cm.

    b. A square with side length 7m.

    c. A rectangle with length 25m and width 12m.

3. Write which shape has the larger area.

    a. A rectangle, length 5cm and width 1cm OR a square of side 2cm?

    b. A rectangle, length 8cm and width 3cm OR a square of side 5cm?

    c. A rectangle, length 7m and width 5m OR a square of side 6m?

    d. A rectangle, length 17km and width 9km OR a square of side 12km?

Problems

Brain-teaser
Annie's garden is 3m long and 5m wide. It was all grass but Annie has cut a square flowerbed, with side length of 1m, in the centre. What area of grass is left?

Brain-buster
A farmer plants nine potatoes in every square metre of earth. How many potatoes will she grow in a field 120m long and 75m wide?

Measurement   59

100 Maths Lessons Year 5 links:

- Autumn 1, Week 6 (pages 37–41): understand and find areas

Year 5 Practice Book links:

- (page 97): Area and perimeter
- (page 98): Finding areas
- (page 99): Living space area

Mass, capacity and volume

Prior learning

- Can weigh and read scales to determine mass.
- Have some experience of measuring liquids, using millilitres and litres.
- Understand that scales are made up of equal divisions.

Learn

- Although these three topics are presented in one unit, you may wish to introduce each measure separately and introduce common links later on. The links to *100 Maths Lessons Year 5* provide ample focused lessons and resources for each area.
- Recap that imperial units are sometimes used for measuring capacity and mass.
- Volume: focus on the concept of cube numbers, ideally working with small 1cm³ plastic or wooden cubes to investigate the relationship of side length and volume of cubes.
- Capacity and mass: spend time ensuring that children understand what these measure, perhaps drawing up sets that might fall into either (or both) categories. In particular, focus on the relationship of grams to kilograms and millilitres to litres. Practise multiplying and dividing by 1000 to convert between each, recapping on working to three decimal places if necessary.

Curriculum objectives

- To convert between different units of metric measure (for example, centimetre and metre; gram and kilogram; litre and millilitre).
- To understand and use approximate equivalences between metric units and common imperial units such as inches, pounds and pints.
- To estimate volume and capacity.
- To use all four operations to solve problems involving measure using decimal notation, including scaling.

Success criteria

- I can convert between different metric units, for example grams and kilograms, litres and millilitres.
- I can make approximate conversions between metric and imperial units.
- I can solve problems involving mass, volume and capacity, including decimals.

Mass, capacity and volume

Learn

Mass is sometimes measured in pounds and ounces.

Capacity is sometimes measured in pints and fluid ounces.

We measure volume in **cubic centimetres** or **cubic metres**. The Volume of this cube is $V = 1 \times 1 \times 1 = 1cm^3$.

Maybe that's why they're called cube numbers!

When we add masses together, the units must be the same.

It's the same with capacity.

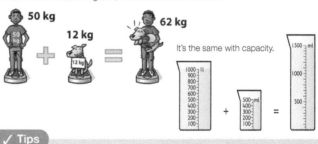

1500ml

✓ Tips

- Essential units for you to know:

Mass	1000g = 1kg
Capacity	1000ml = 1l

Let's make sure we know our units.

- To convert millilitres to litres, and to convert grams to kilograms, divide by 1000.
- To convert litres to millilitres, and kilograms to grams, multiply by 1000.

Talk maths

- This is an exercise in estimation of capacity and volume. Ideally, it should be followed up by using apparatus to measure and check estimates. Although children may need to keep a chart to remind them, try to encourage the actual work to be done collaboratively and orally.

Activities

- Note that this section may require answers of up to three decimal places, as well as adding decimals.
- Before they start, remind the children that it is only possible to add or subtract like units.

Problems

- The problems should be used as useful starting points for context-based work, with the links to *100 Maths Lessons Year 5* and *Year 5 Practice Book* used for extended teaching and practice.

Talk maths

Volume and capacity have similarities.

Volume is usually measured in cubic units, such as cm³. One cubic centimetre equals one millilitre.

Collect some small objects and work with a partner to try and estimate their capacity or weight. If possible use apparatus to check your estimates.

Volume is the amount of space an object takes up. Capacity is used to talk about how much something can hold.

Activities

1. Copy the chart and convert these masses.

Object	Grams	Kilograms
Child		50kg
Dog		12kg
Pencil	75g	
Book	408g	

2. Copy the chart and convert these capacities.

Object	Millilitres	Litres
Teapot		1.25l
Sink		8.5l
Mug	125ml	
Thimble	12ml	

3. Use the completed tables to answer these questions.
   a. What is the mass of a pencil and a book?
   b. What is the capacity of a mug and a thimble?
   c. What is the mass of a child and a book?
   d. What is the capacity of a teapot and a thimble?

Problems

Brain-teaser
Hakan weighs 50kg and his sister Aysha weighs 35kg. Their mum weighs 65kg. How much extra weight would their mum need to add to make a seesaw balance if she sits on one end and the children on the other?

Brain-buster
Françoise has a litre bottle of water. How much will she have left if she fills two thimbles and a mug? The capacity of one thimble is 12ml and of one mug is 125ml.

Measurement   61

100 Maths Lessons Year 5 links:

- Spring 1, Week 6 (pages 119–123): work with mass
- Spring 2, Week 5 (pages 155–159): work with capacity
- Summer 1, Week 6 (pages 201–205): work with volume

Year 5 Practice Book links:

- (page 91): Converting mass
- (page 93): Metric and imperial mass problems
- (page 94): Metric and imperial capacity problems
- (page 95): Ordering masses
- (page 100): Estimate volume
- (page 101): Estimate capacity
- (page 104): Measurement problems (choose appropriate problems)
- (page 105): Summer fete measurement problems (choose appropriate problems)
- (page 107): Outdoor pursuits measurement problems

Time

Prior learning

- Can tell the time using the 12-hour clock.

Learn

- Bring a selection of calendars, clocks and watches into the classroom to discuss the various units and measures of time. Reinforce the irregularity of these units – place value rules do not apply here!

- Remind children of mental methods (for example, multiplying by 60) and consider examples where these are valid and useful.

- Use the chart in the textbook to support quick-fire questions to practise converting between units of time.

- The Tips provide advice for calculating with time. It may be appropriate to spend some time discussing this with the children, aided by card or plastic clocks that the children can freely manipulate.

- *100 Maths Lessons Year 5, Summer 1, Week 6* provides practice in converting between 12- and 24-hour time.

Talk maths

- Ideally, this activity will be supported by bringing as many different timetables and calendars into the classroom. (If this is difficult, the resources in *100 Maths Lessons Year 5* will help).

- For work with timetables, if possible, also provide maps or plans so that children can plan different journeys. This can be extended to role play (older children still love it) for buying tickets and so on.

Curriculum objectives

- To solve problems involving converting between units of time.

- To use all four operations to solve problems involving measure using decimal notation, including scaling.

Success criteria

- I can convert between units of time.

- I can solve problems involving time.

Time

Learn

Seconds, minutes, hours, days, weeks, and **years** – these are all units of time.

Months are a bit different because they are not all the same length.

60 seconds = 1 minute
60 minutes = 1 hour
24 hours = 1 day
7 days = 1 week
365 days = 1 year

Except for leap years – they have an extra day!

Analogue clocks show 12-hour time.
Digital clocks can show **12-hour** or **24-hour time.**

Converting between different units of time is not difficult.

Minutes to seconds	× 60		Seconds to minutes	÷ 60
Hours to minutes	× 60		Minutes to hours	÷ 60
Days to hours	× 24		Hours to days	÷ 24
Weeks to days	× 7		Days to weeks	÷ 7
Years to days	× 365		Days to years	÷ 365

Remainders stay in the same units. For example, change 400 days to years.
400 ÷ 365 = 1 remainder 35 So, 400 days = 1 year and 35 days.

Or one year and five weeks. Can you see that?

✓ Tips

- Be careful adding minutes that move on to a new hour. For example, if a school's lunch break starts at 12:30pm and lasts for 40 minutes, at what time will the break be over? There are 60 minutes in an hour, so 12:30pm + 40 = 1:10pm.

- If you are not sure, use a clock or watch to help you.

- Also, be aware of the 12-hour and 24-hour clocks. Remember that 1pm = 13:00, 6pm = 18:00, and so on.

62 Measurement

- Encourage as much use of precise vocabulary as possible, and use shared information as the starting point for calculations. For example:
  - How many days apart are two people's birthdays?
  - How long before/after noon were you born?

- Converting between 12- and 24-hour clock times can be tricky. The basic rule is that midnight is 'zero' and noon is 'twelve'.
- Before children attempt question 2, recap mental methods for multiplication and division. Challenge more confident learners to solve these problems by using mental methods only.
- The activities in *Year 5 Practice Book* provide further practice.

- The problems provide prompts for many real-life calculations based on children's own lives and families. Challenge the children to create their own set of problems based around the situations in the Brain-teaser and the Brain-buster and challenge one another to solve them.
- *100 Maths Lessons Year 5, Summer 1, Week 6* has problems involving timetables.

Talk maths

Talk to as many people as you can about their birthday. Try to find out what time of day they were born.

Use a calendar to challenge your friends to work out how many days there are between their birthday and yours.

Look at timetables at bus stops or train stations. Can you find out how long different journeys take?

Did you know?

10 years is known as a decade, 100 years is known as a century and 1000 years is known as a millennium.

Activities

1. Copy and complete this chart to convert 12-hour clock times to 24-hour clock times.

12-hour	Midnight	2.10am	9.15am	Noon	3.30pm	9pm	11.59pm
24-hour							

2. Write these times in the unit shown.
   a. 3 hours in minutes
   b. 2 days in hours
   c. 12 weeks in days
   d. 4 years in days
   e. 100 minutes in hours
   f. 100 hours in days
   g. 225 minutes in hours
   h. 500 days in years

3. Add these times.
   a. 8 hours and 25 minutes + 3 hours and 30 minutes
   b. 1 day 7 hours and 25 minutes + 3 days 5 hours and 16 minutes
   c. 2 days 17 hours and 45 minutes + 6 days 9 hours and 13 minutes

Problems

Brain-teaser
Rob's school bus journey takes 17 minutes. If he gets on the bus at 8:20am, what time will he arrive at school?

Brain-buster
Gayle's new baby brother will be exactly one week old at 6pm today. Help Gayle to calculate how many seconds old her new brother will be at 6pm.

100 Maths Lessons Year 5 links:

- Summer 1, Week 6 (pages 201–205): work with time

Year 5 Practice Book links:

- (page 102): Activities diary
- (page 103): Using a calendar
- (page 105): Summer fete measurement problems (choose appropriate problems)

Money

Prior learning

- Can perform written calculations, using either formal or informal methods.
- Can recall number bonds to 100.

Learn

- Remind children of the coins and notes of our currency, ideally bringing examples to class or showing images on the interactive whiteboard. Discuss the value of each coin and note in relation to everyday items. Can the children name items that have a cost that is roughly equal to each coin or note?
- Check that everyone understands the notation used for pounds and pence, and how decimal calculations are accurately written.

- Initially, focus on converting pounds to pence and pence to pounds, consolidating children's skills in multiplying and dividing by 100. Remind the children that amounts are written with either a £ sign or a p for pence, not both.
- Move on to using the four operations to calculate sums of money. Start with addition and consider the example in Tips, reminding the children how numbers with decimal places are added.

- Subtraction, multiplication and division should also be covered, but preferably not within the same session.
- *100 Maths Lessons Year 5, Spring 1, Week 2* covers addition of money.
- *100 Maths Lessons Year 5, Summer 2, Week 2* covers all four operations and money.

Curriculum objectives

- To use all four operations to solve problems involving measure (for example, money) using decimal notation.

Success criteria

- I can solve money problems.

Money

Learn

Money shows us the cost of things. We use pounds (£) and pence (p).

£1 = 100p

We show pence using decimals.

13 pounds and 65 pence = £13.65

If you use the £ sign you don't need to add a p at the end.

You can use all your number skills to solve money problems.

	Example	Try these:
Addition	£13.50 + £6.37 = £19.87	£7.32 + £2.50
Subtraction	£20.00 − £16.25 = £3.75	£10.00 − £8.85
Multiplication	£2.30 × 4 = £9.20	£5.25 × 5
Division	£9.00 ÷ 4 = £2.25	£4.50 ÷ 3
Fractions	$\frac{1}{2}$ of £16.50 = £8.25	$\frac{1}{4}$ of £20

Converting pounds to pence? × 100
Converting pence to pounds? ÷ 100

✓ Tips

- Calculations with money are just the same as using any decimals that have two decimal places.

£47.87 + £38.17

```
    4  7 . 8  7
 +  3  8 . 1  7
 ─────────────
    8  6 . 0  4
    1    1    1
```

Answer: £86.04

Not sure about money? Maybe decimals can help.

- A huge number of calculations are possible with just the items shown in the textbook, and role play can really enhance understanding and mental dexterity for this age group. By placing the children in buyer and seller roles, they will be encouraged to check each other's maths.

Activities

- The charts and calculations will provide enough evidence to assess competence or insecure skills. Remind the children to use written methods if they need to.
- The links to *100 Maths Lessons Year 5* and *Year 5 Practice Book* provide ample further practice in using the four operations with money in a range of context-based problems.

Problems

- Both problems are multi-step and require methodical approaches. Once completed, ask a child who set their work out effectively to talk though their layout with the rest of the class.
- Context-based examples are easy to find and children enjoy practice with money. Teachers usually find that children find this area easier than other measurement work!

Talk maths

Use these items to create multi-step problems to challenge each other. Use written methods to calculate answers if you need to, but be sure to discuss your answers.

Example: If I buy two apples and a banana, how much change will I get from a £2 coin?

2 × 23 + 35 = 81p

2.00 − 0.81 = £1.19

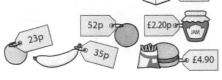

Activities

1. Copy the chart and convert these pence to pounds.

Pence	200p	135p	6325p	9p	10,903p
Pounds					

2. Copy the chart and convert these pounds to pence.

Pounds	£4	£2.56	£0.12	£82	£403.20
Pence					

3. Complete these calculations (use written methods if necessary).

   a. £4.52 + £3.25
   b. £12.35 + £9.80
   c. £10.00 − £8.30
   d. £45.45 − £3.72
   e. £3.35 × 2
   f. £14.08 × 5
   g. £50.00 ÷ 4
   h. $\frac{1}{2}$ of £15.40

Problems

Brain-teaser
Alfie gets £40 for his birthday. He buys a skateboard that is half price in a sale. If the skateboard usually costs £48.50, how much money will Alfie have left?

Brain-buster
A head teacher orders ten desks that cost £35.50 each and 20 chairs for £12.25 each. What will be the total cost?

---

100 Maths Lessons Year 5 links:

- Spring 1, Week 2 (pages 96–101): add and subtract money
- Summer 2, Week 2 (pages 219–224): use all four operations and money

Year 5 Practice Book links:

- (page 104): Measurement problems (choose appropriate problems)
- (page 105): Summer fete measurement problems (choose appropriate problems)
- (page 106): School barbecue measurement problems

Angle facts

Prior learning

- Understand the concepts of whole turns, half turns and quarter turns.
- Know the direction of clockwise and anticlockwise.
- Can read and estimate positions on numbered and unnumbered scales.

Learn

- Spend time looking at protractors with the children, ensuring they know how to use them correctly, and are aware which scale to use depending on the angle being measured (that is, reading clockwise or anticlockwise).
- Early lessons in *100 Maths Year 5, Autumn 1, Week 5* provide practice in measuring angles correctly.
- *100 Maths Lessons Year 5, Summer 1, Week 5* has activities to measure and draw angles to the nearest degree.
- Introduce the different names

of angles (acute, obtuse, reflex, right angle) and provide children with opportunities to learn the names and to become proficient in naming given angles. All the while, reinforce key geometric vocabulary such as 'perpendicular', 'rotation' and 'degree'.

- If 180° protractors are all that are available, show children the 'trick' for calculating reflex angles: measuring the supplementary angle and subtracting it from 360°.

- Note that *100 Maths Lessons Year 5, Autumn 1, Week 5* also provides lessons and activities for developing understanding of using angle properties to deduce other angles (for example, all angles on a straight line add to 180°). These activities are useful for developing reasoning skills while consolidating knowledge.

Angle facts

Learn

We measure angles with a protractor.

A right angle is 90°	A straight line is 180°
90°	180°

Acute angles are between 0° and 90°	Obtuse angles are between 90° and 180°
50°	160°

Angles greater than 180° are called **reflex** angles	A complete turn is 360°
200°	360°

✓ Tips

- Make sure you can use a protractor properly. Check the size of each of the angles on this page.
- Think about it...two lines that make an acute angle on the inside will make a reflex angle on the outside. These two angles add up to 360°.

Stuck? Let's come at things from a different angle.

- Encouraging the children to explain how to use a protractor will help develop their sense of the procedure involved.

- The second part of this task includes drawing angles, estimating their size and then measuring them. This could be extended by challenging the children not only to estimate and measure each other's angles, but also to name each one as they do so.

Activities

- The straightforward practice in this section can be developed further with activities from the links to *100 Maths Lessons Year 5* and *Year 5 Practice Book*.

- Although this chapter's focus is not on shape, investigating regular and irregular polygons by measuring their angles can provide a motivating extension.

Problems

- Note that the Brain-teaser is deliberately open for the children to debate different methods. In the problem, the equipment that Aaron has available would not allow any certainty as to whether a borderline angle (such as 89°) is definitely acute, right-angled or obtuse. However, by drawing straight and perpendicular lines, he should be able to make a good guess.

Talk maths

You will need paper, a pencil, a ruler and a protractor.

Develop and practise a short demonstration about how to use a protractor properly.

Demonstrate the correct way to place it on an angle, and how to measure the angle using the correct readings.

Next, work with a partner to become angle experts: draw a selection of angles and then estimate their size.

Finally, measure each one and compare with your estimates.

How accurate were your angle estimates?

Activities

1. Measure these angles. Write down their size and their name, such as *acute*.

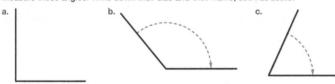

a.   b.   c.

2. Draw these angles, and then name them.

   a. 90°   **b.** 300°   **c.** 15°

Problems

Brain-teaser
Aaron only has a ruler and a pencil, but he can still say if an angle is acute, obtuse or reflex. How can he do this?

Brain-buster
Amy draws a straight line and then draws another line to its middle to make two separate angles. She measures the acute angle to be 42°. She says that the obtuse angle must be 138°. Explain why she is right.

42°

100 Maths Lessons Year 5 links:

- Autumn 1, Week 5 (pages 32–36): estimate, draw and measure acute and obtuse angles; calculate angles on a straight line; calculate reflex angles

- Summer 1, Week 5 (pages 196–200): estimate and measure angles

Year 5 Practice Book links:

- (page 108): Acute, obtuse or right?

- (page 109): What's the angle?

- (page 110): Measuring and drawing angles

Rotating angles

Prior learning

- Understand angles as a measurement of turn.
- Can recognise and name acute, obtuse and right angles.
- Have some understanding of how a protractor is used to measure angles.

- Accurately construct a right angle on the whiteboard, and then extend one side to reveal a second right angle. Discuss how the two right angles make a straight line of 180°, and progress to considering a complete rotation of 360°.
- Give each child a piece of A5 paper (it must be an exact rectangle) and have them write a large number in each corner: 1, 2, 3 and 4. Demonstrate how each corner can be removed (tearing or cutting). Then join all four corners together, revealing that the four right angles make a complete turn, or 360°.
- Displaying a large perpendicular cross, look at the four right angles that are covered in a complete rotation, noting the four main stages of 90°, 180°, 270° and 360°. If possible, allow the children to work with card or plastic clocks and consider the times at which each of these positions occur through the day.

- If appropriate, demonstrate the link between rotations and fractions: 90° is a quarter turn; 180° is a half-turn; 270° is three quarters of a turn; and 360° is a whole turn.

Curriculum objectives

- To identify:
  - angles at a point on a straight line and ½ a turn (total 180°)
  - other multiples of 90°.

Success criteria

- I can identify angles that are multiples of 90.

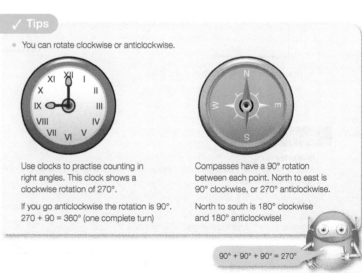

Rotating angles

Learn

A right angle is 90°. Two right angles make 180°.

There are 360° in a complete rotation.

A complete rotation is four right angles.
90° + 90° + 90° + 90° = 360°

Each rotation of 90° is a right angle.

90° + 90° = 180°

Imagine standing at the centre of this circle and turning ninety degrees four times.

Rip the four corners off a piece of A5 paper and put them together. What do you notice?

✓ Tips

- You can rotate clockwise or anticlockwise.

Use clocks to practise counting in right angles. This clock shows a clockwise rotation of 270°.

If you go anticlockwise the rotation is 90°. 270 + 90 = 360° (one complete turn)

Compasses have a 90° rotation between each point. North to east is 90° clockwise, or 270° anticlockwise.

North to south is 180° clockwise and 180° anticlockwise!

90° + 90° + 90° = 270°

- The activity in the textbook can be performed in the playground with chalk, or just with pencil and paper and a small plastic figure. If desired, this can be extended into geography skills by considering compass directions, both for quarter turns and for rotations of amounts other than 90°.

- In particular, check if children understand the difference between representing 360° and 0°.
- The links to *100 Maths Lessons Year 5* and *Year 5 Practice Book* provide further lessons and practice, as well as consolidation for naming and drawing angles, and calculating missing angles in diagrams.

- The problems can be extended to oral challenges for any time or compass bearings, as desired. Extension can be provided by allowing rotations of more or less than 90°.

Talk maths

Use chalk to draw a large cross on the ground and mark the end of each line 1, 2, 3, 4.

Challenge each other to rotate the correct number of right angles. For example, *face number 2 and then rotate 90°*. Which number are you facing now?

You can also try it using compass directions and an obstacle course.

> You can play a mini version of this activity using an action figure on paper!

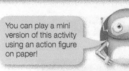

Activities

1. Draw these angles using a protractor.

   a. 90°   b. 180°   c. 270°   d. 360°   e. 0°

2. What angle is shown on each clock? Give your answer in degrees and say if it is clockwise or anti-clockwise.

   a.   b.   c.

3. Say what each of the angles in question 2 would be if you turned in the other direction.

Problems

Brain-teaser
To get from midday to 9pm, how many right angles does the hour hand on a clock have to turn through? How many degrees is this?

Brain-buster
Michael stands facing south. He rotates 270° clockwise, and then he turns an amount. If he finishes facing west, how many degrees did he turn the second time, and in what direction?

Geometry   69

---

100 Maths Lessons Year 5 links:

- Autumn 1, Week 5 (pages 32–36): estimate, draw and measure acute and obtuse angles; calculate angles on a straight line; calculate reflex angles
- Summer 1, Week 5 (pages 196–200): estimate and measure angles

Year 5 Practice Book links:

- (page 111): Angle rules
- (page 112): Missing angles

2D shapes

Prior learning

- Can say some of the properties of triangles.
- Can use some of the vocabulary of shape, for example, 'sides', 'vertices', 'angles', and so on.
- Can use a ruler accurately to draw straight lines.

Learn

- Use flash cards or pictures on the interactive whiteboard to reinforce the names and characteristics of common, regular 2D shapes. If necessary, allow time for the children to play matching or memory games.
- Explain the difference between regular and irregular polygons.

- If possible, provide pegboards and elastic bands or string, for children to investigate how irregular shapes can vary. If this is not possible, there are websites that allow you to manipulate shapes on screen, adjusting the position of any side or angle. This activity can be extended to consider that the sum of the angles for each polygon remains the same no matter how irregular its shape. This can also become a broader investigation that can consolidate children's use of a protractor.
- *100 Maths Lessons Year 5, Summer 1, Week 5* provides activities for investigating regular and irregular polygons.

Curriculum objectives

- To use the properties of rectangles to deduce related facts and find missing lengths and angles.
- To distinguish between regular and irregular polygons based on reasoning about equal sides and angles.

Success criteria

- I can recognise and name regular and irregular polygons.
- I can find missing lengths and angles in rectangles and squares.

2D shapes

Learn

We say that different 2D shapes have different properties.

Each of the angles in a square is 90°. A circle has one side and no corners!

Triangle	Quadrilateral	Pentagon	Hexagon	Heptagon	Octagon
3 sides	4 sides	5 sides	6 sides	7 sides	8 sides

All of these shapes are **regular** – all the sides are the same length, and in each shape all of the angles are the same size.

Irregular shapes have the same number of sides and angles as their corresponding regular shapes, but the sides and angles are not identical.

Triangle	Quadrilateral	Pentagon	Hexagon	Heptagon	Octagon
3 sides	4 sides	5 sides	6 sides	7 sides	8 sides

✓ Tips

- There are several types of quadrilateral that you also need to know about.

Square	Rectangle	Rhombus	Parallelogram	Kite	Trapezium
All sides equal, all angles 90°	Opposite sides equal, all angles 90°	All sides equal, opposite angles equal	Opposite sides equal, and parallel opposite angles equal	Adjacent sides equal	Only one pair of parallel sides

- **Adjacent** means **next to**.

Don't worry, although it's hard to say *quadrilaterals*, they're quite easy really.

70   Geometry

Talk maths

- If plastic shapes are available, these can be put into a 'feelie' bag and children can take turns to name a hidden shape by feeling it only. This can be extended by asking them to describe what they are feeling (without naming it) and asking others to state the name, before revealing the shape to verify their work.

Activities

- If appropriate, children can be introduced to classification of quadrilaterals as described in the Tips. Categories might include:
  - Are all sides equal?
  - Are all angles equal?
  - Are opposite sides parallel?
  - Are any opposite angles equal?
- *100 Maths Lessons Year 5, Summer 1, Week 5* has activities that allow children to investigate regular and irregular polygons and quadrilaterals on isometric paper.

Problems

- The problem can easily be rephrased for different polygons and quadrilaterals, and the links to *100 Maths Lessons Year 5* and *Year 5 Practice Book* also provide a range of investigations to consolidate skills.

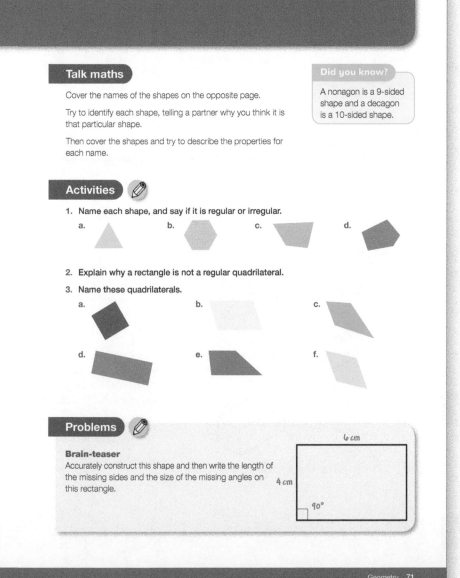

Talk maths

Cover the names of the shapes on the opposite page.

Try to identify each shape, telling a partner why you think it is that particular shape.

Then cover the shapes and try to describe the properties for each name.

Did you know?

A nonagon is a 9-sided shape and a decagon is a 10-sided shape.

Activities

1. Name each shape, and say if it is regular or irregular.

   a.   b.   c.   d.

2. Explain why a rectangle is not a regular quadrilateral.

3. Name these quadrilaterals.

   a.   b.   c.

   d.   e.   f.

Problems

Brain-teaser
Accurately construct this shape and then write the length of the missing sides and the size of the missing angles on this rectangle.

6 cm

4 cm

90°

Geometry   71

100 Maths Lessons Year 5 links:

- Autumn 2, Week 5 (pages 73–77): identify, visualise and describe properties of rectangles, triangles, regular polygons; use knowledge of properties to draw 2D shapes
- Summer 1, Week 5 (pages 196–200): investigate shapes

Year 5 Practice Book links:

- (page 113): Drawing shapes
- (page 115): Find what's missing
- (page 116): Is it a rectangle?
- (page 117): Sorting triangles

3D shapes

Prior learning

- Can say some of the properties of triangles, rectangles and squares.
- Can use some of the vocabulary of shape, for example, 'sides', 'vertices', 'angles', and so on.
- Can use a ruler accurately to draw straight lines.

Learn

- Introduce the topic through a focus on key terminology: 'faces', 'edges' and 'vertices'. Note the singular spelling of each: 'face', 'edge' and 'vertex'.
- By presenting a real or digital cube (some websites have cubes that can be rotated on screen), consider how it is made up of interconnected 2D shapes.
- Look carefully at the shapes in the textbook, and ideally bring real models of each into the classroom. Through looking at

the properties of each shape, consolidate vocabulary. Ensure that children appreciate the key similarity of the cylinder, sphere and cone – they all have a curved face.

- Ask children to think of objects in real life that are examples of the 3D shapes shown. List these and note which objects are not completely accurate 3D shapes (for example, a drinks can).

- Ideally using isometric paper, ask the children to construct a range of cubes and cuboids. If isometric paper is unavailable, demonstrate how to draw with a 3D effect, as shown in the Tips in the textbook. When demonstrating, use dotted lines to show the hidden edges and vertices.

Curriculum objectives

- To identify 3D shapes, including cubes and other cuboids, from 2D representations.

Success criteria

- I can identify and draw 3D shapes.

3D shapes

Learn

3D shapes have faces, edges and vertices.
A corner is a **vertex**. The plural is **vertices**.

Irregular shapes have the same number of sides and angles as their corresponding regular shapes, but the sides and angles are not identical.

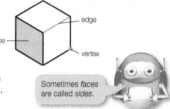

Sometimes *faces* are called *sides*.

Shape	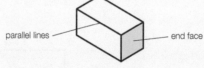					
Name	Cube	Cuboid	Cone	Sphere	Cylinder	Triangular prism
Faces	6	6	2	1	3	5
Edges	12	12	1	0	2	9
Vertices	8	8	0	0	0	6

✓ Tips

- Drawing shapes to look 3D is called isometric drawing.
- The trick is to draw one end face, and then draw the edges as parallel lines.

You don't need special glasses to view 3D shapes!

parallel lines — end face

- Beware: spheres and cones are harder to draw!

Talk maths

- The activity in the textbook can be performed using plastic or wooden shapes or pictures of shapes. These can be displayed behind a child (or on paper stuck to their forehead!) and the child must ask questions to deduce what shape it is. They can only ask questions that can be answered 'yes' or 'no'.

Activities

- Ideally, provide plastic or wooden 3D models to aid children's drawing. Encourage them to try these freehand as well as with rulers.
- For children who are struggling, provide construction kits that have appropriate parts to make either solid or 'skeleton' (edges only) models.

Problems

- In addition to the problems in the textbook, the links to *100 Maths Lessons Year 5* provide suggestions for an activity to construct nets. It challenges children to create them, noticing how nets can vary in their layout yet still produce the correct shape when joined.
- A nice activity to show the difficulties of presenting spheres in 2D is to peel a satsuma – it can't be truly flat. This can lead to links with geography and considerations of different representations of the Earth on maps.

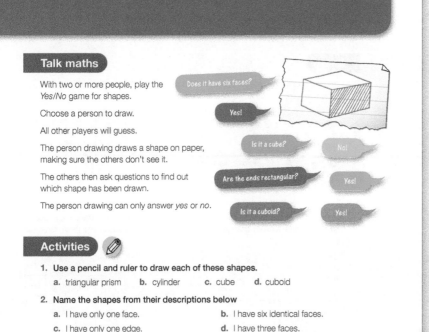

Talk maths

With two or more people, play the *Yes/No* game for shapes.

Choose a person to draw.

All other players will guess.

The person drawing draws a shape on paper, making sure the others don't see it.

The others then ask questions to find out which shape has been drawn.

The person drawing can only answer *yes* or *no*.

Does it have six faces?
Yes!
Is it a cube?
No!
Are the ends rectangular?
Yes!
Is it a cuboid?
Yes!

Activities

1. Use a pencil and ruler to draw each of these shapes.
   a. triangular prism   b. cylinder   c. cube   d. cuboid

2. Name the shapes from their descriptions below
   a. I have only one face.
   b. I have six identical faces.
   c. I have only one edge.
   d. I have three faces.
   e. I have five faces.
   f. I have six faces, some different.

Problems

Brain-teaser
Sanjay draws a 3D shape with a square end; each edge of the square is 4cm. The other sides of his shape are 6cm long. What shape has he drawn?

Brain-buster
A cone and a cylinder are both 10cm long and both have a base with a diameter of 5cm. If they were hollow, which one could hold more water? Explain your answer.

Geometry   73

100 Maths Lessons Year 5 links:

- Autumn 2, Week 5 (pages 73–77): identify and draw nets of 3D shapes

Year 5 Practice Book links:

- (page 114): Shape nets

Year 5 Geometry   79

Reflecting and translating shapes

Prior learning

- Can mark a square and identify a point on a coordinate grid.
- Can name and recall the basic properties of 2D shapes.

Learn

- Draw a simple coordinate grid, like that shown at the top of page 74 the textbook. Work with the children to plot a selection of random points, including actually on each axis, modelling correct vocabulary and appropriate presentation of coordinates.
- Next, revisit children's work on 2D shapes and work together to plot regular and irregular shapes. To conclude, show how a square can be plotted in different positions, from its sides being parallel to the axes to a 'diamond' shape, spotting relationships between the coordinates of the corners for each one.
- Ideally in separate sessions, work with the whole class to demonstrate the reflection and translation of simple 2D shapes. It is only necessary to use vertical or horizontal lines of reflection.

- *100 Maths Lessons Year 5, Spring 1, Week 5* provides a wide range of lessons and resources for consolidating these skills, as well as interactive aids. At this stage Lessons 1 to 3 will be particularly useful.

Reflecting and translating shapes

Learn

We draw coordinate grids with an *x*-axis and a *y*-axis, and we can plot the corners of polygons (2D shapes).

Points on the coordinate grid are shown with the *x*-coordinate first, and then the *y*-coordinate.

Remember, along first, then up.

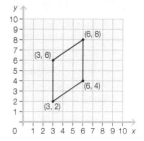

A has been reflected to A¹.
The *x*-coordinate has not changed.

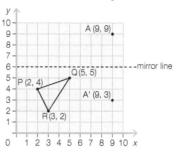

We can also reflect shapes.
What will the coordinates of the reflected triangle be?

We can also **translate** shapes.
The square has been translated (5, 4).

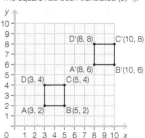

✓ Tips

- **Reflections:**
  In a vertical mirror line, only the *x*-coordinates change. In a horizontal mirror line, only the *y*-coordinates change.
- **Translations:**
  All the *x*-coordinates should change by the same amount. And so should the *y*-coordinates.

74 Geometry

Talk maths

- For the textbook activity, try to provide each group with a large piece of paper with both axes labelled 0 to 10. Ideally, this will be squared paper and children will be able to reflect and translate repeatedly on it using counters or cut-out shapes.
- As children talk, monitor and check that their use of vocabulary is accurate.

Activities

- The two questions should provide a good assessment of whether children understand the concepts involved. You may wish to introduce the notation for reflected points (for example, A reflected becomes A[1], and so on).
- Learning can be extended by using *100 Maths Lessons Year 5, Spring 1, Week 5, Lessons 4 and 5*. These introduce the idea of using formulae to calculate translated coordinates.

Problems

- The Brain-buster requires children to think about how to predict the coordinates of reflected shapes based on how far a point is from a mirror line.
- Challenge the children to devise an explanation for a method of calculating coordinates for a translation.

Talk maths

Take turns to choose a point on the grid and say its coordinates. Challenge someone to reflect or translate it.

Translate the point (0, 5) by (2, 3).

Reflect the point (9, 1) horizontally.

Reflect the point (2, 3) vertically.

Translate the point (4, 4) by (−2, −3).

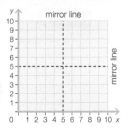

Activities

1. Look at the grid opposite. Using squared paper copy the grid, the square PQRS and the mirror line.
   a. Reflect the square PQRS.
   b. Write the coordinates of the new square.
   c. Plot a triangle ABC: A (6, 5), B (9 ,6), C (7, 9).
   d. Reflect the triangle.

2. Look at the grid opposite. Using squared paper copy the grid and the square WXYZ.
   a. Translate the square WXYZ by (3, 2).
   b. Write the coordinates of the new square.
   c. Plot a triangle DEF: D (2, 7), E (4, 9), F (3, 5).
   d. Translate the triangle by (5, −4).

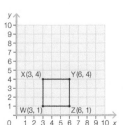

Problems

Brain-buster
Gayle has worked out a method for calculating the coordinates of reflected shapes without drawing them. Explain her method.

Geometry 75

100 Maths Lessons Year 5 links:

- Spring 1, Week 5 (pages 114–118): read and plot coordinates in the first quadrant; draw the position of a shape after a reflection or translation

Year 5 Practice Book links:

- (page 118): Reflect it!
- (page 119): Translate and reflect

Line graphs

Prior learning

- Can create pictograms and simple block and bar charts.
- Can gather information to represent pictorially.

Learn

- Through simple examples, review the different ways the children already know of representing data in graph form. Be sure to cover pictograms and bar charts.
- Create an enlarged version of the line graph about the bike ride on page 76 of the textbook. Stressing that time is always displayed on the x-axis, discuss the graph with the children. Consider the horizontal sections of the line and emphasise that time is passing even though distance is not changing.

- The Tips show how a tree's height varies with time. The children should be able to grasp that the levelling off means that the tree has stopped growing upwards.
- *100 Maths Lessons Year 5, Spring 2, Week 6* and *Summer 2, Week 6* provide activities for assessing data and considering its representation. Use these to consolidate understanding of graph types and the associated vocabulary.

Talk maths

- The graph in the textbook shows the journey of a lorry. Before asking the children to work in pairs or groups, pose a range of questions to aid understanding, such as:
  - Why is one section horizontal?
  - Why is there no vertical section?
  - Why does the graph stop?
- After the children have explored the graph in some detail, encourage them to start forming 'sum' and 'difference' problems,

Curriculum objectives

- To solve comparison, sum and difference problems using information presented in a line graph.

Success criteria

- I can make and interpret line graphs.

Line graphs

Learn

We can represent information and data in different types of charts and graphs.

Each of these graphs has a vertical y-axis and a horizontal x-axis.

Bar charts and pictograms are useful for presenting information from surveys, such as:

- How do you travel to school?
- What is your favourite snack?
- Do you have any pets?

Line graphs are useful to show how things change over time, such as temperature, growth and speed.

bar chart   line graph   pictogram

This graph shows the time taken for an 8km cycle ride.

Find these bits of information on the graph:

- The journey starts at 1pm.
- After 20 minutes the cyclist stops for five minutes.
- The cyclist travels fastest from 25 minutes to 40 minutes.
- The cyclist stops again after 40 minutes.
- The journey finishes at 8km.

Look carefully at the scale on each axis.

✓ Tips

- Line graphs can be used to estimate information.
- This graph shows the height a tree grew every two years for ten years.
- We can draw lines to show its height after three years.

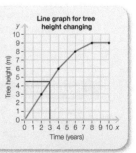

such as:
- How far did the lorry travel between hour 5 and hour 8?
- How long did it take the lorry to travel the first 75km?
- How long did the lorry stop for?
- What was the fastest part of the journey?

- For children who grasp this confidently, you might introduce the concept of speed (and average speed) as distance divided by time.

Activities

- Encourage children to draw the graph as accurately as possible. If necessary, model the plotting of some of the points from the table and connecting them with a ruler.
- Ideally, children should also gain some experience in recording their own data and plotting a line graph of it.

Problems

- The problems in the textbook are made more difficult by the scale on the y-axis. If necessary, spend time with the children looking at the divisions between each number shown, as well as modelling the use of a ruler for reading accurately across the graph.

Talk maths

This line graph shows the distance travelled by a lorry on a long journey.

Look at the graph with a partner and talk about what each part means.

What is each axis for?

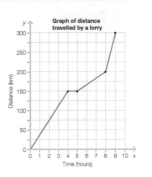
Graph of distance travelled by a lorry

What is the scale for each axis?

How long is the journey?

What is happening when the line is flat?

Activities

1. Philip grows a plant at home. He measures it at the end of each week and records its height in a chart.

Time (weeks)	1	2	3	4	5	6	7	8	9	10
Height (cm)	0	1	3	5	7	10	11	12	12	12

a. Draw a line graph to show how the plant has grown.
b. When was the plant 3cm high?
c. When did the plant stop growing?
d. Which week did the plant grow the most?

Remember to put time on the x-axis.

Problems

Brain-teaser
What is the highest temperature? When was the temperature highest?

Brain-buster
Find the difference between the highest and lowest temperatures.

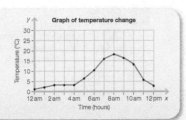
Graph of temperature change

Statistics 77

---

100 Maths Lessons Year 5 links:

- Spring 2, Week 6 (pages 160–164): understand line graphs; construct line graphs; interpret line graphs
- Summer 2, Week 6 (pages 242–246): plan an investigation to collect and represent data

Year 5 Practice Book links:

- (page 120): Comparing data
- (page 121): Missing data
- (page 124): Line graph problems
- (page 125): Every graph tells a story

Tables and timetables

Prior learning

- Can construct frequency tables, pictograms, bar charts and line graphs to represent the frequencies of events and changes over time.
- Can collect, select and organise data to answer questions, draw conclusions and identify further questions to ask.

Learn

- Use the table in the textbook to reinforce effective use of a table of information. This can be extended beyond locating data to making deductions (*Which planet has the shortest orbit time?*), and 'sum' and 'difference' type questions (*How much hotter is Venus than Earth?*).

- The bus timetable provides a range of opportunities for enhancing understanding. Assuming a constant speed for the bus, children should be able to estimate the relative distances between locations. This could lead to a simplified map of the imaginary town. Alternatively, children could question each other about departure and journey times, and/or create further columns for the next three or four buses.

Talk maths

- A range of timetables will be needed for this activity to succeed. If it is impractical to get these from bus and railway stations, remember that a wide range of timetables, including interactive ones, are available online.
- There are ample learning opportunities in planning agendas for day trips, including waiting times. More confident learners can move on to plan world travel via online research.

Curriculum objectives

- To complete, read and interpret information in tables, including timetables.

Success criteria

- I can read and use tables and timetables.

Tables and timetables

Learn

Information is often presented in tables. This table provides complicated information about some planets in our solar system.

You can spot facts about planets and compare them too. Each column has different units.

Planet	Diameter (km)	Day length (hours)	Orbit time (days)	Temp. (°C)
Mercury	4878	4223	88	167
Venus	12,104	2808	225	480
Earth	12,756	24	365	20
Mars	6794	24.5	687	−65

This timetable shows bus times from the bus station to the local school.

Check with a partner that you know how to read the timetable properly. These buses have a circular route. Can you see the halfway point?

Can you see the difference between the number 6 and 7 bus routes? Why wouldn't you go to the supermarket on the number 6 bus? What is the longest time it takes to get between two stops?

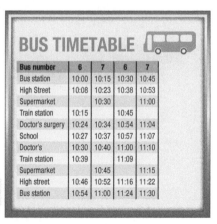

BUS TIMETABLE

Bus number	6	7	6	7
Bus station	10:00	10:15	10:30	10:45
High Street	10:08	10:23	10:38	10:53
Supermarket		10:30		11:00
Train station	10:15		10:45	
Doctor's surgery	10:24	10:34	10:54	11:04
School	10:27	10:37	10:57	11:07
Doctor's	10:30	10:40	11:00	11:10
Train station	10:39		11:09	
Supermarket		10:45		11:15
High street	10:46	10:52	11:16	11:22
Bus station	10:54	11:00	11:24	11:30

Can you spot the patterns for the bus times?

✓ Tips

- Use your fingers to help you trace along timetables and charts. Or if you have a ruler available, using this is even better – it is easy to misread timetables and charts.

Let your fingers do the walking!

Activities

- This section in the textbook will consolidate skills and vocabulary developed so far. To provide extended, context-based work the links to *100 Maths Lessons Year 5* provide scenarios and resources that can be very effective with appropriate planning.

- If further practice in using bar charts or line graphs is required, challenge the children to consider how they would interpret the information in the planets chart and bus timetable. Can they create charts and graphs for these?

Problems

- Once children have solved the problems, encourage them to develop their own, in particular with new bus times for later in the day, which they will need to calculate for themselves.

- *100 Maths Lessons Year 5, Summer 2, Week 6*, which may have been used when studying line graphs, can also provide experience in creating charts and tables.

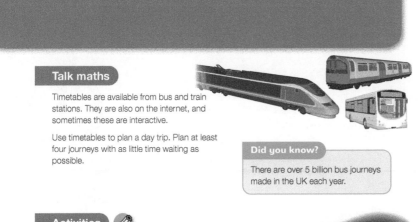

Talk maths

Timetables are available from bus and train stations. They are also on the internet, and sometimes these are interactive.

Use timetables to plan a day trip. Plan at least four journeys with as little time waiting as possible.

Did you know?

There are over 5 billion bus journeys made in the UK each year.

Activities

1. **Use the table on page 78 to answer these questions about our solar system.**
   a. Which is the largest planet?
   b. Which is the coldest planet?
   c. Which planet has the fastest orbit?
   d. Which planets have a similar length of day?

2. **Use the bus timetable on page 78 to answer these questions.**
   a. Which bus has a shorter journey from the bus station to the school?
   b. How often does the number 6 leave the bus station?
   c. How long is the journey from the doctor's surgery to the school?
   d. Why do you think the number 6 round journey takes longer?

Problems

Look at the bus timetable on page 78.

Brain-teaser
Trevor has a doctor's appointment at 10:45am. Which bus should he catch from the bus station?

Brain-buster
A number 7 bus arrives at school at 15:07. What time did it leave the bus station?

100 Maths Lessons Year 5 links:

- Autumn 2, Week 6 (pages 78–82): collect, organise and interpret information in tables and bar charts
- Summer 2, Week 6 (pages 242–246): plan an investigation to collect and represent data

Year 5 Practice Book links:

- (pages 122–123): Complete a timetable

The number system

Prior learning

- Can read and write numbers to at least 100,000 in numerals and words.
- Understand the relationship and value of each digit in a number to at least 100,000.
- Order whole numbers up to 100,000.
- Understands most Roman numerals up to 1000 (M).

Note that this unit is a recap of the previous year's work. Depending on the children's attainment it may be appropriate to cover it in only one or two lessons.

- Display (or draw) two clocks side by side, one with Roman numerals and the other with numbers. As well as recapping the value of Roman numerals (children are expected to know how to read numbers up to 1000), note that the Romans had no symbol for zero, and consider the difficulties this presented them with calculations.
- Discuss the idea of number systems and why our current system might have evolved (the powers of 10 for each column make calculations easier).
- Prepare large digit cards, 0–9, ideally each printed on a sheet of A4 paper. Arrange them in pairs and threes to make a selection of numbers. Ask the children to say each number made. Review the columns in the place-value table and discuss with the children how the position of a digit in a number defines the value of that digit.

Curriculum objectives

- To read, write, order and compare numbers to at least 1,000,000 and determine the value of each digit.
- To read Roman numerals to 1000 (M).

Success criteria

- I can say the value of any digit in a number.
- I can read Roman numerals and convert them to numbers using digits.

The number system

Learn

In the past, some people used the Roman system when writing numbers. The Romans used letters to represent amounts.

Nowadays we use ten digits:

0 1 2 3 4 5 6 7 8 9

All of the maths we do only uses these ten digits. We can do a lot with only ten digits because of **place value**.

The Romans didn't have zero or place value.

Our number system is called **base 10** because it arranges digits in columns that increase in powers of 10.

1,000,000s	100,000s	10,000s	1000s	100s	10s	1s
5	6	4	0	3	4	2

Notice how each digit represents a different amount depending on its place value.

✓ Tips

- Make sure you can read large numbers. It isn't so hard if you take your time. Look at this number:

  2450398

- We can separate the millions and thousands using gaps or commas.

  2,450,398 or 2 450 398

  There's certainly a place for gaps or commas!

- If you are still unsure, write in the place value above each digit.

1,000,000s	100,000s	10,000s	1000s	100s	10s	1s
2	4	5	0	3	9	8

Say it out aloud: two million, four hundred and fifty thousand, three hundred and ninety-eight.

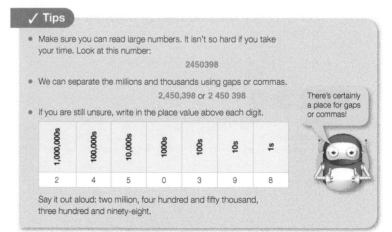

6   Number and place value

Talk maths

- The textbook presents two separate activities, one for converting to and from Roman numerals, the other for correctly reading and saying base 10 numbers. In particular, be sure to model how to read larger numbers correctly, and allow plenty of time for practice and reflection.

Activities

- The questions presented can easily be developed further. If children do need more practice, encourage them to set questions for each other in the same format as those given.

Problems

- The problems can be extended into investigations if desired. For example:
  - Write the number that is two more than two million, three more than three million, and so on.
  - What is the smallest 7-digit number you can make?

Talk maths

Roman numerals

Work with a partner. Challenge each other to say any Roman numeral up to 1000. The table below gives you everything you need to know.

Did you know?

Romanian is the closest living language to Latin, the language of the Romans.

Number	1	2	3	4	5	6	7	8	9	10
Roman numeral	I	II	III	IV	V	VI	VII	VIII	IX	X

Number	50	100	500	1000
Roman numeral	L	C	D	M

It's quite easy once you get the hang of it!

Base 10 numbers

Starting small and getting bigger, write down ten numbers up to 10,000,000 and challenge your partner to say them correctly.

349   9235   400,004   45,202

305,621   3,452,320   90,009

726,817   3,000,003   6,426,208

Activities

1. Change these Roman numerals to base 10 numbers.

   a. CCCL   b. CXC   c. MMMD   d. MDCLXVI

2. Write the value of the underlined digit in each number.

   a. 32,4<u>0</u>2   b. 2<u>3</u>0,508   c. <u>4</u>,730,627   d. 7,<u>6</u>73,205

Problems

Brain-teaser
Write the number that is one more than one million. ·

Brain-buster
What is the biggest 7-digit number? Write it in digits and then in words.

100 Maths Lessons Year 6 links:

- Autumn 1, Week 1 (pages 8–13): place value of 6- and 7-digit numbers

Numbers up to 10,000,000

Prior learning

- Read, write and order numbers up to 1,000,000 and determine the value of each digit in large numbers.

Learn

- Display large place-value tables with columns up to 100,000. Provide a bank of digit cards 0–9, ensuring there are multiple copies of each digit, especially zero. Practise making and saying a range of numbers with the children.

- Stress the importance of zero as a place holder.
- Using the number in the third table on page 8 of the textbook as a starting point, spend time looking at the different powers of 10 in each column.
- Create new numbers and write them on the board. Challenge the children to identify the value of each digit. Model the correct reading of each number carefully and clearly.

- If necessary, be sure to reinforce the school's policy for the use of gaps or commas for separating thousands in large numbers.
- *100 Maths Lessons Year 6, Autumn 1, Week 1* provides a range of activities, many based around mathematical equipment, for reinforcing concepts and vocabulary.

Curriculum objectives

- To read, write, order and compare numbers up to 10,000,000 and determine the value of each digit.
- To solve number and practical problems that involve all of the above.

Success criteria

- I can understand and use numbers up to ten million (10,000,000).

Numbers to 10,000,000

Learn

239,718 in words is two hundred and thirty-nine thousand, seven hundred and eighteen.

100,000s	10,000s	1000s	100s	10s	1s
2	3	9	7	1	8

The **place value** of the **3** digit represents 30,000; the **7** represents 700.
What do the other digits represent?

Zeros are also important.
402,005 in words is four hundred and two thousand and five.

100,000s	10,000s	1000s	100s	10s	1s
4	0	2	0	0	5

This number is twelve million, seven hundred and sixty-four thousand, three hundred and five.

10,000,000	1,000,000s	100,000s	10,000s	1000s	100s	10s	1s
1	2	7	6	4	3	0	5

Use a comma after the millions and after the thousands column.
The number above should be written as 12,764,305.

What number does each of the digits represent?

✓ Tips

- Write the place value in columns above numbers if you're stuck.
- < means less than and > means more than.

Did you know?

A billion is a thousand million. One billion has nine zeros.

Talk maths

- Create sets of digit cards, ensuring that each digit is repeated several times. Allow children to work in groups and create numbers that they can read aloud fluently. Encourage them to identify larger numbers that they find tricky, and focus on these.

- Also, try displaying large numbers with one digit covered. Say the number to the children and ask them to identify the missing digit.

Activities

- Before attempting the textbook questions, provide practice in writing larger numbers in words. Consider, in particular, how zeros affect the words used (for example, six hundred and four thousand).

Problems

- The textbook problems focus on populations. For more confident learners, this can be extended into investigations of cities and countries around the world, looking at populations, GDP, and so on.

- *100 Maths Lessons Year 6, Spring 1, Week 1* has activities for this, and the *Year 6 Practice Book* has number problems involving large numbers.

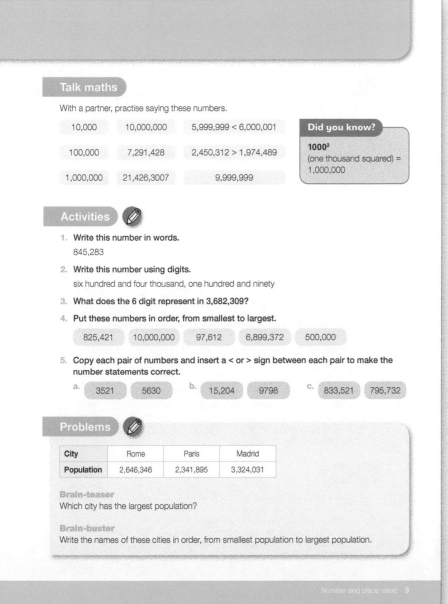

Talk maths

With a partner, practise saying these numbers.

10,000	10,000,000	5,999,999 < 6,000,001
100,000	7,291,428	2,450,312 > 1,974,489
1,000,000	21,426,3007	9,999,999

Did you know?

1000^2
(one thousand squared) = 1,000,000

Activities

1. Write this number in words.
   845,283

2. Write this number using digits.
   six hundred and four thousand, one hundred and ninety

3. What does the 6 digit represent in 3,682,309?

4. Put these numbers in order, from smallest to largest.

   | 825,421 | 10,000,000 | 97,612 | 6,899,372 | 500,000 |

5. Copy each pair of numbers and insert a < or > sign between each pair to make the number statements correct.

   a. 3521 5630   b. 15,204 9798   c. 833,521 795,732

Problems

City	Rome	Paris	Madrid
Population	2,646,346	2,341,895	3,324,031

Brain-teaser
Which city has the largest population?

Brain-buster
Write the names of these cities in order, from smallest population to largest population.

Number and place value 9

100 Maths Lessons Year 6 links:

- Autumn 1, Week 1 (pages 8–13): read, write, order, compare and convert numbers to words and vice versa, up to 10 million

- Spring 1, Week 1 (pages 90–95): order and compare numbers to at least 10,000,000

- Summer, 1, Week 1 (pages 172–176): say, read and write numbers to 10,000,000; know the values of each digit in a 7-digit number

Year 6 Practice Book links:

- (pages 6–7): Read and write numbers to 10,000,000

- (page 8): Ordering whole numbers

- (page 13): Number problems with big numbers

Estimation and rounding

Prior learning

- Round integers to the nearest 10, 100 and 1000.
- Use rounding to check answers to calculations and determine, in the context of a problem, levels of accuracy.

Learn

- Working with numbers below 1000, practise rounding up and down to the nearest 10, and then 100. Point out the rule that 5 and 50 always round up.

- Move on to considering how rounding can help with estimation, stressing the importance of this not just in real life, but also as a rapid way of roughly checking answers.
- Move on to rounding larger numbers, considering how any larger number can be rounded to different powers of 10. The Tips in the textbook show this for 837,635. Work through the different ways this number can be rounded, and then try others.

- Move on to considering how rounding can be used to help with estimating calculations involving larger numbers.
- *100 Maths Lessons Year 6, Summer 1, Week 1* develops skills of rounding and estimating in context to solve problems.

Curriculum objectives

- To round any whole number to a required degree of accuracy.
- To solve number and practical problems that involve all of the above.

Success criteria

- I can round any whole number to any power of 10.

Estimation and rounding

Learn

To round a number to the nearest **power of 10** we look at it on a number line.

We use powers of 10 for rounding, counting and estimating.

620 rounded down to the nearest hundred is 600   670 rounded up is 700

649 and below will round down to 600; 650 and above round up to 700.

We can do the same with thousands and millions.

12,368 rounded down to the nearest thousand is 12,000

12,547 rounds up to 13,000

1,355,721 rounded down to the nearest million is 1,000,000

1,631,570 rounds up to 2,000,000

We can also use these skills to estimate answers, for example,
103 + 98 + 204 + 195 is approximately 100 + 100 + 200 + 200 = 600
To estimate the answer to 45,231 + 23,876 we could say 45,000 + 24,000 = 69,000.
To estimate the answer to 7,235,421 − 5,862,403 we could say:
7,000,000 − 6,000,000 = 1,000,000.

✓ Tips

- Always think carefully about what you want to round to: thousands, ten thousands, millions, and so on. Then think about the part of the number line the number is on. So:
  - 837,635 rounds to the nearest thousand as 838,000
  - 837,635 rounds to the nearest ten thousand as 840,000
  - 837,635 rounds to the nearest hundred thousand as 800,000
  - 837,635 rounds to the nearest million as 1,000,000

10   Number and place value

Talk maths

- In doing the textbook activity, stress to the children that they can only challenge each other with numbers that they themselves can read and round – they must be able to tell if their partner's answers are right or wrong.
- Children who find this activity difficult could be placed in larger groups so that they hear lots of mathematical language being used correctly.

Activities

- As well as the textbook questions, use the links to *100 Maths Lessons Year 6* to provide activities that combine both rounding and estimation skills.
- The *Year 6 Practice Book* has rounding in the context of different measures.

Problems

- 'Numbers up to 10,000.000' on pages 88–89 of this book suggested that more confident learners investigate the populations of different countries and cities. This information could be used to pose further rounding and estimation problems.

Talk maths

Work with a partner. Each write six different numbers between 10,000 and 10,000,000. Say aloud each other's numbers and then challenge each other to round any of the numbers to a power of 10.

What is 5,348,325 rounded to the nearest 100,000?

Activities

1. Round these numbers to the nearest 1000.
   a. 4567   b. 23,145   c. 45,320   d. 78,649

2. Round these numbers to the nearest 100,000.
   a. 120,367   b. 450,000   c. 1,382,320   d. 7,976,311

3. Round these numbers to the nearest 1,000,000.
   a. 6,435,207   b. 845,453   c. 3,500,000   d. 9,724,500

4. Copy and continue the sequence with three more numbers each.
   a. 0; 100,000; 200,000
   b. 370,000; 380,000
   c. 7,500,000; 8,500,000

Problems

Brain-teaser
Round each city's population to the nearest million.

City	Rome	Paris	Madrid
Population	2,646,346	2,341,895	3,324,031

Brain-buster
Estimate, to the nearest million, the total population of Madrid, Rome and Paris. Do you think your estimate is higher or lower than the actual total? Explain your answer.

Number and place value   11

100 Maths Lessons Year 6 links:

- Autumn 1, Week 1 (pages 8–13): round numbers to the nearest 100 and 1000 and round in practical situations
- Summer 1, Week 1 (pages 172–176): round whole numbers and decimals

Year 6 Practice Book links:

- (page 9): Rounding whole numbers
- (page 14): Stadium rounding
- (page 48): Estimating costs
- (page 51): Use your squares
- (page 55): Estimate before solving

Negative numbers

Prior learning

- Interpret negative numbers in context.
- Count forwards and backwards with positive and negative whole numbers, including through zero.

Learn

- Using a drawn or digital simulation of a thermometer, spend time exploring it as a vertical number line, practising counting back and forward through zero. Stress that the children must always include

zero, as they do any other number when counting. For example, when counting back 8 from 6, they must remember to count zero within that step of 8, and so end at −2. If they miss it out, then they would end at −3, which is incorrect.

- Still using the thermometer as a reference, move on to representing counting on and back as written number

sentences, limiting work to between −10 and +10 initially. Move on to −20 to +20 if appropriate.

- *100 Maths Lessons Year 6*, Spring 1, Week 1, Lessons 4 and 5 have activities for working with negative numbers both in and out of practical contexts.

Curriculum objectives

- To use negative numbers in context, and calculate intervals across zero.
- To solve number and practical problems that involve all of the above.

Success criteria

- I can read, use and carry out simple calculations with positive and negative numbers.

Negative numbers

Learn

Numbers can be negative as well as positive.

−10 −9 −8 −7 −6 −5 −4 −3 −2 −1 0 1 2 3 4 5 6 7 8 9 10

Remember you can use a number line to help you. Don't forget to include zero when you are counting!

When we add numbers on a number line we move to the right. When we take away numbers we move to the left.

Temperature is a great way to practise using positive and negative numbers.
If you start at +2 and count back 6 you stop at −4.
If you start at +15 and count back 16 you end at −1.
If you start at −8 and count on 16 you stop at +8.
If you start at −13 and count on 24 you stop at +11.

We can do simple calculations with positive and negative numbers to check the answer. For example:

$2 - 3 = -1$ **so** $-3 + 2 = -1$ $-14 + 18 = 4$ **so** $18 - 14 = 4$

+20
+18
+16
+14
+12
+10
+8
+6
+4
+2
0
−2
−4
−6
−8
−10
−12
−14
−16
−18
−20

✓ Tips

- Can you spot the connections between positive and negative numbers? Look at the connections in the box. If you understand this, negative numbers will be easy for you!

$8 - 4 = 4$	$4 + 8 = 12$	$12 - 8 = 4$	$12 - 8 = 4$
$4 - 8 = -4$	$-4 - 8 = -12$	$8 - 12 = -4$	$4 - 12 = -8$

- Try choosing some other numbers and see if you can spot patterns.

Talk maths

- Provide pairs or small groups with a number line, either −10 to +10 or −20 to +20. Encourage children both to use their fingers to support movement along the line, and to say their calculation aloud, as this provides strong reinforcement of the ideas.
- As children progress they might move to mental calculation and final statements, for example four minus seven equals minus three, and so on.

Activities

- Question 2 challenges children to count from −20 to + 20 in steps of 4. This particular activity can be altered and extended as appropriate.
- The *Year 6 Practice Book* links have useful reinforcement activities.

Problems

- Temperature variation lends itself to ample investigation of temperatures around the world (see *100 Maths Lessons Year 6, Spring 1, Week 1, Lesson 5*).
- In addition, temperature variation through the day can be plotted in line graphs if desired.

Talk maths

What's minus ten plus fifteen?

Minus five.

7	9	12
4	16	20
−3	−12	−8
−20	−17	−5

With a partner, choose two numbers from the box and ask them to either subtract or add them together. For example, say: *What is nine minus twelve?* Now ask them to ask you some questions. Use the number line below to help you.

−20 −19 −18 −17 −16 −15 −14 −13 −12 −11 −10 −9 −8 −7 −6 −5 −4 −3 −2 −1 0 1 2 3 4 5 6 7 8 9 10 11 12 13 14 15 16 17 18 19 20

Activities

1. Complete these calculations.
   a. 3 − 5   b. 5 − 9   c. −4 + 7   d. −8 + 8

2. Count on from −20 to +20 in steps of 4. Write each number.

3. Copy these number sentences and insert the missing signs + or −.
   a. 7 ___ 7 = 0   b. −12 ___ 13 = 1   c. 14 ___ 21 = −7   d. 2 ___ 18 = −16

4. Copy these number sentences and insert the missing numbers.
   a. −13 + ___ = 1   b. 14 − ___ = −5   c. ___ − 15 = −8   d. ___ + 10 = 1

Problems

Brain-teaser
One winter morning the temperature at dawn is −4 degrees Celsius (−4°C). If the temperature rises 12°C by noon, what will the temperature be then?

Brain-buster
The temperature in the desert is 49.7°C and in the mountains is −19.7°C. What is the difference between the two places?

> **Did you know?**
> Even though deserts are hot places, they can get very cold at night.

Number and place value   13

100 Maths Lessons Year 6 links:

- Spring 1, Week 1 (pages 90–95): use negative numbers in context

Year 6 Practice Book links:

- (page 10): Positive and negative
- (page 11): Using negative numbers
- (page 16): Negative number problems
- (page 17): Bank account problems

Addition and subtraction

Prior learning

- Add and subtract numbers mentally with increasingly large numbers.
- Use formal written methods to add and subtract whole numbers with more than four digits.

Note that this unit is a recap of previous years' work. However, it is suggested that several lessons are given to this work. In particular, the links to the Year 6 Practice Book *point to a wide range of reinforcement and extension work.*

- Consider how these skills can be applied to larger numbers that are manageable mentally. If desirable, look at how children might assess a calculation for its potential to be solved mentally.
- Recap formal written methods for both addition and subtraction, stressing the importance of understanding place value in exchanging and carrying forward.

- The inverse nature of addition and subtraction should be clear to children of this age. Use examples to remind them of this and check their understanding.
- *100 Maths Lessons Year 6, Autumn 1, Week 2* provides varied activities and investigations.

Learn

- Spend time covering mental methods that the children should already know, such as number bonds, partitioning and bridging.

Curriculum objectives

- To perform mental calculations, including with mixed operations and large numbers.
- To solve problems involving addition, subtraction, multiplication and division.

Success criteria

- I can use and apply mental methods to add and subtract some large numbers.
- I can use and apply formal written methods to add and subtract large numbers.

Addition and subtraction

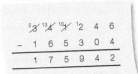

To add 999, just add 1000 and subtract 1.
45,362 + 999 = 46,361

Learn

You will probably know several mental methods for addition and subtraction.

You must learn your number bonds: 7 + 8 = 15   15 − 8 = 7   15 − 7 = 8
Partitioning numbers is important too: 25 + 12 = 37

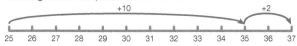

We can use formal written methods for adding and subtracting larger numbers.

The first step is to neatly lay out the numbers in columns according to place value.

```
    6  6  4  5  7  2
 +  1  5  3  0  5  4
 ─────────────────────
    8  1  7  6  2  6
          1        1
```

Just like addition, we can use the place-value columns to subtract larger numbers.

```
   2  13   3  13      12
   3   4   4   1    2  4  6
 −     1   6   5    3  0  4
 ──────────────────────────
       1   7   5    9  4  2
```

✓ Tips

- Remember, you can check your subtractions by adding your answer to the number you took away.

```
   12  13   3  13  3  13
    2   3   4   4      13
 −          6   1   7   5
 ─────────────────────────
        1   7   2   6   8   checking...
```

```
    1   7   2   6   8
 +      6   1   7   5
 ─────────────────────
    2   3   4   4   3   correct! ☺
        1   1   1
```

- Only use written methods that you are sure you understand. If you have a method you like, stick to it, practise it, and always check your answers!

14   Calculations

Talk maths

- Encourage the children to be able to explain their thought processes when deciding whether to use a mental method. Where they elect to use written methods, ask them to explain each step as if giving a mini-presentation.

Activities

- The questions can be extended by providing children with additions of more than two numbers. There is also ample practice in the *Year 6 Practice Book*, including many context-based problems.

Problems

- Data lists, such as populations, planet sizes, animal weights and so on, provide rich material for children to use to develop their own problems and challenges.

Talk maths

Think of two numbers and write them down. Challenge your partner to add them using a mental or written method, and then explain their method to you. Repeat this five or six times, then do the same for subtractions.

Try it with three numbers, or even four!

Activities

1. Add these numbers using mental methods.
   a. 452 + 340   b. 5127 + 399   c. 425,364 + 54,005

2. Subtract these numbers using mental methods.
   a. 800 − 260   b. 146,450 − 29,000   c. 2,754 − 399

3. Add these numbers using a written method.
   a. 234,482 + 314,222   b. 635,231 + 327,594   c. 1,342,435 + 3,825,032

4. Subtract these numbers using a written method.
   a. 314,222 − 234,482   b. 962,825 − 327,594   c. 3,825,032 − 1,342,435

Problems

City	Rome	Paris	Madrid
Population	2,646,346	2,341,895	3,324,031

Brain-teaser
How many more people live in Madrid than Paris?

Brain-buster
Calculate the combined population of Rome, Paris and Madrid.

Calculations   15

100 Maths Lessons Year 6 links:

- Autumn 1, Week 2 (pages 14–19): use mental and written methods for addition and subtraction of large numbers
- Summer 1, Week 2 (pages 177–181): solve addition and subtraction problems

Year 6 Practice Book links:

- (page 36): Adding order
- (page 37): Bridging and adjusting
- (page 38): Partition to add and multiply
- (page 46): Postal addition problem
- (page 49): Addition and subtraction problem
- (page 56): What's wrong?

Multiplication and division facts and skills

Prior learning

- Recall all their times-tables up to and including 12 × 12.
- Be aware of the differences between the terms 'multiple', 'factor', and 'prime number'.
- Identify some prime numbers.

Learn

- Display a large multiplication square and use it for quick-fire multiplication and division questions, reinforcing the inverse relationship between the two.

- Show the children how this can be used for multiplying and dividing some larger numbers mentally, such as 40 × 5, 20 × 30, 640 ÷ 8, and so on.
- The links to *100 Maths Lessons Year 6* provide further guidance for recapping knowledge and facts, including squared numbers.

- Focus on multiplying and dividing by powers of 10 (this may include decimals). It is important for children to see this as numbers moving through place-value columns, not just 'adding zeros' as is sometimes done. This will help them to appreciate that they are becoming 'ten times bigger', 'one hundred times bigger' and so on.

Curriculum objectives

- To perform mental calculations, including with mixed operations and large numbers.
- To solve problems involving addition, subtraction, multiplication and division.

Success criteria

- I can use and apply mental methods to multiply and divide some large numbers.
- I can mentally multiply and divide numbers by powers of 10.

Multiplication and division facts and skills

Learn

Multiplication squares show us that division is the *inverse* of multiplication.

So, we can say:
$8 \times 9 = 72$
$9 \times 8 = 72$

$72 \div 9 = 8$
$72 \div 8 = 9$

×	1	2	3	4	5	6	7	8	9	10	11	12
1	1	2	3	4	5	6	7	8	9	10	11	12
2	2	4	6	8	10	12	14	16	18	20	22	24
3	3	6	9	12	15	18	21	24	27	30	33	36
4	4	8	12	16	20	24	28	32	36	40	44	48
5	5	10	15	20	25	30	35	40	45	50	55	60
6	6	12	18	24	30	36	42	48	54	60	66	72
7	7	14	21	28	35	42	49	56	63	70	77	84
8	8	16	24	32	40	48	56	64	(72)	80	88	96
9	9	18	27	36	45	54	63	72	81	90	99	108
10	10	20	30	40	50	60	70	80	90	100	110	120
11	11	22	33	44	55	66	77	88	99	110	121	132
12	12	24	36	48	60	72	84	96	108	120	132	144

You already know some square and cube number facts, and you can calculate others.

Five squared = $5^2 = 5 \times 5 = 25$ Five cubed = $5^3 = 5 \times 5 \times 5 = 125$

Remember the inverses: $25 \div 5 = 5$, $125 \div 5 = 25$

Also, you should now be able to multiply and divide by **powers of 10.**

Operation	Fact	Example
×10	Move one place left	65 × 10 = 650
÷10	Move one place right	65 ÷ 10 = 6.5
×1000	Move three places left	65 × 1000 = 65,000
÷1000	Move three places right	65 ÷ 1000 = 0.065

✓ Tips

- When multiplying by larger numbers, we can separate the powers of 10.

  7 × 12,000 is the same as 7 × 12 × 1000 = 84 × 1000 = 84,000

  Or   for 24,000 ÷ 6, just do 24 ÷ 6 = 4, then times by 1000 = 4 × 1000 = 4000

Talk maths

- The activity in the textbook requires children to challenge their peers. Remind the children that they should only be challenging their peers with questions that they think they know the answer to, or at very least they could calculate with appropriate support (not a calculator!). In particular, ensure that children are using the appropriate vocabulary.

Activities

- The textbook questions focus on methods presented in earlier sections.
- *100 Maths Lessons Year 6, Autumn 1, Week 4, Lesson 4* provides further resources for focused practice.
- Also of use are *Year 6 Practice Book* 'Is it correct?' and 'Divisibility facts'. These focus on divisibility rules as well as providing practice in checking if calculations are correct. (Note that some of the questions involve addition and subtraction.)

Problems

- If desired, each of the problems in the textbook can be easily extended by creating charts showing different revenues, ticket prices and attendances. Note that the Brain-teaser focuses on multiplication and the Brain-buster on division.

Talk maths

Ask your partner to solve a calculation mentally, then give them a challenge such as to multiply a square or cube number by a power of 10. For example:

- What is seven squared times a thousand?
- What is three cubed times one hundred thousand?

> **Did you know?**
>
> $10^3 = 1000$
> $100^3 = 1,000,000$

If you are feeling brave, work out some answers in advance and then try a mental division, for example:

- What is forty-nine thousand divided by seven?
- What is two thousand seven hundred divided by three?

Activities

1. Solve these multiplications mentally.

   a. 24×200 b. 62×1000 c. 40×40
   d. 25×2000 e. $43 \times 10,000$ f. $100 \times 10,000$

2. Now solve these divisions using mental methods.

   a. $6000 \div 3$ b. $125 \div 5$ c. $125,000 \div 5$
   d. $360,000 \div 4$ e. $640,008 \div 8$ f. $125,000 \div 5$

3. Use your knowledge of inverses to solve these.

   a. If $27,072 \div 576 = 47$, what does 576×47 equal?
   b. If $4320 \times 723 = 3,123,360$, what does $3,123,360 \div 4320$ equal?

Problems

Brain-teaser
A football stadium holds 8000 people. How much money would be collected for a sell-out match if each ticket was £20?

Brain-buster
For a different football match, tickets are sold for £30, but only £90,000 is collected. How many tickets were sold?

---

100 Maths Lessons Year 6 links:

- Autumn 1, Week 3 (pages 20–25): recall all multiplication and division tables to 12×12; solve problems
- Autumn 1, Week 4 (pages 26–31): mental methods for multiplication and division
- Spring 1, Week 3 (pages 101–106): solve problems with all four operations

Year 6 Practice Book links:

- (page 22): Is it correct?
- (page 23): Divisibility facts
- (page 39): Using related multiplication and division facts
- (page 51): Use your squares

Written methods for long multiplication

Prior learning

- Use mental and written methods for multiplication.

Learn

- Although the children should be familiar with at least one formal method for long multiplication, it is worth spending time recapping the layout and process to ensure clear, accurate working. In particular, when referring to 10s and 100s digits, it's most helpful to use the value of the digit not just its name. For example, saying 30 for the 3 in 237.

- Move on to multiplying 3- and 4-digit numbers by 2-digit numbers, stressing the order of operations. Note that the textbook multiplies first by the 1s and then by the 10s, though some schools prefer to do this the other way around.

- The links to *100 Maths Lessons Year 6* provide a range of lesson and activity ideas. Note that these units also cover division, so lessons will need to be selected carefully depending on whether you wish to cover division alongside or separately to long multiplication.

Curriculum objectives

- To multiply multi-digit numbers up to four digits by a 2-digit whole number using the formal written method of long multiplication.

- To solve problems involving addition, subtraction, multiplication and division.

- To use estimation to check answers to calculations and determine, in the context of a problem, an appropriate degree of accuracy.

Success criteria

- I can use and apply formal written methods for long multiplication.

Written methods for long multiplication

Learn

There are several formal written methods for multiplying numbers. You may have been taught methods a bit different from this one. You should use whichever method you are comfortable with.

Remember, the numbers are arranged in their place-value columns: 100s, 10s and 1s.

	3	6
×	2	4
1	4²	4	(← × 4)
7¹	2	0	+ (← × 20)
8	6	4	

Answer: 864

	4	7
×	1	8
3	7⁵	6	(← × 8)
4	7	0	+ (← × 10)
8	4	6	
1			

Answer: 846

We can use formal written methods for all numbers, no matter how large they are. Multiplying two numbers that are both larger than 10 is called long multiplication. We multiply each digit on the top by each digit on the bottom, carrying forward powers of 10.

Remember, always put the larger number on the top.

		3	2	6
	×		4	5
1	6¹	3³	0	(← × 5)
1	3¹	0²	4	0	+ (← × 40)
1	4	6	7	0

Answer: 14,670

		4	2	0	8
	×			6	3
1	2	6	2²	4	(← × 3)
2	5¹	2	4⁴	8	0	+ (← × 60)
2	6	5	1	0	4
		1	1		

Answer: 265,104

✓ Tips

- Lay out your work neatly and you'll probably get the right answer.

Watch how to do huge calculations and get them right!

		8	6	9	5
	×			6	7
	6	0⁴	8⁶	6³	5	(← × 7)
5	2⁴	1⁵	7³	0	0	+ (← × 60)
5	8	2	5	6	5
		1			

Answer: 582,565

Talk maths

- The activity in the textbook involves children explaining the steps involved in two long multiplications. Check if the process in the book matches the standard process in the school mathematics policy and, if necessary, adjust accordingly.

Activities

- The textbook and the *Year 6 Practice Book* offer a great deal of practice material. Although quantity of practice is important, it is vital that children have a secure grasp of the process before starting extended practice sessions.

- For less confident learners, draw up the list of steps for laying out and performing long multiplication calculations and have them check each step as they perform it.

- More confident learners might be challenged to consider whether any calculations might be solved mentally through partitioning.

Problems

- Note that both of the textbook problems are difficult. The *Year 6 Practice Book* provides a wide range of practice and problems to support and extend learning.

Talk maths

Look at each of these long multiplications and talk it through aloud, explaining how each stage was done. Make sure you work in the correct order.

Remember that zeros still have to be multiplied and recorded, and anything times zero is... zero!

		4	8
×		3	1
		4	8
1	4^2	4	0	+
1	4	8	8

Answer: 1488

		6	0	7
	×		2	5
	3	0	3^3	5
1	2	1^1	4	0	+
1	5	1	7	5

Answer: 15,175

Activities

1. Complete each of these long multiplications using a written method.
   a. 62 × 14   b. 325 × 22   c. 405 × 34   d. 6338 × 52

2. Complete each of these long multiplications using a written method.
   a. 425 × 21   b. 1267 × 30   c. 5326 × 15   d. 8736 × 65

Problems

Brain-teaser
A head teacher estimates that every child in her school does 72 pieces of homework each year (that is around two pieces per week). If there are 347 children in the school, how many pieces of homework must be marked each year?

Brain-buster
A supermarket chain sells 9237 RoboDog toys in a year. They cost £79 each. How much money does the supermarket make in total?

100 Maths Lessons Year 6 links:

- Autumn 1, Week 4 (pages 26–31): multiply 2- and 3-digit numbers by 1- and 2-digit numbers

- Autumn 2, Week 1 (pages 49–54): multiply 4-digit numbers by 2-digit numbers

- Summer 1, Week 3 (pages 182–186): use long multiplication

Year 6 Practice Book links:

- (pages 24–25): Long multiplication

- (page 26): Long multiplication problem

- (page 27): Show time

- (page 50): Wedding madness!

- (page 57): Ink blots

Written methods for short division

Prior learning

- Can understand the close relationship between multiplication and division.
- Can use mental and written methods for division.

100 Maths Lessons Year 6, Spring 1, Week 3, Lesson 3 covers this, as does the *Year 6 Practice Book* 'Divisibility facts'.

Learn

- Prior to using the textbook, review children's existing division skills, in particular their knowledge of how to assess if larger numbers are multiples of single-digit numbers.
- *100 Maths Lessons Year 6, Spring 1, Week 3, Lesson 3* covers this, as does the *Year 6 Practice Book* 'Divisibility facts'.
- Progress to reviewing the school's preferred method for short division with the children, using only numbers that are exactly divisible by single-digit numbers, as per the first textbook example.
- The focus should now move to remainders, both in simple practical contexts, such as sharing items between groups, dividing the cost of a bill, and so on. Move on to formal written methods that include remainders.
- Drawing on the examples in the Tips, remind children how multiplication can be used as an inverse to check a division, remembering to add any remainder at the end.

Curriculum objectives

- To divide numbers up to four digits by a 2-digit number using the formal written method of short division where appropriate, interpreting remainders according to the context.
- To solve problems involving addition, subtraction, multiplication and division.

Success criteria

- I can use and apply the formal written method for short division.

Written methods for short division

Learn

There are several formal written methods for dividing numbers. You may have been taught methods a bit different to those in this book. You should use whichever method you are comfortable with – as long as you get the right answers!

		0	8	6
3	2	²5	¹8	

Answer: 258 ÷ 3 = 86

Remember what divide means. It tells you how many times one number goes into another number.

For 72 ÷ 8 = 9 we say, 72 divided by 8 equals 9.

In short division we carry forward remainders. Sometimes there is a remainder in the answer at the end.

		0	6	3	r1
4	2	²5	¹3		

Answer: 253 ÷ 4 = 63 r1

		0	2	2	5	r2
7	1	¹5	¹7	³7		

Answer: 1577 ÷ 7 = 225 r2

You can learn about long division in the next unit.

✓ Tips

- Lay out your work carefully and think about the place value of every digit. Use squared paper to help you.

		0	8	5	8	6	9	r1
3	2	²5	¹7	²6	²0	²8		

Answer: 257,608 ÷ 3 = 85,869 r1

I'll keep this tip short – get it?

- You can check your answer by multiplying the answer by the number you divided by, and then add the remainder. Look:

		8	5	8	6	9
×						3
2	5	7	6	0	7	
		1	2	2	2	

Answer: 257,607 + 1 remainder = 257,608

- This activity focuses on children developing a stronger sense of the steps needed to complete a short division calculation.
- A difficulty in dealing with larger numbers is children's ability to read them clearly in the division context. As in the division example given, encouraging children first to write a summary of their calculation underneath the formal method and then to read it aloud can support this.

Activities

- Note that the Activities section includes division by 12, although this can still be performed as a short division.
- Extended practice and reinforcement can be found in the links to *100 Maths Lessons Year 6* and to the *Year 6 Practice Book*.

Problems

- Before the children try the problems in the textbook, provide them with opportunities to complete the many different problem-based activities in the links to *100 Maths Lessons Year 6* and to the *Year 6 Practice Book*.

Talk maths

Look at this short division and explain it aloud, saying how each stage was done.

Answer: 8,712,034 ÷ 6 = 1,452,005 r4

Activities

1. Complete each of these short divisions.
   a. 92 ÷ 4   b. 123 ÷ 5   c. 2605 ÷ 6   d. 3758 ÷ 12

2. Complete each of these short divisions using a written method.
   a. 86 ÷ 7   b. 322 ÷ 5   c. 3685 ÷ 8   d. 13,588 ÷ 12

Problems

Brain-teaser
A teacher shares out 93 stickers between seven children. How many stickers will each child receive, and how many will be left over?

Brain-buster
Tickets for a pop concert cost £18 each. If the total amount taken for tickets was £22,464, how many tickets were sold? Explain how you could check your answer.

100 Maths Lessons Year 6 links:

- Autumn 2, Week 1 (pages 49–54): written methods for division

Year 6 Practice Book links:

- (page 23): Divisibility facts
- (pages 28–29): School trip division
- (page 31): Divide the bill
- (page 39): Using related multiplication and division facts

Written methods for long division

Prior learning

- Understand the close relationship between multiplication and division.
- Can use the formal written method of short division.

Learn

- Briefly review your school's preferred method for written short division with the children.
- Remind the children of the relationship between multiplication and division. Model using inverse calculations to check answers.

- Note that the focus is still on dividing and writing whole numbers and remainders, not giving answers as decimals.
- Depending on prior knowledge and abilities, it may be necessary to spend considerable time working through the procedures for long division. When presenting methods, try to help the children just to focus on the numbers currently being divided. This will help them realise that each step happens in isolation. Long division, like multiplication, is usually successful when children can focus only on the numbers involved in each step.
- *100 Maths Lessons Year 6, Autumn 1, Week 4, Lesson 4* also has useful guidance on building children's skills.

Curriculum objectives

- To divide numbers up to four digits by a 2-digit whole number using the formal written method of long division, and interpret remainders as whole number remainders, fractions, or by rounding, as appropriate for the context.
- To solve problems involving addition, subtraction, multiplication and division.
- To use estimation to check answers to calculations and determine, in the context of a problem, an appropriate degree of accuracy.

Success criteria

- I can use and apply the formal written method for long division.

Written methods for long division

Learn

To divide something means to share it into equal amounts. Twelve divided by three equals four.

For larger numbers we sometimes need to use formal methods to help us calculate accurate answers.

In short division we carry on the remainder at each stage.

	0	4	2	6	r2
8	3	^{3}4	^{2}1	^{5}0	

Answer: 426 r2

Turn back a page to see formal methods for short division.

When we are dividing larger numbers we may need to use long division. This example shows you one method.

Can you see the difference between long division and short division? With long division we are calculating the remainder at each stage, so that there is less chance of making an error.

Whichever method you use, make sure you understand it!

				2	2	3	r3
	1	6	3	5	7	1	
(2 × 16 =) −			3	2			
				3	7		
(2 × 16 =) −			3	2			
				5	1		
(3 × 16 =) −			4	8			
					3		

Answer: 223 r3

✓ Tips

- In calculations it is fine to leave a remainder, but in problem solving these need to be presented carefully. You may need to show the remainder, write the remainder as a fraction or a decimal, or round off the answer.

  For example:
  If five pizzas are shared between four people you wouldn't say each person receives one pizza remainder one. You would say they get $1\frac{1}{4}$ pizzas each.

  Or, if a problem asks how many rows of ten can 93 seats be arranged in, the answer is nine. We round the answer and ignore the remainder.

Here's a bit of friendly advice about remainders.

Talk maths

- This activity aims to help focus children's attention on the step-by-step nature of long division. This will help to show that the whole point of the written method is to simplify complex calculations. In examining the formal method used, stress the importance of neat and accurate layout, as well as the use of estimation and inverses (multiplication) for checking work.

Activities

- Use the children's answers to assess who is having difficulties. Review any misunderstandings by providing simpler calculations before moving on to the problems.

Problems

- A particularly important aspect of solving problems with long division is whether answers should be rounded up or down. For example, in arranging cars to take a school football team away, the context dictates that the number of cars must be rounded up: 11 children divided by three per car, thus requires four cars, with only two children in the fourth car. Alternatively, if pencils are packed in boxes of 12, 13 pencils will only fill one box with one pencil left over. The *Year 6 Practice Book* presents lots of material to consolidate these ideas.

Talk maths

Look at this long division and explain it aloud, saying how each stage was done.

Now try writing down and explaining the steps for this long division: 2878 ÷ 13

Remember that zero divided by anything is… zero.

						2	2	1	r5
		1	3	2	8	7	8		
(2 × 13 =) −				2	6				
					2	7			
(2 × 13 =) −					2	6			
						1	8		
(1 × 13 =) −						1	3		
							5		

Answer: 221 r5

Activities

1. Copy and complete each of these long divisions.

   a.
      12 | 1 6 0

   b.
      16 | 3 6 8

   c.
      25 | 5 2 6 4

   d.
      15 | 3 8 1 8

2. On squared paper, complete each of these long divisions using a written method.

   a. 338 ÷ 15   b. 4438 ÷ 21   c. 6358 ÷ 18   d. 7318 ÷ 32

Problems

Brain-teaser
A theatre has 2010 seats. If there are 15 seats per row, how many rows are there?

Brain-buster
Sixteen people buy a lottery ticket and, altogether, they win £37,468. They agree to share it equally. How much will they each receive, to the nearest 1p?

Calculations 23

---

100 Maths Lessons Year 6 links:

- Autumn 1, Week 4 (pages 26–31): divide 2- and 3-digit numbers by a 2-digit number
- Autumn 2, Week 1 (pages 49–54): divide a 4-digit number by a 2-digit number
- Spring 2, Week 1 (pages 131–135): use long division formally
- Summer 1, Week 3 (pages 182–186): solve long division calculations

Year 6 Practice Book links:

- (page 30): Round up and down
- (pages 32–33): Long division
- (page 34): Long division target practice
- (page 35): Soup factory division

Ordering operations

Prior learning

- Can calculate using all four operations.
- Can carry out mental calculations with mixed operations.

Learn

- Use a selection of examples to cover the basic order of operations in complex number sentences. Use simple numbers and avoid using brackets or indices initially. (If required, there are several examples in the textbook and in the links to *100 Maths Lessons Year 6*.)

- Starting with the example 18 − 3 × 5 in the textbook, demonstrate to the children how brackets can be used to alter the order of operations. Stress that the calculations in brackets are always carried out first. If appropriate, create number sentences with more than one set of brackets in them to exemplify this.

- The Tips introduce BIDMAS – remember that the 'I' stands for Indices.
- *100 Maths Lessons Year 6, Autumn 2, Week 4, Lesson 4* also covers BIDMAS.

Curriculum objectives

- To perform mental calculations, including with mixed operations and large numbers.
- To use their knowledge of the order of operations to carry out calculations involving the four operations.
- To solve addition and subtraction multi-step problems in contexts, deciding which operations and methods to use and why.

Success criteria

- I can use operations in the correct order to carry out calculations and solve problems.

Ordering operations

Learn

Calculations and problems involving more than one operation are called **multi-step**. You must only do one calculation at a time, and you must do them in the right order!

The right order is division and multiplication first, followed by addition and subtraction, working from left to right.

Look at this calculation:	$25 \div 5 + 3 \times 7 - 6 \times 4$
Division first ($25 \div 5 = 5$)	$5 + 3 \times 7 - 6 \times 4$
Multiplication next ($3 \times 7 = 21$)	$5 + 21 - 6 \times 4$
And another multiplication ($6 \times 4 = 24$)	$5 + 21 - 24$
Then addition ($5 + 21 = 26$)	$26 - 24$
And last subtraction ($26 - 24 = 2$)	Answer = 2

You can control the order in which calculations are done by using brackets.
Calculations inside brackets come first. Look at this example:

$18 - 3 \times 5 = 18 - 15 = 3$ But $(18 - 3) \times 5 = 15 \times 5 = 75$

Or this one:

$21 \div 3 + 4 = 7 + 4 = 11$ But $21 \div (3 + 4) = 21 \div 7 = 3$

Brackets make a *big* difference.

✓ Tips

- If you understand this you are ready for BIDMAS:
  Brackets
  Indices (such as square and cube numbers)
  Division ⎤ ← Do multiplication and division together in the
  Multiplication ⎦   order they come, left to right.
  Addition ⎤ ← Do addition and subtraction together in the
  Subtraction ⎦   order they come, left to right.
- Indices are a bit tricky. They tell us the power of a number, for example, a square number such as 7^2 is 7 to the power of 2; 7^3 is 7 to the power of 3 and so on.

Here's a top tip to keep your maths in order.

- This section encourages children to investigate the effect that the position of brackets has on a calculation. They should be encouraged to discuss this for a selection of straightforward number sentences. Ask them to stay with each sentence until they reach agreement on the correct answer for a particular arrangement of brackets. A plenary focused on this work can reveal interesting pitfalls and ideas for checking work.

Activities

- The textbook questions are quite tricky. Support work is available in the links to *100 Maths Lessons Year 6*. When moving on to the harder questions, encourage children to rewrite the number sentence after each operation to encourage methodical and neat working.
- Children's answers to the questions in the textbook should provide adequate opportunities for assessment of their grasp of the concepts.

Problems

- Children may benefit from doing the many activities available in the *Year 6 Practice Book* before attempting those in the textbook, both of which are tricky.
- *100 Maths Lessons Year 6, Spring 2, Week 1, Lesson 3* provides structured support for developing effective approaches to problem solving.

Talk maths

Look at the calculation below. Try inserting a pair of brackets in different places and discuss, with a partner, what answer it gives you. Remember, do only one calculation at a time, and think BIDMAS.

$$24 + 48 \div 8 - 2 \times 5 - 4 =$$

Activities

1. Solve these.
   a. $24 \div 2 - 3 \times 4$ b. $23 - 7 \times 2 - 18 \div 6$ c. $3 \times 45 \div 5$

2. Now solve these.
   a. $16 \div (3 + 5)$ b. $47 - 7 \times (18 \div 6 + 2)$ c. $(7 + 8) \div (12 - 9)$

3. Copy and then mark each of these calculations right (✓) or wrong (✗).
   a. $5 \times 3 - 14 \div 2 = 8$ b. $(25 - 6) \times 10 \div 5 = 38$
   c. $(8 + 6) - 15 \div 5 \times (4 + 3) = 77$ d. $(3 \times 7 - 45 \div 5) + 22 - 88 \div (5 + 2 \times 3) = 26$

4. Copy these number sentences, then add the missing brackets to complete each.
   a. $8 \times 5 + 2 - 3 = 53$ b. $14 \div 7 + 2 \times 11 - 6 = 12$ c. $64 - 12 + 5 \times 3 = 37$

Problems

Brain-teaser
The prize for a charity raffle is £20. Tickets cost £2 each. Charlie sells 34 tickets, Georgina sells 17 tickets and Jayden sells 43 tickets. Georgina says they have made a profit of £168. Is she right? Write the calculation needed to work out the profit.

Brain-buster
A car showroom sells new cars for £12,000. It also buys second-hand cars for £2,500 and sells them for £7,000. At the end of a week, the car showroom has received £37,500. Explain how many new cars have been sold, and how many second-hand cars have been bought and sold. Write the calculation then work out the answer.

Calculations 25

---

100 Maths Lessons Year 6 links:

- Autumn 2, Week 4 (pages 66–71): order of operations
- Spring 2, Week 1 (pages 131–135): solve problems using all four operations
- Summer 2, Week 1 (pages 213–217): solve problems involving large numbers

Year 6 Practice Book links:

- (page 40): Order of operations
- (page 41): Operations with brackets
- (page 42–45): Mental calculations using mixed operations (1), (2), (3) and (4)
- (page 47): Missing information problems
- (page 53): Measure up
- (page 54): You choose the problem

Factors, multiples and prime numbers

Prior learning

- Can recall all their times tables up to and including 12 × 12.
- Are aware of the differences between the terms 'multiple', 'factor' and 'prime number'.
- Can identify some prime numbers.

Learn

- Using examples, revisit the meaning of factors, multiples and primes. Some people muddle factors and multiples at times. An easy way to remember which is which is that F comes before M, so factors come before multiples (in other words, they are smaller than multiples).

- Next, look at prime numbers in more detail. Displaying a large 100-square, ideally on an interactive whiteboard, 'sieve' through the square to identify prime numbers. This will also help consolidate children's understanding of factors and multiples.
- *100 Maths Lessons Year 6, Autumn 1, Week 3* provides a range of ideas and activities for consolidating children's understanding of the terms and concepts.
- Separately, introduce the ideas of factor pairs, common factors and common multiples. (The Tips illustrate how some numbers have several sets of factor pairs.)

Curriculum objectives

- To identify common factors, common multiples and prime numbers.

Success criteria

- I can identify and use common factors, multiples and prime numbers.

Factors, multiples and prime numbers

Learn

A **multiple** is a number that is made by multiplying two numbers.

$$5 \times 7 = 35$$

35 is a multiple of both 5 and 7.
We can also say that 5 and 7 are factors of 35.

Factors are easy to list in pairs: The factors of 35 are 1 and 35, 5 and 7. Factors are the numbers that we multiply together to get multiples.

A **common factor** is a factor shared by two or more numbers. For example, 7 is a common factor of 14 and 77.

A **common multiple** is a multiple shared by two or more numbers. For example, 20 is a common multiple of 2 and 5 (and of 1, 4, 10 and 20!).

Prime numbers can only be divided by themselves and one.

Factors and multiples are easy if you really know your times tables. Try to learn your primes up to 100.

Remember, 1 is not a prime number, and 2 is the only even prime number.

Did you know?

A *titanic* prime is a prime number that has over 1000 digits!

Prime numbers on a 100-square

1	②	③	4	⑤	6	⑦	8	9	10
⑪	12	⑬	14	15	16	⑰	18	⑲	20
21	22	㉓	24	25	26	27	28	㉙	30
㉛	32	33	34	35	36	㊲	38	39	40
㊶	42	㊸	44	45	46	㊼	48	49	50
51	52	㊿	54	55	56	57	58	㊾	60
㉖①	62	63	64	65	66	㊻⑦	68	69	70
㉗①	72	㊆③	74	75	76	77	78	㊉⑨	80
81	82	㊌③	84	85	86	87	88	㊎⑨	90
91	92	93	94	95	96	㊐⑦	98	99	100

✓ Tips

- Remember that factors always come in pairs. It can help to list them in pairs too, for example:

  Look at 96 (it has the most factors for any number under 100, 12 altogether):

  96 = 1 × 96, 2 × 48, 3 × 32, 4 × 24, 6 × 16, 8 × 12

Talk maths

- The activity in the textbook can be developed further by creating a bank of cards with a mixture of true and false facts on them (these could be differentiated). As with all talk-based activities, encourage a focus on correct and consistent use of mathematical vocabulary, and use a plenary session to correct any misconceptions.

Activities

- The textbook questions are straightforward, and can easily be used as starting points for further similar questions.

- Children whose grasp of the concepts is secure could be moved on to using and investigating prime factors. There are two useful activities in the *Year 6 Practice Book*. Children should have been introduced to the idea of factor trees (see 'Factors and prime numbers' in the *Year 6 Practice Book*).

Problems

- Children who solve the two problems without difficulty might be set a challenge to investigate higher prime numbers. Amazingly, new (enormous) prime numbers are still found from time to time, but asking children to investigate up to 200 should be more than enough for the time being!

- In addition, there is a problem-solving activity on the CD-ROM for *100 Maths Lessons Year 6, Autumn 1, Week 3*.

Talk maths

Play *True or False* with a partner. Spend ten minutes writing down a collection of facts about factors, multiples and primes, and then take turns challenging your partner to decide if your facts are true or false. If you give false facts you must know what the true answer should be.

For example:

- 24 has eight factors (True: 1, 2, 3, 4, 6, 8, 12, 24)
- 100 is a common multiple of 4, 5 and 6 (False: 100 is not a multiple of 6)
- 38 has two prime factors (True: 2 and 19 are both prime numbers)

Activities

1. What are the common factors of 12 and 20?
2. What are the common factors of 30 and 50?
3. Write three common multiples of 3 and 5.
4. What is the lowest common multiple of 2, 5 and 7?
5. 30 has three prime factors. What are they?
6. What is the largest number between 1 and 100 that has two prime factors?

Problems

Brain-teaser
David says, "2 is a prime number and 19 is a prime number. 2 × 19 = 38, so 38 must be a prime number too." Can you explain why David has made a mistake?

Brain-buster
Find the highest factor that is shared by 96 and 150.

Did you know?

The highest factor that is shared by two numbers is called the highest common factor, or HCF.

100 Maths Lessons Year 6 links:

- Autumn 1, Week 3 (pages 20–25): identify and use multiples, factors and prime numbers

Year 6 Practice Book links:

- (page 18): Fact finder
- (page 19): Factors and prime numbers
- (page 20): Prime factors
- (page 21): Prime investigation

Simplifying fractions

Prior learning

- Can identify multiples, common multiples, factors and common factors.
- Understand the terms 'numerator' and 'denominator'.

Learn

- Re-introduce the children to fractions by spending time considering the concept of what they are: proportions.
- Using both single objects that can be cut or divided, such as pizzas, and groups of objects, such as pencils or marbles, consider how different objects and quantities can be divided into halves, quarters and thirds.
- Be sure to reinforce the relationship between quarters and halves, and that one whole is equivalent to two halves, four quarters, and so on.

- Stressing the relationship between numerator and denominator, spend time considering how fractions can be simplified while representing the same proportion. To make this concrete, take a set of 24 blocks and show that 12 out of 24 is the same as one half, eight out of 24 is one third, and so on. Be sure to show lots of written equivalents and focus on simplifying them by dividing numerator and denominator by a common factor.

- It may also be helpful to create a fraction wall, and keep this on display on the classroom wall or on the interactive whiteboard.
- *100 Maths Lessons Year 6, Autumn 2, Week 2, Lessons 2 and 4* provide additional lessons on simplifying fractions.

Curriculum objectives

- To use common factors to simplify fractions; use common multiples to express fractions in the same denomination.

Success criteria

- I can use common factors to simplify fractions.

Simplifying fractions

Learn

Fractions show proportions of a whole.

They have a **numerator** on the top, and a **denominator** on the bottom.

numerator ⟶ $\dfrac{1}{2}$ ⟵ denominator

One half is *one* out of *two* equal parts!

We usually simplify fractions to make them easier to understand.

$\dfrac{250}{500}$ is the same as $\dfrac{1}{2}$

Simplified fractions are easier to read and understand.

To simplify fractions you must understand factors.

Look at the dots. These statements are true:

Three out of 12 are red. One in every four is red.

So, $\dfrac{3}{12}$ is the same as $\dfrac{1}{4}$.

We say that the fraction has been **simplified**.

We can also simplify fractions using common factors.

To simplify $\dfrac{24}{30}$ we can separate each number into suitable factor pairs:

- Factors of 24 = 1 × 24, 2 × 12, 3 × 8, 4 × 6
- Factors of 30 = 1 × 30, 2 × 15, 3 × 10, 5 × 6

6 is the highest common factor of both 24 and 30. Therefore...

$$\dfrac{24}{30} = \dfrac{4 \times 6}{5 \times 6} \qquad \dfrac{24 \div 6}{30 \div 6} = \dfrac{4}{5}$$

To simplify to the smallest fraction, look for the highest common factor.

✓ Tips

- If you can't spot the highest common factor, look for a lower common factor for the numerator and the denominator and divide the numerator and the denominator to simplify and keep going until you get to the smallest number, for example:

$$\dfrac{18 \div 2}{48 \div 2} = \dfrac{9 \div 3}{24 \div 3} = \dfrac{3}{8}$$

Or, just divide 18 and 48 by 6!

Simple tips for simplifying fractions!

Talk maths

- The activity in the textbook can be played in groups or with the whole class. If preferred, you can create a bank of appropriate question on cards in advance.

- When discussing fractions, remember to focus on the correct terminology: 'numerator', 'denominator' and 'common factor'.

Activities

- Written practice in finding equivalent fractions can be continued for as long as desired. The questions in the book can easily be adapted to different fractions. For children who need support, provide the fractions in visual form, preferably as circles, so that they can see how simplified fractions continue to represent the same proportion.

Problems

- As with the Activities questions, the two problems can be rewritten to match the abilities of different children, such as six out of eight children have school dinners, and so on.

Talk maths

Play *Bing Bang Bong*.

Any number of people can play.
You will each need a pencil and paper.

Take turns to call out a fraction (such as, twelve fifteenths). Everyone must write down the fraction in numerator and denominator form, and then it is a race to simplify the fraction as much as possible.

The first person to simplify the fraction must shout *bing*! Everyone must then agree that they are right.

If they have made a mistake, the first person to spot and correct it shouts *bang*!

If a fraction has been suggested that cannot be simplified (such as seven sixteenths), the first person to realise this must shout *bong*!

> The player with the most correct **bings**, **bangs** and **bongs** wins the game!

Activities

1. Write the highest common factor of each pair of numbers.
   a. 6 and 10
   b. 15 and 24
   c. 45 and 17
   d. 100 and 40
   e. 30 and 300
   f. 11 and 88

2. Say if these simplifications are true or false.
   a. $\frac{43}{86} = \frac{1}{2}$
   b. $\frac{12}{60} = \frac{1}{5}$
   c. $\frac{21}{49} = \frac{3}{8}$
   d. $\frac{64}{100} = \frac{16}{25}$

3. Simplify these fractions.
   a. $\frac{6}{8}$
   b. $\frac{15}{20}$
   c. $\frac{24}{32}$
   d. $\frac{75}{100}$
   e. $\frac{36}{80}$
   f. $\frac{45}{72}$
   g. $\frac{128}{300}$
   h. $\frac{64}{200}$

Problems

Brain-teaser
128 out of 400 children have school dinners. Write this as a fraction in its simplest form.

Brain-buster
What fraction of the children do not have school dinners? Write the answer in its simplest form.

Fractions, decimals and percentages   29

100 Maths Lessons Year 6 links:

- Autumn 2, Week 2 (pages 55–60): use common factors to simplify fractions

Year 6 Practice Book links:

- (page 60–61): Common factors and simplifying fractions

Comparing and ordering fractions

Prior learning

- Can identify common multiples and common factors.
- Understand the terms 'mixed number' and 'improper fraction'.

Learn

- Review learning from 'Simplifying fractions' on pages 108–109 of this book, looking at how fractions can be simplified by finding common factors in the numerator and the denominator. Demonstrate that the simplified fraction is equivalent to the original.

- Repeat this for a range of fractions, and also show how the numerator and denominator can both be multiplied by the same number to create an equivalent fraction with larger numbers at the top and bottom.

- Move on to demonstrating how fractions can be compared. Start by using visual illustrations, for example one third of a circle is greater than one quarter, and so on. Progress to looking at fractions that are harder to compare. This may require a separate session to recap the concept of common multiples, as it is the denominators that must be made the same (common denominators) to compare the size of two fractions.

- *100 Maths Lessons Year 6, Autumn 2, Week 2* provides a variety of lessons for comparing and ordering fractions.

Curriculum objectives

- To compare and order fractions, including fractions > 1.

Success criteria

- I can compare and order fractions.
- I can identify and find equivalent fractions.

Comparing and ordering fractions

Learn

We can compare and order fractions by giving them the same denominators. To do this we must understand **equivalent fractions**.

This rectangle has been cut into eight equal pieces, or eighths.

$$\frac{2}{8} = \frac{1}{4}$$ because we have divided the numerator and denominator by 2.

Two eighths is *equivalent* to one quarter because they are the same proportion of the whole.

We can check this by changing either one of them:

$$\frac{2 \div 2}{8 \div 2} = \frac{1}{4} \qquad \frac{1 \times 2}{4 \times 2} = \frac{2}{8}$$

> When simplifying a fraction, whatever you do to the numerator, you must do the same to the denominator.

To compare and order fractions, we must give them the same denominator. Which is bigger, $\frac{2}{5}$ or $\frac{1}{4}$?

We need to find the lowest common multiple which is 20 for 4 and 5, so we must convert each fraction into twentieths.

$$\frac{2 \times 4}{5 \times 4} = \frac{8}{20} \qquad \frac{1 \times 5}{4 \times 5} = \frac{5}{20} \qquad \text{So, } \frac{2}{5} \text{ is bigger than } \frac{1}{4}.$$

Let's try something harder. Which of these fractions is bigger, $\frac{7}{8}$ or $\frac{17}{20}$? The lowest common multiple for 8 and 20 is 40.

$$\frac{7 \times 5}{8 \times 5} = \frac{35}{40} \qquad \frac{17 \times 2}{20 \times 2} = \frac{34}{40} \qquad \text{So, } \frac{7}{8} \text{ is bigger than } \frac{17}{20}.$$

✓ Tips

- Remember, when we give each fraction the same denominator, it is called a **common denominator**.
- To compare any number of fractions, you need to give each fraction the same common denominator by finding the **lowest common multiple**. Look at page 26 if you are not certain.
- Remember, > means is bigger than, and < means is smaller than.

Talk maths

- Arrange the children in pairs or small groups, and provide a range of fractions on cards. Challenge them to take two cards at a time and find a common denominator for the fractions, and then make a statement comparing the two fractions.

- This activity can be developed by asking the children to compare three or more fractions, as well as by providing mixed numbers or improper fractions if appropriate.

Activities

- This section can be reinforced with activities from the *Year 6 Practice Book*. On its own, it should provide sufficient information for you to assess children's understanding.

Problems

- Not all children need attempt the Brain-buster problem.

- Try challenging children to create their own problems that they can pose to each other.

Talk maths

Write down a selection of fractions, making sure each one has a different numerator and denominator, such as $\frac{3}{7}$ $\frac{2}{3}$ $\frac{5}{8}$ $\frac{1}{9}$ $\frac{4}{6}$.

Try this with improper fractions, where the numerator is bigger. The same rules apply!

Next, choose any pair of fractions and change them to give them the same denominator. Then make a statement about them, such as:

$\frac{3}{7}$ and $\frac{2}{3}$ have a common denominator of 21.

$\frac{3}{7} = \frac{9}{21}$ and $\frac{2}{3} = \frac{14}{21}$ so $\frac{2}{3} > \frac{3}{7}$.

Activities

1. Change each fraction to give it a denominator of 30.

    a. $\frac{1}{2}$ b. $\frac{2}{3}$ c. $\frac{3}{5}$ d. $\frac{5}{6}$

2. Copy and insert the correct sign, =, < or >.

    a. $1\frac{1}{2}$ $1\frac{3}{6}$ b. $3\frac{3}{4}$ $3\frac{2}{3}$ c. $\frac{20}{6}$ $\frac{13}{4}$ d. $\frac{12}{5}$ $\frac{15}{6}$

3. True or false?

    a. $\frac{3}{7} > \frac{1}{3}$ b. $\frac{15}{9} > \frac{7}{5}$ c. $\frac{7}{11} > \frac{13}{20}$

4. Arrange these fractions in order, smallest to largest. Place a less than sign (<) between each one.

    a. $\frac{3}{4}, \frac{5}{8}, \frac{2}{3}$ b. $\frac{4}{9}, \frac{3}{7}, \frac{1}{3}$ c. $\frac{13}{24}, \frac{5}{9}, \frac{7}{12}$

Problems

Brain-teaser

Eva's mum has some money in her purse. She says that Eva can have a fraction of it. She offers Eva $\frac{3}{8}$ or $\frac{7}{20}$ of the money.

Which fraction will give Eva more money?

Brain-buster

In a survey, some children were asked which pets they owned. $\frac{2}{7}$ of the children owned dogs and $\frac{3}{12}$ owned cats. The others owned no pets. Arrange the three sets of children in order, showing the fraction of each.

100 Maths Lessons Year 6 links:

- Autumn 2, Week 2 (pages 55–60): compare and order fractions

Year 6 Practice Book links:

- (page 62): Comparing fractions
- (page 63): Equal match

Adding and subtracting fractions

Prior learning

- Can add and subtract simple fractions with the same denominator.
- Recognise and find equivalent fractions.

Learn

- Drawing circles on the whiteboard, illustrate how quarters can easily be added to quarters, but not to thirds.
- Review the concept of common denominators and the creation of equivalent fractions. Demonstrate the complete process in order to add one half and one third.

- Starting with pairs of fractions that require only one of the fractions to be adjusted (for example, fifths and tenths), practise a range of additions with the children. Move on to two or three fractions which require the creation of a lowest common multiple before any addition can be performed. Stress the importance of carefully adjusting each fraction in turn to ensure that it remains equivalent to the original.

- Note that the Tips provide information on using mixed numbers and improper fractions. If further support is needed with these concepts, use *100 Maths Lessons Year 6 Spring 1, Week 4, Lesson 2* and *Summer 1, Week 4, Lesson 1*.

Curriculum objectives

- To add and subtract fractions with different denominators and mixed numbers, using the concept of equivalent fractions.

Success criteria

- I can add and subtract fractions with different denominators and mixed numbers.

Adding and subtracting fractions

Learn

To add and subtract fractions, they must have the same denominator.

To add $\frac{1}{2}$ and $\frac{1}{3}$, first find the lowest common denominator ($2 \times 3 = 6$).

Next, convert each fraction to give it a denominator of 6.

$$\frac{1 \times 3 = 3}{2 \times 3 = 6} \qquad \frac{1 \times 2 = 2}{3 \times 2 = 6}$$

And you must only add the numerators!
$$\frac{3}{12} + \frac{4}{12} = \frac{7}{12}$$

Then, add the new fractions: $\frac{3}{6} + \frac{2}{6} = \frac{5}{6}$

Taking away is exactly the same – you only subtract the numerators. $\frac{7}{10} - \frac{3}{10} = \frac{4}{10}$

The common denominator will usually be the lowest common multiple of all the fractions involved.

If one denominator is a multiple of the other, you only need to change one. For example: $\frac{3}{5} + \frac{1}{10} = \frac{6}{10} + \frac{1}{10} = \frac{7}{10}$

Sometimes you will need to think more, for example:

$\frac{3}{5} + \frac{1}{8}$ 40 is the lowest common multiple of 5 and 8.

$\frac{3}{5} = \frac{24}{40}$ and $\frac{1}{8} = \frac{5}{40}$ $\frac{24}{40} + \frac{5}{40} = \frac{29}{40}$

✓ Tips

Here's how to add mixed numbers and improper fractions.

- There are two ways to deal with improper fractions and mixed numbers.

  1. Add the whole numbers and the fractions separately.

  $1\frac{1}{3} + 3\frac{5}{6}$

  $= 1 + 3 + \frac{1}{3} + \frac{5}{6}$

  $= 4 + \frac{2}{6} + \frac{5}{6}$

  $= 4\frac{7}{6}$

  $= 5\frac{1}{6}$ It works for subtraction too!

  2. Use improper fractions.

  $1\frac{1}{3} + 3\frac{5}{6}$

  $= \frac{4}{3} + \frac{23}{6}$

  $= \frac{8}{6} + \frac{23}{6}$

  $= \frac{31}{6}$

  $= 5\frac{1}{6}$

- Try to provide several opportunities for children to become familiar with the vocabulary and processes involved in adding and subtracting fractions, challenging them to collaborate in finding common denominators. Also, remind them that when they have their answer they should always check to see if it can be simplified.

- When children subtract fractions, reinforce that, as with whole numbers, fractions can be added in any order, but not subtracted in any order. Avoid negative fractions.

Activities

- The questions should provide enough material for assessment of children's understanding of the concepts. Further practice can be provided through activities in the *Year 6 Practice Book*.

Problems

- Further problems can easily be created using fraction cards as prompts.

Talk maths

Work with a partner and challenge them to add and subtract fractions. You can *only* say fractions that have one denominator that is a multiple of the other. Use the fractions in the box, or make up some of your own, for example:

$$\frac{1}{2} \quad \frac{3}{4} \quad \frac{7}{12} \quad \frac{1}{6} \quad \frac{2}{3} \quad \frac{5}{9}$$
$$\frac{5}{8} \quad \frac{3}{10} \quad \frac{4}{5} \quad \frac{3}{4} \quad \frac{5}{6} \quad \frac{1}{3}$$

Add one third and five sixths
$(\frac{1}{3} + \frac{5}{6} = \frac{2}{6} + \frac{5}{6} = \frac{7}{6} = 1\frac{1}{6})$

One third plus five sixths equals seven sixths, or one and one sixth.

Challenge your partner to work it out then read their answer to you.

Activities

1. **Add these fractions.**
   a. $\frac{1}{6} + \frac{2}{3}$
   b. $\frac{2}{5} + \frac{3}{10}$
   c. $\frac{1}{4} + \frac{1}{8} + \frac{1}{2}$

2. **Subtract these fractions.**
   a. $\frac{5}{8} - \frac{1}{2}$
   b. $\frac{7}{9} - \frac{1}{3}$
   c. $\frac{7}{12} - \frac{2}{5}$

3. **Copy these fraction sentences and insert the missing sign (+ or –).**
   a. $\frac{1}{2} \square \frac{1}{4} = \frac{3}{4}$
   b. $\frac{1}{2} \square \frac{1}{3} = \frac{1}{6}$
   c. $\frac{1}{2} \square \frac{2}{5} = \frac{9}{10}$
   d. $\frac{2}{7} \square \frac{1}{6} = \frac{5}{42}$
   e. $\frac{7}{10} \square \frac{1}{4} = \frac{9}{20}$
   f. $\frac{3}{8} \square \frac{1}{12} = \frac{11}{24}$

4. **Complete these calculations. Show your answers as a mixed number.**
   a. $\frac{5}{2} + \frac{7}{4}$
   b. $2\frac{1}{2} - 1\frac{1}{4}$
   c. $\frac{10}{3} - \frac{11}{5}$
   d. $2\frac{2}{3} + 1\frac{4}{5}$

Problems

Brain-teaser
Jin and Tom buy a pizza. If Jin eats $\frac{1}{2}$ of it and Tom eats $\frac{1}{3}$, how much pizza is left over?

Brain-buster
Tulga and Amy have some popcorn. Tulga eats three sevenths of it and Amy eats four elevenths of it. How much popcorn is left?

100 Maths Lessons Year 6 links:

- Autumn 2, Week 2 (pages 55–60): add and subtract simple fractions

- Spring 1, Week 4 (pages 107–112): use equivalent fractions knowledge to add and subtract fractions with different denominators

- Summer 1, Week 4 (pages 187–192): add and subtract fractions by finding common denominators

- Summer 2, Week 3 (pages 223–227): calculate with fractions and mixed numbers

Year 6 Practice Book links:

- (page 64): Add and subtract fractions

- (page 65): Adding and subtracting mixed numbers

Multiplying fractions

Prior learning

- Can multiply simple fractions by whole numbers.
- Can convert improper fractions to mixed numbers and vice versa.

Learn

- Using a variety of arrays of dots, work with the children to divide them into equal groups that are fractions of the whole, such as halves, thirds, quarters and fifths. Modelling the word 'of', as in *half of six is three*.
- Point out the relationship between the denominator and division. For example, in a fraction like $\frac{1}{5}$, 1 is divided by 5. Move on to fractions with a numerator larger than 1, for example $\frac{3}{7}$ is equivalent to 3 divided by 7.

- Continue with the arrays introduced above, and demonstrate how one half of 24 is 12, and that one third of 12 is 4. Show that this means that one third of one half is equivalent to one sixth, representing the calculation thus: $\frac{1}{3} \times \frac{1}{2} = \frac{1}{6}$
- Develop this further by demonstrating the process with fractions that have larger numerators, such as two fifths multiplied by three quarters,

showing how simplification can be introduced at any stage.

- Depending on children's confidence and competence, this can be progressed to more complex calculations where common factors can be cancelled out. The Tips give an example of this.

Multiplying fractions

Learn

We can multiply whole numbers by fractions.

When multiplying by a fraction we use the word **of**.

- $\frac{1}{2}$ of 10 = 5.
- One quarter of 12 is 3.
- $\frac{1}{3}$ of 9 is 3.

Remember, multiplication works in any order: $\frac{1}{2} \times 24$ is the same as $24 \times \frac{1}{2}$.

We can also multiply fractions by other fractions.

Watch carefully: when we multiply fractions together we multiply the numerators with each other *and* we multiply the denominators with each other.

$$\frac{1}{2} \times \frac{3}{4} = \frac{1 \times 3}{2 \times 4} = \frac{3}{8}$$

Look at the circle opposite. Can you see how half of three quarters equals three eighths?

Let's try something harder:

$$\frac{5}{6} \times \frac{2}{3} = \frac{5 \times 2}{6 \times 3} = \frac{10}{18}$$ (we can simplify this to $\frac{5}{9}$)

$\frac{3}{4}$

All whole numbers can be written as fractions with a denominator of 1.

So, $5 \times \frac{3}{8}$ is the same as saying $\frac{5}{1} \times \frac{3}{8} = \frac{15}{8}$ (or $1\frac{7}{8}$).

✓ Tips

- Look at this calculation: $\frac{2}{3} \times \frac{3}{5} = \frac{2 \times 3}{3 \times 5} = \frac{6}{15} = \frac{2}{5}$

  We didn't really need to do a calculation because the three on the top cancels out with the three on the bottom (3 ÷ 3 = 1).
- Can you see the quick way to solve this calculation?

  $$\frac{3}{7} \times \frac{7}{9} = \frac{3 \times 7}{7 \times 9} = \frac{3}{9} = \frac{1}{3}$$
- Remember to simplify fractions as much as possible.

This trick might save you time, but only use it if you understand it!

Talk maths

- If the textbook activity is too difficult for children to solve mentally, challenge them to work in pairs to carry out multiplications, writing an explanation for each one. Children should be encouraged to select fractions that they are confident in working with.

Activities

- Before attempting the questions in the textbook, children may need additional demonstrations of how to multiply whole numbers by fractions: change the whole number to a fraction with a denominator of 1.

- In completing these questions, children should come to appreciate that simplifying common factors before multiplying is usually an easier approach.

- The *Year 6 Practice Book* provides additional practice, and *100 Maths Lessons Year 6, Summer 1, Week 4, Lessons 2 and 3* provide activities which will be useful for support and extension.

Problems

- Encourage the children to develop their own fraction multiplication problems. In particular, they could consider two-step problems which require a degree of reasoning. For example, If one fifth of a class of 30 children have blonde hair, how many do not have blonde hair?

Talk maths

Choose any two fractions from the examples in the box.
Read them aloud as a multiplication.
Try solving the problem mentally, explaining your answer.

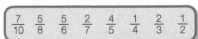

$$\frac{7}{10} \quad \frac{5}{8} \quad \frac{5}{6} \quad \frac{2}{7} \quad \frac{4}{5} \quad \frac{1}{4} \quad \frac{2}{3} \quad \frac{1}{2}$$

$\frac{7}{10} \times \frac{4}{5} = \frac{28}{50}$ because 7 × 4 = 28, and 10 × 5 = 50.

Also, 2 is a common factor of 28 and 50, so we can simplify to $\frac{14}{25}$.

Activities

1. Copy and complete these multiplications.
   a. $\frac{1}{2}$ of 20   b. $\frac{1}{4}$ of 24   c. $\frac{3}{4}$ of 24
   d. $\frac{2}{5} \times 25$ e. $\frac{5}{6}$ of 30   f. $\frac{2}{3} \times 39$

2. Write these answers as mixed numbers.
   a. $14 \times \frac{1}{4}$ b. $25 \times \frac{1}{2}$ c. $40 \times \frac{1}{3}$
   d. $14 \times \frac{3}{7}$ e. $12 \times \frac{3}{5}$ f. $100 \times \frac{1}{6}$

3. Multiply these fractions.
   a. $\frac{1}{2} \times \frac{1}{3}$ b. $\frac{2}{5} \times \frac{3}{4}$ c. $\frac{3}{8} \times \frac{8}{9}$
   d. $\frac{5}{6} \times \frac{4}{5}$ e. $\frac{2}{3} \times \frac{5}{8}$ f. $\frac{10}{7} \times \frac{4}{5}$

Problems

Brain-teaser
Tinashe usually takes ten and a half minutes to run one lap of the park. In her roller skates she can do the same lap in half this time. How long will it take her in roller skates?

Brain-buster
A second is $\frac{1}{60}$ of a minute, and a minute is $\frac{1}{60}$ of an hour. What is a second as a fraction of an hour?

100 Maths Lessons Year 6 links:

- Spring 1, Week 4 (pages 107–112): multiply pairs of simple fractions

- Summer 1, Week 4 (pages 187–192): understand that multiplying with fractions gives a smaller answer; multiply pairs of fractions

- Summer 2, Week 3 (pages 223–227): multiply proper fractions

Year 6 Practice Book links:

- (pages 66–67): Multiply pairs of fractions

- (page 73): Fraction match

Dividing fractions

Prior learning

- Can recognise and find equivalent fractions.
- Can multiply simple fractions by whole numbers.

Learn

- Ensure that children are comfortable with the terms 'numerator', 'denominator' and 'inverse'.
- Also, demonstrate how a whole number can be written as a fraction with a denominator of 1.
- Once grasped, dividing fractions by whole numbers is straightforward. However, initially it often muddles children. Therefore, they need a careful introduction to this area.

- The emphasis in the textbook is on multiplying by the inverse of the whole number (in other words, dividing by 2 is the same as multiplying by ½). However, for children who are struggling to grasp the concept, it may be beneficial to use concrete examples and to consider sharing, such as half a pizza shared between three people gives them one sixth of the whole pizza each.

- *100 Maths Lessons Year 6, Spring 1, Week 4, Lesson 5* and *Summer 1, Week 4, Lesson 4* provide further advice and ideas.

Curriculum objectives

- To divide proper fractions by whole numbers.

Success criteria

- I can divide fractions by whole numbers.

Dividing fractions

Learn

When multiplying by a fraction we multiply the numerators together, and we multiply the denominators together.

$$\frac{1}{5} \times \frac{3}{4} = \frac{1 \times 3}{5 \times 4} = \frac{3}{20}$$

Just as we can multiply fractions, we can also divide fractions. Look at the circle opposite. Half has been shaded.

If we divide the shaded half in two we get quarters.

So: $\frac{1}{2} \div 2 = \frac{1}{4}$.

Remember $\frac{1}{2} \times \frac{1}{2} = \frac{1}{4}$. So, dividing by 2 is the same as multiplying by $\frac{1}{2}$.

Now try this one: $\frac{1}{4} \div 3$

This is the same as saying $\frac{1}{4} \times \frac{1}{3} = \frac{1}{12}$.

Try drawing a circle and dividing it into fractions to prove this.

✓ Tips

- Dividing fractions is tricky.
  But remember that dividing by a whole number is the same as multiplying by one over that number, such as:

  $\frac{2}{3} \div 5$ is the same as $\frac{2}{3} \div \frac{5}{1}$ which is the same as $\frac{2}{3} \times \frac{1}{5} = \frac{2}{15}$.

  So, $\frac{2}{3} \div 5 = \frac{2}{15}$.

Talk maths

• Encourage children to develop their understanding of the concept by drawing circles and dividing these into halves, quarters and thirds. They should then consider how each fraction is affected if divided by 2, 3, 4 or 5. They can both draw and discuss the resulting quantities, and finally record what they've done as a calculation.

Activities

• Remember to encourage children to sketch the fractions if they are unsure of the calculations. The *Year 6 Practice Book* provides further support.

Problems

• These problems are fairly tricky, but should be achievable with sketches to support children's calculations. This topic provides plenty of opportunities to practise reasoning skills, and as always children should be encouraged to consider how realistic their answers are, and to check their work accordingly.

Talk maths

These circles have been divided into halves, quarters and thirds. Use them to help you discuss dividing simple fractions by whole numbers.

> A half divided by three equals one sixth.

> A quarter divided by two equals one eighth.

> A third divided by five equals one fifteenth.

Activities

1. Is each calculation right or wrong?

   a. $\frac{1}{2} \div 3 = \frac{1}{6}$ b. $\frac{1}{4} \div 2 = \frac{1}{8}$ c. $\frac{1}{3} \div 3 = \frac{1}{6}$

   d. $\frac{2}{5} \div 4 = \frac{1}{10}$ e. $\frac{3}{4} \div 2 = \frac{1}{2}$ f. $\frac{6}{3} \div 4 = \frac{1}{2}$

2. Copy and complete these divisions.

   a. $\frac{1}{2} \div 2$ b. $\frac{1}{4} \div 3$ c. $\frac{1}{3} \div 5$

   d. $\frac{2}{3} \div 4$ e. $\frac{3}{4} \div 4$ f. $\frac{2}{3} \div 20$

Problems

Brain-teaser
Jem shares half a cake between seven people. What fraction of the whole cake will they each receive?

Brain-buster
A teacher has three tenths of a sheet of stickers left and wants to share them equally among her class of 24 children.

What fraction of the sheet of stickers will each child receive? If a full sheet holds 240 stickers, how many will each child receive?

100 Maths Lessons Year 6 links:

• Spring 1, Week 4 (pages 107–112): divide fractions by whole numbers

• Summer 1, Week 4 (pages 187–192): understand that dividing fractions by a whole number gives a larger answer

• Summer 2, Week 3 (pages 223–227): solve problems involving dividing fractions by whole numbers

Year 6 Practice Book links:

• (page 68): Dividing proper fractions by a whole number

Decimal equivalents

Prior learning

- Can convert a fraction to a decimal.

Learn

- Recap the terminology of fractions and decimals, covering key vocabulary: 'numerator', 'denominator', 'decimal place', 'tenths' and 'hundredths'.

- Create a set of cards showing fractions and their decimal equivalents, each on a separate piece of card. Shuffle the cards and give out to volunteers at the front of the classroom. Ask the children to hold up their decimals and fractions, and get the rest of the class to pair them with their equivalent by instructing them only by their mathematical names. For example: *Half stand next to 0.5.*

- The textbook gives examples of finding decimal equivalents of fractions by dividing the numerator by the denominator. Talk through the use of short division, paying close attention to zero used as a place holder and the positioning of the decimal point. Demonstrate how zeros can be added after a decimal point (for example, 3.000) to allow the formal division process to be completed.

- *100 Maths Lessons Year 6, Autumn 2, Week 2, Lesson 3* covers decimal equivalents calculated by dividing fractions.

Curriculum objectives

- To associate a fraction with division and calculate decimal fraction equivalents for a simple fraction.

Success criteria

- I can convert between fractions and decimals.
- I understand the relationship between fractions and division.

Decimal equivalents

Learn

A proper fraction is a proportion of one whole.

$$\frac{1}{4}, \frac{1}{3}, \frac{1}{2}, \frac{2}{3}, \frac{3}{4}$$ are all proper fractions.

A fraction is a numerator divided by a denominator, such as:

$\frac{1}{2}$ is 1 divided by 2, so $\frac{1}{2}$ = 0.5

You need to learn these common fractions and their decimal equivalents:

Fraction	$\frac{1}{2}$	$\frac{1}{4}$	$\frac{3}{4}$	$\frac{1}{5}$	$\frac{1}{10}$
Decimal	0.5	0.25	0.75	0.2	0.1

Any fraction can be written as a decimal.
If you need to calculate the decimal equivalent of a fraction, just do a short division.

$$\frac{1}{4} = 4\overline{\smash{)}1.{}^{1}0\,{}^{2}0}\quad \begin{array}{c}0.25\end{array}$$

Notice that a whole number can be written with zeros in the decimal places.

$$\frac{3}{8} = 8\overline{\smash{)}3.{}^{3}0\,{}^{6}0\,{}^{4}0}\quad\begin{array}{c}0.375\end{array}$$

Remember to keep the decimal point in the right place!

✓ Tips

Time for some decimal tips!

- Remember that, after a decimal point, the first column is tenths, the second column is hundredths, and the third column is thousandths.
- We read decimals aloud using the numbers zero to nine.
  - We say 0.5 is zero point five.
  - We say 0.75 is zero point seven five.
  - We say 0.375 is zero point three seven five.
  - We say 0.666 is zero point six six six.

Talk maths

- The textbook contains a small uncompleted chart. Children should work in pairs to copy and extend this chart on paper, and work together to create a bank of simplified fractions and their decimal equivalents.

- Depending on children's abilities, try to encourage the learning of a range of fraction–decimal equivalents. Ideally, this would include halves, quarters, thirds, fifths and tenths. More confident learners should move on to eighths. (There is a question focusing on eighths in Activities.)

Activities

- While children work through the questions, encourage them to spot relationships between fraction increments and decimal increments. For example, counting in fifths is in steps of 0.2, tenths is 0.1, and so on. More confident learners should be encouraged to count in steps of quarters and eighths.

- If appropriate, introduce work on decimal number lines. Add decimals and their fraction equivalents to the lines to help children appreciate their relative sizes.

Problems

- Both problems move on to more complex fractions (sixths and twelfths). Also, the problems in the *Year 6 Practice Book* include giving the answers to short divisions as fractions and decimals.

Talk maths

You know about fraction equivalents, such as $\frac{2}{4} = \frac{1}{2}$.

Now look at what happens when they are changed to decimals.

$$\frac{2}{4} = 0.5 \qquad \frac{1}{2} = 0.5$$

> Because the fractions are equivalent, they both equal 0.5.

Discuss this with a partner. Copy and complete this chart as you go.

Fraction	$\frac{2}{8} = \frac{1}{4}$	$\frac{4}{10} = \frac{2}{5}$	$\frac{2}{6} = \frac{1}{3}$	$\frac{6}{8} = \frac{3}{4}$	$\frac{10}{12} = \frac{5}{6}$
Decimal	0.25	0.4			

Activities

1. Convert these fractions to decimals.
   a. $\frac{2}{5}$ b. $\frac{6}{10}$ c. $\frac{3}{8}$

2. Copy and complete this chart.

Fraction	$\frac{1}{8}$	$\frac{2}{8}$	$\frac{3}{8}$	$\frac{4}{8}$	$\frac{5}{8}$	$\frac{6}{8}$	$\frac{7}{8}$	$\frac{8}{8}$
Decimal	0.125	0.25						

3. Copy then match each fraction to its decimal equivalent.

   $\frac{3}{4}$ $\frac{5}{8}$ $\frac{4}{5}$ $\frac{1}{3}$

   0.625   0.8   0.333   0.75

4. Copy then match each decimal to its fraction equivalent.

   0.166   0.4   0.7   0.125

   $\frac{1}{8}$ $\frac{1}{6}$ $\frac{7}{10}$ $\frac{2}{5}$

Problems

Brain-teaser
Which is more, $\frac{5}{6}$ or 0.8?

Brain-buster
A bag of popcorn is shared equally between 12 people. Tim says that each person will receive 0.1 of the popcorn. Is he right? Explain your answer.

---

100 Maths Lessons Year 6 links:

- Autumn 2, Week 2 (pages 55–60): use division to convert fractions to decimals

- Spring 1, Week 4 (pages 107–112): convert fractions to decimals.

Year 6 Practice Book links:

- (page 71): Fractions of curtains

Decimal places

Prior learning

- Can round decimal numbers to one decimal place.
- Can multiply and divide decimal numbers by 10 and 100.

Learn

- Draw a chart on the whiteboard using the column headings from the first table on page 40 of the textbook. Work with the children to choose a selection of simple fractions and insert them along with their decimal equivalents. Model the correct vocabulary for each so that the different names for an equivalent fraction and decimal is noted, for example one half, zero point five.

- Progress to decimal fractions. That is, fractions with denominators of 10, 100 and 1000. Stress the mathematical implications of multiplying and dividing by powers of 10, showing how the digits move places in a place-value table accordingly.

- One tricky thing for children to understand is the relative sizes of tenths, hundredths and thousandths. It is difficult to convey this, but explain that numbers after the decimal point continue with the trend before it. In other words, as we move from left to right the size of the value of each digit decreases by a factor of 10.

- The textbook provides information and explanations for rounding, including recurring numbers. It is important for children to be able to read the decimals correctly in order to round them.

Curriculum objectives

- To identify the value of each digit in numbers given to three decimal places and multiply and divide numbers by 10, 100 and 1000 giving answers up to three decimal places.

Success criteria

- I can use and understand decimals with up to three decimal places.

Decimal places

Learn

A decimal fraction has 10, 100 or 1000 as its denominator, such as $\frac{4}{10}$.

We can say $\frac{4}{10}$ as 4 divided by 10.

When we divide a number by 10, 100 or 1000, we move the numbers to the right.

Fraction name	Fraction	Decimal	Decimal name
Seven tenths	$\frac{7}{10}$	0.7	Zero point seven
Twenty-three hundredths	$\frac{23}{100}$	0.23	Zero point two three
Four hundred and thirty-five thousandths	$\frac{435}{1000}$	0.435	Zero point four three five

The place value of each digit changes.

Decimals can have more than three decimal places, but usually we round decimals, just like we round other numbers.

A basic rule for rounding is if the next number is five or more, round up, if not, round down.

| 0.87 = 0.9 to one decimal place | 0.435 = 0.44 to two decimal places |

| 0.2574 = 0.257 to three decimal places |

Money usually needs to be rounded to two decimal places.

Look at these examples.

Fraction	$\frac{1}{7}$	$\frac{4}{13}$	$\frac{7}{17}$
Decimal	0.142857	0.307692	0.411764
Rounded to three decimal places	0.143	0.308	0.412
Rounded to two decimal places	0.14	0.31	0.41
Rounded to one decimal place	0.1	0.3	0.4

✓ Tips

- Some decimals have the same number that goes on forever, such as
  $\frac{1}{6}$ = 0.16666666666666666666666666666666666666

  We call this a recurring decimal. We usually round these decimals to three decimal places.

  So $\frac{1}{6}$ = 0.167 to three decimal places.

- $\frac{1}{3}$ and $\frac{2}{3}$ also make recurring decimals.

- $\frac{1}{3}$ = 0.333 to three decimal places. $\frac{2}{3}$ = 0.667 to three decimal places.

• The textbook activity requires division. Children can practise reading the decimal answers. This can be taken further by creating a chart and ordering decimals in order of size, ideally rounded to three decimal places.

• The chart requires in question 2 children to write down each decimal rounded to three, two and one decimal places.

• For consolidation, *100 Maths Lessons Year 6, Autumn 2, Week 3* provides further practice in multiplying and dividing numbers by powers of 10.

• Note that *100 Maths Lessons Year 6, Spring 1, Week 2* provides activities for addition and subtraction of decimals

and money in problem-solving contexts. Working with pounds and pence can help children appreciate the relative size of tenths and hundredths.

• The Brain-teaser is a tricky one, but provides scope for further practice and investigation. The suggested *Year 6 Practice Book* activities can consolidate this.

You will need two or more people.

Think of a fraction with demoninators of 2, 4, 5 or 8 and then use division to calculate the decimal equivalent.

$\frac{2}{5} = 0.4$

Take turns to challenge each other to say the decimal to one, two or three decimal places, checking each other's answers.

1. Look at these decimals and say how many thousandths, hundredths and tenths each one has.
   a. 0.375
   b. 0.903

2. Copy and complete this chart.

Fraction	Decimal	Rounded to three decimal places	Rounded to two decimal places	Rounded to one decimal place
$\frac{2}{7}$	0.285714			
$\frac{3}{13}$	0.230769			
$\frac{4}{11}$	0.363636			
$\frac{2}{3}$	0.66666			
$\frac{8}{9}$	0.88888			

Brain-teaser
Jared says that 0.001 rounded to the nearest tenth is 0.1. Is he right? Explain your answer.

Brain-buster
Explain why $\frac{3}{11}$ is a recurring number, and round it to three decimal places.

100 Maths Lessons Year 6 links:

• Autumn 2, Week 3 (pages 61–65): identify the value of decimals; round and order decimals to two places; multiply decimals by 10, 100 and 1000

• Spring 1, Week 2 (pages 96–100): addition and subtraction of decimals and money

Year 6 Practice Book links:

• (page 15): Decimal rounding problems

• (page 76): Place value in decimals

• (page 77): Ordering decimals

Multiplying decimals

Prior learning

- Can read and write decimals as fractions.
- Can read, write, order and compare numbers with up to three decimal places.
- Can round numbers to the nearest whole number and to one decimal place.

- Spend time reviewing the formal written method for long multiplication that the children are familiar with. (If they have only covered short multiplication to date, multiplying decimals by a single-digit whole number is still possible, but avoid using the textbook activities at present. Instead, *100 Maths Lessons Year 6, Spring 2, Week 2* provides simpler examples.)

- If the children are comfortable with this work, spend time looking at carrying forward between columns. This is exactly the same for decimals as it is for whole numbers, although children may need support to appreciate the concept of ten thousandths being equal to one hundredth, and so on.
- If children need further support, work on problems and calculations involving money.

Learn

- Start by writing a selection of decimals on the board (to a maximum of two decimal places) and work with the children to read and arrange them in order of size. Discuss how they might be written as equivalent fractions and how they might be rounded to the nearest whole number or tenth. Use this as an opportunity to model correct mathematical vocabulary and terminology.

Curriculum objectives

- To multiply 1-digit numbers with up to two decimal places by whole numbers.
- To solve problems which require answers to be rounded to specified degrees of accuracy.

Success criteria

- I can multiply decimals by whole numbers.
- I can solve problems involving decimals with up to three decimal places and rounding.

Multiplying decimals

Learn

Do you remember what tenths, hundredths and thousands are?
Tenths are bigger than hundredths, and hundredths are bigger than thousandths.

| $0.6 > 0.5$ | $0.431 > 0.429$ | $0.1 > 0.099$ | $0.3 > 0.28$ | $0.515 > 0.4$ |

- There are ten tenths in a whole.
- There are one hundred hundredths in a whole, but ten hundredths in one tenth.
- There are one thousand thousandths in a whole, but ten thousandths in one hundredth.

one hundred and twenty-three thousandths = zero point one two three

$$\frac{123}{1000} = 0.123$$

We can multiply any two numbers together, including numbers that are decimals. For the moment, we will learn how to multiply a decimal by a whole number. This will come in very handy for solving money problems!

Do you remember how to use formal written methods for multiplication?

```
    3  2  4
 ×     1  3
 ─────────────
    9  7¹ 2
 3  2  4  0  +
 ─────────────
 4  2  1  2
 ─────────────
 1  1
```
Answer: 4212

Well, the same method works for decimals.

```
    4 · 1  3
 ×     2  3
 ─────────────
 1  2 . 3  9
 8  2 . 6  0  +
 ─────────────
 9  4 · 9  9
```
Answer: 94.99

It's all about place value. Just remember to keep the decimal point in the right place.

✓ Tips

- When you multiply a decimal by a whole number, make sure you give your answer as a decimal too, with the same number of decimal places, for example:
  $6.35 × 2 = 12.70$ or $£1.25 × 4 = £5.00$
  Keeping the zeros helps with checking work later on.

- The introduction in the textbook tries to convey the relationship between multiplications involving whole numbers and decimals (for example, 12 × 3 and 0.12 × 3). Try to develop this activity by using a wide range of small decimals and whole numbers, initially avoiding any carrying forward between columns.

Activities

- It may be beneficial for children to practise multiplying decimals by single-digit whole numbers as in question 1.
- More confident learners might be introduced to mental methods for some of the calculations, at least as initial estimates. Demonstrate to them how 1.8 × 2 can be done mentally as: 18 times 2, and then divide by 10 to give 3.6. Or 0.05 × 5 is: 5 times 5 divided by 100.

Problems

- Note that the Brain-buster is a multi-step problem.
- Most problems involving decimals will involve measures, such as 'Home decorating' in the *Year 6 Practice Book*. Children could be encouraged to start creating their own problems, perhaps based on price lists from local shops or online shops.

Talk maths

With a partner, investigate multiplying decimals by whole numbers. Use small numbers to see if you can spot any handy patterns, such as

$3 \times 4 = 12, 0.3 \times 4 = 1.2$ or $6 \times 8 = 48, 6 \times 0.8 = 4.8$

Activities

1. Copy and complete each of these decimal multiplications using a written method.

a.	b.	c.	d.
0.2	3.3	0.23	0.34
× 3	× 2	× 4	× 6

e.	f.	g.	h.
0.46	2.6	0.66	0.19
× 8	× 5	× 4	× 6

2. Copy and complete each of these decimal multiplications using a written method.
   - a. 0.23 × 21
   - b. 0.45 × 15
   - c. 0.25 × 25
   - d. 3.33 × 33

Problems

Brain-teaser
A group of eight friends decide to buy their teacher some flowers. If they each contribute £1.15, how much will they have?

Brain-buster
A school trip is going to cost exactly £100. A letter is sent home asking for a donation of £2.65 per child towards the trip. If there are 32 children in the class and they all make the contribution, how much more will the school have to contribute?

100 Maths Lessons Year 6 links:

- Spring 2, Week 2 (pages 136–140): multiply and divide decimals by whole numbers

Year 6 Practice Book links:

- (page 52): Home decorating

Dividing decimals

Prior learning

- Can read and write decimals as fractions.
- Can read, write, order and compare numbers with up to three decimal places.

Learn

- This section is best tackled once children are secure with both short and long division.
- Revise the standard methods used in your school for short and long division. Discuss how remainders come about and how they are represented.
- Demonstrate short division for dividing a whole number into a number with two decimal places. (Choose a calculation with no 'remainder'.) Focus on dividing the tenths and hundredths, which follow the same procedure. Ensure the decimal point is kept in position.

Curriculum objectives

- To use written division methods in cases where the answer has up to two decimal places.
- To solve problems which require answers to be rounded to specified degrees of accuracy.

Success criteria

- I can divide decimals by whole numbers.
- I can solve problems involving decimals with up to three decimal places and rounding.

100 Maths Lessons Year 6 links:

- Spring 2, Week 2 (pages 136–140): divide decimals

- Next, or in a separate session, move on to long division of a decimal by a larger number. (It may be appropriate to differentiate.)

Talk maths

- Children could prepare a presentation where they explain, step-by-step, the stages of a short or long division of a decimal number. Encourage them to think of each stage, including the layout, as well as the correct use of terminology.

Activities

- Question 1 focuses on short division, and question 2 on long division. You could generate more questions at appropriate levels.

Problems

- Further practice of problems involving money would be beneficial. If possible, provide mixtures of problems involving decimals so that children have to choose the appropriate operation(s).

Dividing decimals

Learn

Short division

In short division we carry on the remainder at each stage, but with long division we are calculating the remainder at each stage, so that there is less chance of errors.

		0	4	2	6	r2
8	3	³4	²1	⁵0		

We can use short and long division for dividing decimals. Just remember to keep the decimal point in the same place.

	0	.	8	7
4	3	.	³4	²8

Long division

				2	2	3	r3
1	6	3	5	7	1		
	–	3	2				
			3	7			
		–	3	2			
				5	1		
			–	4	8		
					3		

				1	.	6	4
	1	3	2	1	.	3	2
(13 × 1 →) –		1	3				
			8	3			
(13 × 6 →) –		7	8				
			5	2			
(13 × 4 →) –		5	2				
			0	0			

Activities

1. Copy and complete each of these short divisions of decimals.
   - a. 0.39 ÷ 3
   - b. 0.54 ÷ 2
   - c. 0.49 ÷ 12

2. On paper, complete these long divisions of decimals using a written method.
   - a. 0.6 ÷ 15
   - b. 7.04 ÷ 32
   - c. 3.30 ÷ 22
   - d. 77.4 ÷ 15

Problems

Brain-teaser
Aysha has a brother and a sister. Their mum gives them £10.44 pocket money, to share equally between the three of them. How much will they each get?

44   Fractions, decimals and percentages

Percentage equivalents

Prior learning

- Understand percentage as the number of parts in 100.
- Can find simple percentages of numbers.

Learn

- Revisit this topic two or three times over the course of the year.
- Remind the children how a fraction can be converted to its decimal equivalent, creating a grid like the one at the top of page 45 in the textbook.

- Move on to the concepts of per cent and out of 100. Review the chart in the textbook. Use tenths and hundredths, and then move on to common fraction–decimal–percentage equivalents, such as one half and one quarter.

Talk maths

- Create cards showing ten different fractions and their decimal and percentage equivalents. The children can play games such as 'Snap' before arranging the cards in order in their equivalent groups.

Activities

- Ask the children to create a set of step-by-step rules to show how to convert from any one representation to any other.

Problems

- The *Year 6 Practice Book* has simpler problems.

Curriculum objectives

- To recall and use equivalences between simple fractions, decimals and percentages, including in different contexts.

Success criteria

- I can convert between fractions, decimals and percentages.

100 Maths Lessons Year 6 links:

- Spring 2, Week 3 (pages 141–145): solve problems involving percentages, fractions and decimals
- Summer 1, Week 5 (pages 193–197): fractions, decimals and percentages
- Summer 2, Week 3 (pages 223–227): work with fractions, decimals and percentages

Year 6 Practice Book links:

- (page 58): Day trip
- (page 59): Ferry crossing
- (page 70): Fraction action
- (page 72): Equivalence bingo
- (page 74): Percentage maker
- (page 75): Credit crunch

Percentage equivalents

Learn

$\frac{65}{100}$ is a decimal fraction.
We can say 65 over 100 or 65 out of 100.

Per cent means parts of a hundred or out of 100. Look at the 100 grid. 65 out of the 100 squares are shaded, this is 65%.

$0.65 = \frac{65}{100} = 65\%$

Decimal fractions can be called percentages.

It is easy to find the equivalents of simple fractions and decimals.

We can use our knowledge of decimal places and rounding to help us find trickier equivalents.

Fraction	$\frac{1}{2}$	$\frac{1}{4}$	$\frac{1}{10}$	$\frac{1}{5}$	$\frac{3}{4}$	$\frac{1}{1}$
Decimal	0.5	0.25	0.1	0.2	0.75	1.0
Per cent	50%	25%	10%	20%	75%	100%

$\frac{3}{8} = 0.375 = 37.5\%$ $\frac{5}{6} = 0.833 = 83.3\%$

Activities

1. Copy and complete the chart.

Percentage	Decimal	Fraction
33.3%		
	0.125	
		$\frac{2}{5}$
	0.85	
		$\frac{7}{8}$

Problems

Brain-teaser
12 out of 30 children have blond hair. What is that as a percentage?

Ratio and proportion: numbers

Prior learning

- Can solve problems involving fractions.

Learn

- Start with the example of the red and blue square in the textbook, and progress to a variety of groupings, such as sets of shapes, beads, cars, and so on. Demonstrate and discuss the difference between fractions and proportions. For each example, move on to showing the difference between fractions, proportion and ratio. Present each one clearly, separately, and with the appropriate notation.

- In particular, point out how proportions and ratios can be simplified to their lowest terms, just as fractions can be.

- Using the information about animals on a farm in the textbook, extend ratio and proportion to larger numbers. The textbook prompts children to consider other statements. Children can also discuss these ideas in other contexts, for example using information about the children in the class: eye colours, hair colours.

- The first two lessons of *100 Maths Lessons Year 6, Summer 1, Week 6* provide useful ideas and resources for consolidating children's understanding.

Curriculum objectives

- To solve problems involving the relative sizes of two quantities where missing values can be found by using integer multiplication and division facts.

- To solve problems involving unequal sharing and grouping using knowledge of fractions and multiples.

Success criteria

- I can compare quantities using ratio and proportion.

Talk maths

- After allowing the children to make statements about the coloured squares in the textbook, arrange the children into small groups to prepare four or five questions about the squares, focusing on ratio and proportion. Explain that they will be challenging other groups with their questions, and introduce them to negative statements, such as: *What proportion of the tiles are not red?*

Ratio and proportion: numbers

Learn

A fraction shows us one number compared to a whole. In the shape opposite, one out of four of the squares is blue.

Proportion is the fraction of a whole.
For this shape, the proportion of blue squares is one in four, or one out of four.
And the proportion of red squares is three in four, or three out of four.

Ratio is different, because it compares amounts.
For this shape above, the ratio of blue squares to red squares is 1 to 3, or 1:3.

Look at these examples.
In total there are 100 animals on a farm. There are two dogs, three cats, five rabbits, 20 cows, 30 sheep and 40 chickens.

Proportion
The proportion of dogs is two out of 100 animals. As a fraction this is $\frac{2}{100}$ or $\frac{1}{50}$.

The proportion of rabbits is $\frac{5}{100}$ or $\frac{1}{20}$. One in every 20 animals is a rabbit.

Ratio
The ratio of dogs to cows is 2:20. This can be simplified to 1:10. There are 10 cows for every dog.

The ratio of cows to chickens is 20:40. This can be simplified to 1:2. For every cow there are two chickens.

✓ Tips

- Proportion is a fraction of the whole; ratio compares different amounts.
- One in every five adults play computer games (so four out of five do not play).
  As a *proportion* this is one out of five, or $\frac{1}{5}$.
  But the *ratio* of adults who do play to adults who don't play computer games is 1:4.

- While listening to their question-and-answer exchanges, ensure that the children are clear about the differences between ratio and proportion. Note those children who are simplifying these with ease. If appropriate, recap work on fractions and multiples for simplifying fractions and apply this to proportions and ratios.

Activities

- If desired, the questions in this section can be expanded to cover other proportions and ratios.
- In addition, the *Year 6 Practice Book* has good consolidation activities. You can also use the 'Recipe' activity in *100 Maths Lessons Year 6, Summer 1, Week 6, Lesson 2*.

Problems

- Be sure to work though the Brain-teaser with the children once they have tried it. Check that they are able to simplify both proportion and ratio.
- Note that the Brain-buster is much trickier, as children must use a given ratio to calculate a quantity. Ideally, children should receive more practice with this type of calculation through practical problems.

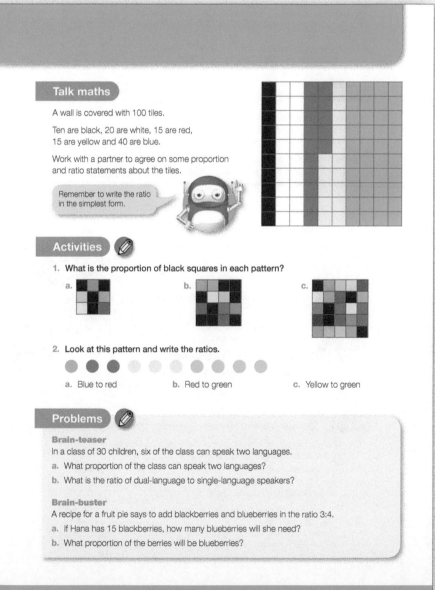

Talk maths

A wall is covered with 100 tiles.

Ten are black, 20 are white, 15 are red, 15 are yellow and 40 are blue.

Work with a partner to agree on some proportion and ratio statements about the tiles.

Remember to write the ratio in the simplest form.

Activities

1. What is the proportion of black squares in each pattern?

   a.   b.   c.

2. Look at this pattern and write the ratios.

   a. Blue to red   b. Red to green   c. Yellow to green

Problems

Brain-teaser
In a class of 30 children, six of the class can speak two languages.
a. What proportion of the class can speak two languages?
b. What is the ratio of dual-language to single-language speakers?

Brain-buster
A recipe for a fruit pie says to add blackberries and blueberries in the ratio 3:4.
a. If Hana has 15 blackberries, how many blueberries will she need?
b. What proportion of the berries will be blueberries?

Ratio and proportion   47

100 Maths Lessons Year 6 links:

- Summer 1, Week 6 (pages 198–202): understand and use ratio and proportion

Year 6 Practice Book links:

- (page 78): Baking time
- (page 80): All in a day

Ratio and proportion: percentages

Prior learning

- Can solve problems involving fractions.
- Can solve problems involving the calculation of percentages.

Learn

- Review the concepts of proportion and ratio and elicit the key differences between them. When appropriate, review the identification of factors and multiples of numbers and how they're used when simplifying proportions and ratios.

- Spend time ensuring that children understand the concept of per cent. If necessary, explain that it is a proportion which is always expressed out of 100. Start with examples that have 100 items as their basis, such as the example of children with brown eyes in the textbook. Then move on to data groups that are both under 100 (for example, a class of 25 children) and over 100 (for example, 360° in a pie chart).

Consider how proportions of these amounts can be converted to percentages.

- Note that this work may take more than one session. The *100 Maths Lessons Year 6* links for this section have a wide range of lesson ideas and resources to help with this topic.

Curriculum objectives

- To solve problems involving the calculation of percentages and the use of percentages for comparison.
- To solve problems involving unequal sharing and grouping using knowledge of fractions and multiples.

Success criteria

- I can use percentages for comparison and problem solving.

Ratio and proportion: percentages

Learn

Proportion is the fraction of a whole. For this shape, the proportion of yellow triangles is one in three, or one out of three.

Ratio compares amounts. For this shape, the ratio of yellow to green triangles is one to two, or 1:2.

And the proportion of green triangles is two in three, or two out of three.

And the ratio of *green to yellow* triangles is two to one or 2:1.

Percentages are a type of proportion. They represent an amount out of 100.

35 children out of 100 have packed lunches, which is $\frac{35}{100}$ or 35%.

If 17 children out of 50 have brown eyes, as a proportion it is $\frac{17}{50}$.

Percentages must be out of 100, so we must adjust the fraction.

$\frac{17}{50} = \frac{34}{100}$ so 34% have brown eyes.

That's easy. What if there were only 50 children?

Remember that 100% is everything, so, if 34% of the children have brown eyes, 66% do not, because 34% + 66% = 100%.

✓ Tips

- When calculating percentages, choose the order of calculations you find easier, for example, to find 26% of 360:
- you can either find 25% ($\frac{1}{4}$) of 360 = 90, plus 1% of 360 = 3.6. 90 + 3.6 = 93.6.
  - Or you can do 26 × 360, then divide by 100.

  360 ÷ 25 = 90 **plus** 360 ÷ 1 = 3.6 so 90 + 3.6 = 93.6

  26 × 360 = 9360 9360 ÷ 100 = 93.6

- The activity in the textbook (involving statements about ratio, proportion and percentages, using a pack of playing cards) can be differentiated by asking groups to focus solely on ratio, proportion or percentage statements.

- For some children, percentage statements will be difficult as with only 40 cards (all of the picture cards are removed for the activity) numbers will need to be multiplied by a factor of 2.5. However, it may also be appropriate to show children how they can quickly state some percentages, such as 20 out of 40 cards is half, therefore 50%.

Activities

- Children's answers to this section will show you if children have grasped the essence of what percentages are. Further material is available in the *100s Maths Lessons Year 6* links below.

Problems

- The Brain-teaser is straightforward, and several other problems could be developed from it, based on new data such as car colour.

- The Brain-buster is very tricky, but the *Year 6 Practice Book* provides further problems involving percentages. Also, be sure to spend time relating pie charts to percentages and vice versa.

Talk maths

You will need a pack of playing cards with the picture cards removed.
This will leave 40 cards, 1–10 in each suit of clubs, diamonds, spades and hearts.

Sort the pack in different ways and then make statements of proportion, ratio and percentage, such as:
One in four cards is a diamond.
The ratio of diamonds to other cards is 1:3.
25% of the pack is diamonds.

Did you know?

1 in 40 is 2.5%

Activities

1. Write these proportions as a percentage.

   a. 1 in 4   b. 7 in 10   c. 2 in 5   d. 3 in 8

2. Write these percentages as a proportion in their simplest form.

   a. 25%   b. 40%   c. 26%   d. 87.5%

3. Calculate these percentages.

   a. 25% of 200   b. 50% of 1   c. 10% of 624

   d. 95% of 300   e. 60% of 24   f. 15% of 360

4. Explain what each of these mathematical terms mean.
   a. Percentage   b. Proportion   c. Ratio

Problems

Brain-teaser
In a traffic survey, children counted 220 cars. 25% were driving over the speed limit. How many cars were driving too fast?

Brain-buster
The percentage of homes in the UK where a dog is kept as a pet is 18%. If there are 42 million homes in total, how many of these will keep a dog?

100 Maths Lessons Year 6 links:

- Summer 1, Week 5 (pages 193–197): solve problems involving percentages

- Summer 2, Week 3 (pages 223–227): use percentages for comparison; solve problems using percentages

Year 6 Practice Book links:

- (page 79): School travel plan

- (page 83): Dinner arrangements

Scale factors

Prior learning

- Can multiply by 10, 100 and 1000.
- Can recall multiplication facts up to 12 × 12.

Learn

- Review all the work done so far on proportion, ratio and percentage.
- Looking at the beads in the textbook, or something similar, focus on ratio as a way of comparing quantities.

- Using simple examples such as those in the textbook, explain the concept of scale, noting that scale works like ratio. For example, 1:25 means that an enlargement is 25 times bigger. Encourage the children to create scale drawings of small images. This can be done to good effect by drawing a 1cm grid over a small image, and then, for example, enlarging this to a grid of 4cm-sided squares.

- Finally, if possible, introduce the children to a selection of maps – paper or digital – and consider how scales affect what content is shown or is visible.
- *100 Maths Lessons Year 6, Summer 1, Week 6, Lessons 3 and 4 focus on scale and how this affects drawings of 2D shapes.*

Curriculum objectives

- To solve problems involving similar shapes where the scale factor is known or can be found.
- To solve problems involving unequal sharing and grouping using knowledge of fractions and multiples.

Success criteria

- I can use scale factors to enlarge, reduce and compare shapes and other objects.

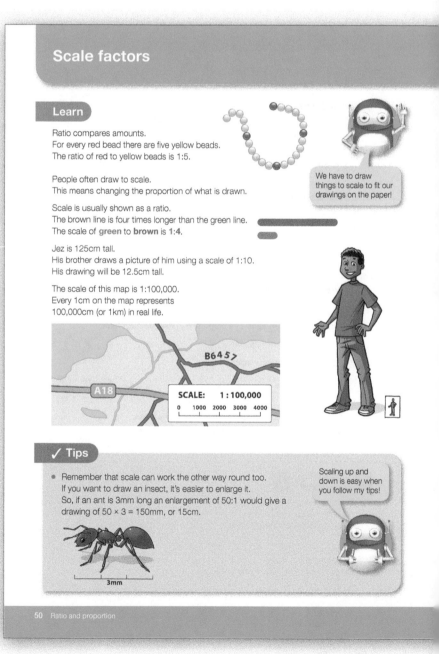

- The textbook activity encourages children to collaborate on producing enlargements using a given scale factor. This can be easily extended or adapted to actual items available to them.

- Note also that the final sentence suggests that children attempt a scale reduction. This is a good way to develop a feel for the effects of scales on the final drawings. (The *Year 6 Practice Book* activity 'Playground scale drawing' requires such thinking.)

- Remind children to check whether each question is asking for enlargement or reduction – the clue is usually in the wording.

- Also try to use the ideas in the links to *100 Maths Lessons Year 6* to practise enlarging and reducing regular polygons.

- Both of the problems can easily be adapted to create further work, either with simpler or harder numbers. Further extension can come from activities in the *Year 6 Practice Book*, or from extended investigations with real-life maps and plans.

Talk maths

You will need a sheet of paper, a pencil and a ruler. Measure these objects, and then try to draw an enlargement of each object, using a scale of 5:1. Take your drawings and explain them to a partner. To finish, try drawing your partner at a scale of 1:10.

Or just draw their hand – remember to measure it before you start.

Activities

1. **This line is 4cm long.**

   How long would these enlargements be?

   a. 2:1   b. 5:1   c. 10:1

2. **This square has a side of 1cm.**

   Copy and complete this chart for different scale enlargements.

Scale of enlargement	Side length	Area
5:1		
10:1		
25:1		

3. **A table is 1m high.**

   What height would models be if they were made to these scales?

   a. 1:2   b. 1:5   c. 1:20

Problems

Brain-teaser
A model of a house is made to a scale of 1:25. If the model is 22cm high, what height is the actual house?

Brain-buster
Anita makes a sculpture of a mouse. The actual mouse is 8cm high. The sculpture is 60cm high. What is the scale of the enlargement?

Ratio and proportion   51

---

100 Maths Lessons Year 6 links:

- Summer 1, Week 6 (pages 198–202): solve problems involving scale factors

Year 6 Practice Book links:

- (page 81): Scale up
- (page 82): Playground scale drawing

Using simple formulae

Prior learning

- Can recognise and use common formulae such as A (area of rectangle) = l (length) × w (width).

Learn

- Spend as much time as necessary revising the area of rectangles or squares. (If the children are unsure of the concept, return to counting squares to work out area.) Move on to presenting just the length and width of a rectangle or square, and ask the children to calculate area by using the formula. Move on to presenting the area and the width so that the length might be deduced. This last step is important as it involves manipulating the formula.

- Point out the units, and how when multiplying centimetres by centimetres, we get cm².

- Continue working with the formula for area, showing how equations are like scales. They must be kept balanced at all times – whatever is done to one side must be done to the other. Show how dividing each side by 'w' we can adjust the formula to have $l = A/w$.

- Move on to perimeter, in particular showing how the formula can be simplified to $P = 2(w + l)$.

- *100 Maths Lessons Year 6, Spring 2, Week 4, Lessons 1 and 2* provide further ideas and practice with simple formula.

Curriculum objectives

- To use simple formulae.
- To generate and describe linear number sequences.

Success criteria

- I can use simple formulae.
- I can identify and make linear number sequences.

Using simple formulae

Learn

If we need to calculate the perimeter or area of a regular shape, we can use a formula.

For the rectangle, we can say,
Area equals length multiplied by width.
In a formula, we can use a letter for each part.
So, **area equals length multiplied by width**
becomes $A = l \times w$.

| A = area | l = length | w = width |

In formulae, we can drop the multiplication sign. If a letter and a number, or two letters, are together, it means that they are being multiplied. The area of a rectangle is $A = lw$.
For the red rectangle, $A = 4 \times 3 = 12cm^2$

For a rectangle that is 7m long and 2m wide: $A = 7 \times 2 = 14m^2$.
For a rectangular field that is 90m long and 30m wide:
$A = 90 \times 30 = 2700m^2$.

Notice that area has square units. It is shown with this symbol ².

Perimeter is the distance around a shape.
For a rectangle $P = l + w + l + w$ or, $P = 2l + 2w$.
Remember, multiplication before addition.
For the red rectangle, $P = 2 \times 4 + 2 \times 3 = 14cm$.

You can use other formulas in the same way. Just replace the letters with the numbers.

Did you know?

Using letters to represent numbers is called *algebra*.

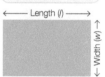
←—— Length (l) ——→ Width (w)

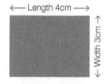
←—— Length 4cm ——→ Width 3cm

The great thing about a formula is that you can use it again and again. The letters always stay the same but they represent different numbers.

✓ Tips

- Be sure to get your units right. Formulae are used to calculate all sorts of things: distance, area, temperature, weight, volume, and so on. You must be sure to keep everything in the same units.

- If you are calculating with different units, you must convert one unit to the other first: you must multiply centimetres by centimetres, add grams to grams, and so on.

Talk maths

In addition to the textbook activity, organise group oral work sessions based around *100 Maths Lessons Year 6, Summer 2, Week 2*. This looks at the creation of linear patterns from a formula, based on the 'nth term'. Begin by providing a small selection of simple formulae, such as $n + 4$, $2n + 1$, $3n - 2$, where n is the position of each number in the sequence. For $n + 4$, the first number in the sequence is 5, the second 6, and so on.

Activities

The textbook activities focus on the given formulae for perimeter and area, and completing a chart to show how a formula generates a range of values. The *Year 6 Practice Book* provides a wide range of further practice in using formula and linear sequences.

Problems

Both of the textbook problems are tricky. It may be appropriate to work through these with the children altogether. Both questions can be used to create straight-line graphs, which provide an alternative way of looking at the data created by a formula, as well as generating new data without actually calculating it.

Talk maths

Try inventing your own simple formulae, and then test them on a partner, for example:

- Some new houses are being built. If every house has seven windows, a formula for windows is: $w = 7h$, where h = the number of houses, and w = the number of windows.
- How about cars? You need five tyres per car.
- Or currant buns? There are 24 currants per bun!

If there are six houses there must be 42 windows!

If there are 100 houses, there will be 700 windows!

Activities

1. Copy and complete the chart for perimeters and areas of rectangles.

Length	Width	Perimeter	Area
5cm	2cm		
5m	4m		
7km	1.5km		
3.2m	2.3m		

2. Copy and complete this chart using the formula: $h = 3f + 8$

h					
f	1	2	4	9	100

Problems

Brain-teaser

Beth wants to change some dollars to pounds. The formula for calculating the amount of pounds she receives is $ = 1.67 × £. £ is the amount of pounds Beth has and $ is the dollars she will receive. (1.67 is called the exchange rate.) If Beth has £200 to change, how many dollars will she receive?

Brain-buster

Here is the formula for changing degrees Fahrenheit to degrees Celsius: $C = \frac{5}{9} × (F - 32)$. Copy this chart, then use the formula to complete it.

Fahrenheit	32°	104°	212°
Celsius			

Algebra   53

100 Maths Lessons Year 6 links:

- Spring 2, Week 4 (pages 146–151): use and devise simple formulae
- Summer 2, Week 2 (pages 218–222): make and describe number sequences

Year 6 Practice Book links:

- (page 85): Express it!
- (page 90): What's next?
- (page 91): Jumping frog number patterns
- (page 92): In sequence
- (page 93): Algebra problems

Missing numbers

Prior learning

- Can recognise and use common formulae such as *A* (area of rectangle) = *l* (length) × *w* (width).
- Can calculate a simple statement where a letter represents a number.

Learn

- Present a selection of simple calculations with one number missing, like the one at the top of page 54 in the textbook. You may want to include all four operations straightaway, or just start with simpler addition and subtractions. Challenge the children to identify the missing number in each calculation.
- As described in the Tips, demonstrate how missing numbers can be negative numbers. Demonstrating this through a range of examples.

- If desired, try a small selection of simple 'missing decimal' problems.
- Using the textbook example ☐ − 9 = 23 as a basis, demonstrate how substituting a missing number with a letter can make it easier to visualise and manipulate equations. In particular, use this opportunity to focus on manipulating equations to make the letter the 'subject'.

- Note that a common error in solving equations is for children to move a letter or number to the other side. It is very important to clearly negate this perception. Use the analogy of balance scales to show that the same thing must be done to each side to keep them balanced.
- *100 Maths Lessons Year 6, Spring 2, Week 4, Lesson 4* provides further ideas and guidance.

Curriculum objectives

- To express missing number problems algebraically.

Success criteria

- I can use algebra to solve missing number problems.

Missing numbers

Learn

Sometimes equations have missing numbers.

4 + ◯ = 12

Easy! The missing number is 8. Count on from 4 to 12. Or you can take away four from both sides:

4 + ◯ − 4 = 12 − 4

◯ = 8

Because the equation must balance, you must add or subtract the same amount to each side of the equals sign.

4.3 − ◯ = 3.1

Not so easy! The missing number is 1.2. You have to add ◯ to both sides and take away 3.1 from both sides.

4.3 − ◯ + ◯ = 3.1 + ◯

4.3 = 3.1 + ◯

4.3 − 3.1 = ◯

1.2 = ◯

For harder problems, it can help to put a letter in the place of the missing number.

◯ − 9 = 23

h − 9 = 23

h − 9 **+ 9** = 23 **+ 9**

h = 32

Now try this one: 3 × ◯ = 30

And this one: 4 + 2 × ◯ = 30

✓ Tips

- Don't forget that missing numbers could be negative numbers or decimals. Can you see the answers for these two?

  ◯ + 3 = 2   3.1 + ◯ = 7.5

  (missing number = −1)   (missing number = 4.4)

Did you know?

An equation must always balance, like scales. Everything on one side of the equals sign must equal everything on the other side.

Talk maths

- The activity requires knowledge of the order of operations as children present multi-operation equations to each other.
- Try to allow plenty of opportunities for children to discuss their methods for finding the missing numbers. They will not always need to manipulate the equation to make the unknown number the subject. Many may well find themselves using logic and mental calculation skills to good effect.

Activities

- Most of the questions involve a single operation, but provide a good basis for consolidating understanding. The *Year 6 Practice Book* provides further practice to extend this learning.

Problems

- Although the two problems are challenging, they provide good support to enable children to create their own equations or formulae for solving practical problems. (Remember that many practical areas of the curriculum lend themselves to formulae.)

Talk maths

Test a partner with some missing numbers. Secretly write a calculation nice and large, and make sure that you have the right answer, for example:

$$13 - 3 \times 4 = 1$$

Cover any one of the numbers with your finger, and challenge them to calculate the hidden number.

Activities

1. **Copy these equations and insert the missing numbers.**

   a. $23 - \bigcirc = 15$ b. $\bigcirc - 7 = 11$ c. $6 + \bigcirc = 31$ d. $\bigcirc + 13 = 11$

   e. $4 \times \bigcirc = 24$ f. $49 \div \bigcirc = 7$ g. $23 + 4 \times \bigcirc = 39$ h. $\bigcirc \div 3 - 4 = 7$

2. **Copy and complete these problems.**

   a. $45 = \bigcirc - 17$ b. $23 = 11 + 2 \times \bigcirc$ c. $7.3 = \bigcirc - 2.7$ d. $6 = \bigcirc + 9$

Problems

Brain-teaser
A teacher has been collecting dinner money, but she dropped some of her own money into the bowl by accident. She knows that 25 children each gave her £1.50, and that there is £42.50 in the bowl. Write an equation for the missing money, and use it to find out how much money the teacher should take back.

Brain-buster
Some children are raising money for charity. They *each* raise £5.60. An anonymous donor says that they will match the amount raised. The total amount raised, including the donation, is £190.40. Write an equation for the money, and use it to find out how many children took part.

Algebra 55

100 Maths Lessons Year 6 links:

- Spring 2, Week 4 (pages 146–151): find unknowns that will satisfy number sentences
- Summer 2, Week 2 (pages 218–222): find the value of letters in calculations

Year 6 Practice Book links:

- (page 87): Letter time
- (page 89): Finding other unknowns

Equations with two unknowns

Prior learning

- Can recognise and use simple formulae.
- Can calculate a simple statement where a letter represents a number.

Learn

- Review the work covered so far for using letters in equations, and manipulating those equations to find the value of the missing numbers.
- Also, review the use of formulae for defining and generating linear sequences.

- Starting with a very simple equation involving the adding of two unknowns, work with the children to look at how each missing number can have multiple values, depending on the value of the other number.
- A simple activity to demonstrate this is the game 'Equation Partners'. Hand out a range of number cards (for example, 0–10). Then, write an appropriate formula on the whiteboard (for example, $x + y = 10$) and ask the children to find a partner that they can team up with to solve the equation. Can they agree on who is which unknown? This can be extended to wider number ranges and formulae with different operations.
- *100 Maths Lessons Year 6, Spring 2, Week 4, Lesson 5* and *Summer 2, Week 2, Lesson 4* both provide ideas for introducing this topic.

Curriculum objectives

- To find pairs of numbers that satisfy an equation with two unknowns.
- To enumerate possibilities of combinations of two variables.

Success criteria

- I can solve equations that have two variables.

Equations with two unknowns

Learn

Algebra uses letters as well as numbers.
Letters are sometimes referred to as **variables**, or **unknowns**.
The letters **represent** numbers.

We can solve an equation to find the value of an unknown number. $16 - a = 7$

We can move letters and numbers around, but we must keep the calculation balanced.

How to find a:

$16 - a = 7$

$16 = 7 + a$ (we added a to each side)

$9 = a$ (we took away 7 from each side)

$a = 9$ (we wrote the equation starting with 'a = ...')

> Whatever we do to one side, we must do to the other!

Equations can have more than one variable or unknown.

$x + y = 6$

The problem with equations that have two variables is that there can be more than one answer.

$x = 0, y = 6$	$x = 1, y = 5$	$x = 2, y = 4$
$x = 3, y = 3$	$x = 4, y = 2$	$x = 5, y = 1$
$x = 6, y = 0$	$x = 7, y = -1$	$x = -1, y = 7$

> It goes on forever!

Did you know?

In real life scientists find equations like this very useful.

✓ Tips

- Spend time practising balancing equations with two unknowns. It will really help you to see how they work. These equations are all the same:

$p + q = 4$ $p = 4 - q$ $q = 4 - p$

Try putting $p = 3$ and $q = 1$ into each equation to check!

> It's a balancing act!

Talk maths

- Encourage the children to work in pairs or small groups to investigate each of the equations shown in the textbook. The important thing is for the children to understand that variables are exactly that – they can vary in value.

Activities

- The tables have been designed to show children that their answer might be numbers of any sign or magnitude. This could be extended by creating additional charts for each formula and assigning a selection of decimal values to one of the variables.
- Repeating this with one variable increasing from −5 to + 5, including zero, will allow children to see the linear nature of the equations. This will be helpful to them in studying and creating line graphs.

Problems

- Children who find the problems too difficult should be directed to the suggested *Year 6 Practice Book* activities, especially the questions on 'Equations with two unknowns'.

Talk maths

Working with a partner, choose one of the equations in the box and choose a variable each. The first person calls out a number for their letter, and the second person must find the value of the second variable. Try it for all the equations.

$p = q + 4$

$a + b = 18$

$2x - y = 7$

$s + 3 = t - 4$

$23 - y = z$

Start off by using small numbers only, but have a go with bigger ones too!

Activities

1. Copy and complete the table for each equation.

a. $y = x + 2$

x	0	1	2	3	4	5	−1	−2	−3
y									

b. $s + t = 8$

s	0	2	5	6	7	8	9	10	−1
t									

c. $p = 2q - 3$

q	0	1	1.5	2	5	10	100	−1	−10
p									

Problems

Brain-teaser

Entry to the school disco is £2. The cost for disco hire is £120.
The head teacher writes a formula to calculate the money they will raise.

$m = 2t - 120$

(m = the money they will make, and t = the number of tickets they will sell)

a. How many tickets must they sell to 'break even'?

b. How many tickets must they sell to make a profit of £50?

Break even means to lose nothing and gain nothing.

Brain-buster

Rashid writes an equation. He says that there is only one possible answer for x and y if they are positive whole numbers.

$x^2 - y^2 = 32$ What are the numbers he is thinking of?

Algebra 57

100 Maths Lessons Year 6 links:

- Spring 2, Week 4 (pages 146–151): find two unknowns to satisfy number sentences
- Summer 2, Week 2 (pages 218–222): identify unknown numbers in algebraic sentences

Year 6 Practice Book links:

- (page 86): Algy and Brian
- (page 87): Letter time
- (page 88): Equations with two unknowns

Converting units

Prior learning

- Can use standard metric units.
- Can read scales on a measuring devices.
- Can carry out problem-solving tasks involving measures.

Learn

- Work with the children to refresh their knowledge of the different units used for measuring time, length, mass and capacity. There are many different aspects and variations to remember. As such, it may be better to introduce each area in separate sessions. Also, if possible, display a chart in the classroom showing the units of measurement and their abbreviations.

- Stress, in particular, that time differs from the others in that it does not use a number system involving base 10.

- Focusing initially on length, capacity and mass, review the procedures which the children should already know for multiplying and dividing by powers of 10, considering how these can be used to convert between units.

- Be careful to stress that the conversion of units of time requires varied and individual calculations. Although there are mental methods for multiplying and dividing by 60, if converting between days and hours (or years and days) long multiplication or division may be required.

- In addition, *100 Maths Lessons Year 6, Autumn 1, Week 6* provides a comprehensive range of lessons and resources that cover all areas of measurement.

Curriculum objectives

- To use, read, write and convert between standard units, converting measurements of length, mass, volume and time from a smaller unit of measure to a larger unit, and vice versa, using decimal notation to up to three decimal places.

Success criteria

- I can convert between different units of measurement, including those for length, mass, capacity and time.

Converting units

Learn

Different quantities are measured in different ways.

Measure	Units of measurement	Abbreviations	
Time (years)	1 year = 12 months, = $365\frac{1}{4}$ days 1 year = approximately 52 weeks 1 week = 7 days	years = y months = m	weeks = w days = d
Time (days)	1 day = 24 hours 1 hour = 60 minutes 1 minute = 60 seconds	hours = h minutes = m	seconds = s
Length	1 kilometre = 1000 metres 1 metre = 100 centimetres 1 centimetre = 10 millimetres	kilometres = km metres = m	centimetres = cm millimetres = mm
Mass	1 kilogram = 1000 grams	kilograms = kg	grams = g
Capacity	1 litre = 100 centilitres 1 centilitre = 10 millilitres	litre = l centilitre = cl	millilitre = ml

Look at these conversion charts.

Converting length

Conversion	Operation	Example
mm to cm	÷ 10	12mm = 1.2cm
cm to m	÷ 100	256cm = 2.56m
m to km	÷ 1000	467m = 0.467km
cm to mm	× 10	3.5cm = 35mm
m to cm	× 100	1.85m = 185cm
km to m	× 1000	4.3km = 4300m

Converting mass

Conversion	Operation	Example
grams to kg	÷ 1000	250g = 0.25kg
kg to grams	× 1000	7.3kg = 7300g

Converting time

Conversion	Operation	Example
hours to days	÷ 24	48h = 2d
mins to hours	÷ 60	240m = 4h
seconds to mins	÷ 60	600s = 10m
days to hours	× 24	2d = 48h
hours to mins	× 60	7h = 420m
mins to seconds	× 60	10m = 600s

Converting capacity

Conversion	Operation	Example
cl to litres	÷ 100	7000cl = 70l
ml to litres	÷ 1000	3000ml = 3l
litres to cl	× 100	3l = 300cl
litres to ml	× 1000	2.3l = 2300ml

- Using the textbook activity as a basis, encourage groups to practise simple mental conversions, either creating their own challenges or working from prompts or flashcards. Of particular importance is that children develop the ability to gauge the sort of questions they should ask one another. Rather than creating challenges that are obviously too difficult, encourage them to only ask questions that they know the answer to.

- Practical support can be provided by providing measuring equipment and objects, although this is also covered in 'Using measures' on pages 140–141 of this book.

Activities

- The questions in the textbook cover essential conversions, which can easily be extended or consolidated with different quantities. In addition, the *Year 6 Practice Book* provides further practice.

- *100 Maths Lessons Year 6, Spring 2, Week 5, Lessons 1 and 2* provide further support for converting units of distance, mass, capacity and time.

Problems

- The Brain-buster in particular requires children to work methodically step-by-step.

- 'Using measures' on pages 140–141 of this book provides ample practice in solving further problems using different measures.

Talk maths

Work with a partner to practise converting units in your head. Using the charts on the page opposite, ask each other questions that you know will be possible to calculate mentally.

> How many centimetres in 3m?
> How many seconds in 5 minutes?
> How many millilitres in 2.5l?

✓ Tips

- You must always make sure that you are using the right units.
- To solve problems that have different quantities that can be measured, you may have to convert the units, such as 1kg + 340g = 1340g or 1.34kg

Activities

1. **Convert these times.**
   a. 5 hours into minutes
   b. 2 hours into seconds
   c. 510 seconds into minutes
   d. 1 day into seconds

2. **Convert these lengths.**
   a. 23m into millimetres
   b. 2.4km into metres
   c. 1km into centimetres
   d. 685mm into metres

3. **Convert these weights.**
   a. 750g into kilograms
   b. 32.5kg into grams
   c. 1g into kilograms
   d. 0.35kg into grams

4. **Convert these lengths.**
   a. 2.5l into millilitres
   b. 75cl into litres
   c. 63,425ml into litres
   d. 0.25l into millilitres

Problems

Brain-teaser
The distance from Evie's front door to her school gate is exactly 242,637mm! How far is that in metres, centimetres and millimetres? (For example, 31,456mm is 31m, 45cm and 6mm.)

Brain-buster
How many seconds are there in a leap year?

100 Maths Lessons Year 6 links:

- Autumn 1, Week 6 (pages 37–41): read, write and convert units of measure
- Spring 2, Week 5 (pages 152–156): convert between standard units of measurement, using up to three decimal places

Year 6 Practice Book links:

- (page 95): Ordering lengths
- (page 98): Converting units of measures
- (page 99): Converting and ordering units
- (page 100): Happy hundred!

Using measures

Prior learning

- Can convert between units of measure.
- Can carry out problem-solving tasks involving measures.

Learn

- Review the units of measurement covered so far. If possible, look at the equipment used to measure each quantity at different sizes. Consider everyday objects and the attributes that they may have – the weight and height of people, the capacity of a mug or bathtub, the length of the school day, and so on.

- Although the textbook presents imperial units for all measures, it is probably wise to introduce these separately. In particular, conversion between miles to kilometres is still pertinent today and probably warrants more attention than the others.

- Recap the conversion of time. Although there is no imperial equivalent, the units for measures of time are idiosyncratic and children will require a lot of practice at converting between units.

Curriculum objectives

- To solve problems involving the calculation and conversion of units of measure, using decimal notation up to three decimal places where appropriate.
- To convert between miles and kilometres.

Success criteria

- I can solve problems involving different measures, including time, length, mass and capacity, using appropriate units.

Using measures

Learn

Measures you should understand include:

Measure	Used for	Units
Capacity	Volumes of containers, quantities of liquid	1cl = 10ml 1l = 100cl 1l = 1000ml 1ml = 0.1cl 1ml = 0.001l
Length	Distances, lengths and areas	1km = 1000m 1m = 100cm 1cm = 10mm 1m = 0.001km 1cm = 0.01m 1mm = 0.1cm
Mass	Weights	1kg = 1000g 1g = 0.001kg
Time	Times, timetables, speed	1d = 24h 1h = 60m 1m = 60s

How many kilometres is 10 miles?

Arranging quantities with units in powers of 10 is called **metric**. Metric systems make conversion easy by multiplying or dividing by 10, 10^2 (100) or 10^3 (1000).

Remember, you can only add like units:
1.1l + 357ml = 1.457l or 1457ml
1.45km + 257m = 1.707km or 1707m
3.23m – 122.6cm = 2.004m or 200.4cm
0.24kg + 3245g = 3.485kg or 3485g

Time is a bit different. We give answers to time in hours, minutes and seconds.
45s + 25s = 70s = 1m 10s
40m + 50m = 90m = $1\frac{1}{2}$h
3h 50m – 100m = 2h 10m

Imperial units
We sometimes use imperial units for:

lengths
1 mile = 1760 yards   1 yard = 3 feet
1 foot = 12 inches

1 inch = 2.54cm	1cm = 0.394 inches
1 mile = 1.61km	1km = 0.621 miles

weights
1 stone = 14 pounds (lb)
1lb = 16 ounces (oz)

1lb = 0.454kg	1kg = 2.205lb
1oz = 28.35g	1g = 0.035oz

capacity
1 gallon = 8 pints

1 pint = 0.57 litres	1 litre = 1.76 pints

✓ Tips

Metric or imperial? Learn both!

- We still have imperial units in daily life. In the past, everything was measured in imperial units. These are sometimes used in other countries, but in most of the world metric units are used. The key facts in the box above are worth learning by heart so that you can do quick mental conversions.

- Arrange children in small groups. Provide each group with a selection of objects that vary in capacity, weight or length (some will lend themselves to both). Using the chart on page 61 of the textbook as a guide, challenge the children to plan how to measure attributes of the different objects. In particular, discuss how children can estimate the different measures.

Activities

- Ask the children to use the conversion charts in the textbook to calculate imperial equivalents of their actual measurements. (Alternatively, provide a list of measurements for them to convert.)
- The *Year 6 Practice Book* provides ample further practice, especially in estimating. This is an essential skill as it helps the children to develop a feel for the meaning of units of measurement.

Problems

- The problems are tricky, but might prompt children to create their own variations to challenge each other with. In addition, *100 Maths Lessons Year 6* provides many other problems in the context of measurement.

Talk maths

You will need a tape measure, some scales and a measuring jug.

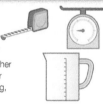

Work with a partner to measure a range of objects. Discuss whether you will measure the length, weight or capacity of each object (for some objects you can measure more than one). Before measuring, make some estimates and write these down.

Activities

1. Now find the actual measures of all your objects, using the appropriate equipment. With practice, you will find that your estimates become better and better.

Object	Measure	Estimate	Actual	Imperial units
Mug	Capacity	260ml	215ml	
Pencil	Length	12cm	10.7cm	
Banana	Weight	90g	130g	

Now try to calculate the imperial units for each object.

Problems

Brain-teaser

If it takes 25 seconds to fill a 1 litre jug from a tap, how long will it take to fill three 250ml cups from the same tap? (You can assume that there is no time lost when changing cups.)

The 1 litre jug weighs 1.79kg when full of water. What is the weight of the empty jug?
The 250ml cup weighs 483g when full of water. What is the weight of the empty cup?

Brain-buster

Brian's grandad says that when he was at school he was 4 feet 11 inches tall and weighed 6 stone, 3 pounds. Convert his height and weight to metric units.
If Brian's grandad is 80 on his next birthday, calculate how many days he has lived. (There will have been 20 leap years in his life so far.) How many hours has he lived? How many minutes is this?

Did you know?

1ml of water weighs 1g. 1l of water weighs 1kg.

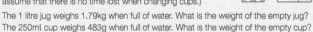

---

100 Maths Lessons Year 6 links:

- Autumn 1, Week 6 (pages 37–41): solve problems using units of measure
- Spring 2, Week 5 (pages 152–156): solve problems involving units of measure up to three decimal places
- Summer 2, Week 5 (pages 234–238): solve problems involving measures

Year 6 Practice Book links:

- (page 94): Estimating length
- (page 96): Estimating mass
- (page 97): Liquid measures
- (page 101): How long?
- (page 102): Moon traveller
- (page 103): Converting miles to kilometres and vice versa

Perimeter and area

Prior learning

- Can calculate the perimeter of a rectangle and related shapes.
- Can calculate the area of scale drawings of rectangles using given measurements.

Learn

- Review the children's knowledge of formulae. Ideally, they will already have encountered these in studying basic algebra.
- Work through a range of examples of rectangles and squares drawn on a square grid. Use counting methods as well as calculation to work out simple perimeters and areas.
- Using the examples Shape 1 and Shape 2 in the textbook as a starting point, look at a range of pairs of rectangles (including squares) to demonstrate how shapes with the same areas can have different perimeters and vice versa.

- *100 Maths Lessons Year 6, Spring 1, Week 6, Lesson 1* provides structured guidance around the interactive teaching resource 'Squared paper' on the accompanying CD-ROM.
- If appropriate, progress to looking at composite shapes, where two or more rectangles are joined together, or rectangles that have rectangular holes in them. Ask the children to consider the difficulties in calculating area and perimeter. Children should be

particularly aware of dealing with the perimeters of those shapes, where joined edges must be discarded from calculations. A simple tip is that the perimeter is the distance that they would travel if they (or an ant for small shapes!) were to walk around the edge.

Curriculum objectives

- To recognise that shapes with the same areas can have different perimeters and vice versa.
- To recognise when it is possible to use formulae for area and volume of shapes.

Success criteria

- I can calculate the perimeter and area of regular shapes and shapes made from rectangles.

Perimeter and area

Learn

Perimeter is the distance around the outside of a shape. All rectangles have a width and a height. Perimeter can be calculated with a formula:
$P = 2l + 2w$ Or we can say $P = 2(l + w)$.

Area is measured in square units. For rectangles we multiply the length by the width: $A = lw$
For this rectangle, $P = 2(3 + 2) = 10\text{cm}$, and $A = 3 \times 2 = 6\text{cm}^2$.

The perimeter of a square is four times the length of a side: $P = 4s$.
The area of a square is side length times side length: $A = s^2$.
The perimeter of this square is: $P = 4 \times 1.5 = 6\text{cm}$
The area of this square is: $A = 1.5 \times 1.5 = 2.25\text{cm}^2$

Shapes that have the same perimeter do not necessarily have the same area as each other.

Shape 1
5cm

Perimeter = 2(5 + 1) = 12cm
Area = 5 × 1 = 5cm²

Shape 2
4cm

Perimeter = 2(4 + 2) = 12cm
Area = 4 × 2 = 8cm²

Remember to do any calculations in brackets first.

✓ Tips

Here's how to get your perimeters and areas right.

- Watch out for silly mistakes when you find the perimeters and areas of composite shapes. This shape has a square with a hole in it, joined to a rectangle. There are two mistakes that people often make.
  1. They include the perimeter where the shapes are joined. *Don't!*
  2. They forget to take away the area of the hole. *Do!*

- It may be more practical to set the activity as homework or, if not, as a rotation for small groups. An excellent extension is to have children, in pairs or small groups, to prepare their charts in advance, visualising and deciding on what they are going to measure, and then estimating lengths, perimeters and areas, and then making measurements and comparing.

- The textbook questions can be extended by challenging children to create their own shapes, including composite shapes and those with rectangular or square sections that have been removed.

- A useful tip for finding the perimeters of composite shapes is to draw around the actual perimeter in colour, and then to write the length of each section.

- Encourage the children to draw the shapes described before attempting any calculation, and to consider the steps involved in each calculation, laying them out methodically and neatly.

- Note that the suggested *Year 6 Practice Book* activities tend to focus on area, but these can easily be adjusted to incorporate the calculation of perimeter too.

Talk maths

You will need a tape measure. Investigate the perimeter and area of different rectangles and squares around your school. Measure their lengths and widths then use formulae to calculate their areas and perimeters. Explain anything you discover.

Object	Shape	Dimensions	Perimeter	Area
Table	Square	$s = 80cm$	320cm	6400cm²
Television	Rectangle	$l = 125cm, w = 75cm$	400cm	9375cm²
Door				

Activities

1. Accurately copy these shapes and then calculate their perimeter and area.

a.

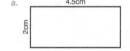
4.5cm / 2cm

b.

1.5cm

Did you know?

The plural of formula is formulae.

2. Accurately copy these shapes and then calculate their perimeter and area.

a.

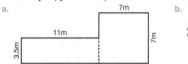
7m / 11m / 7m / 3.5m

b.

1m / 1m / 3.5m / 4.5m / 2m

Problems

Brain-teaser
Ben's rectangular garden is 5m long and has a total perimeter of 16m. What is its area?

Brain-buster
Some square wall tiles are 20cm wide. How many tiles would be needed to cover a wall 3m high and 2.4m long?

100 Maths Lessons Year 6 links:

- Spring 1, Week 6 (pages 118–122): work with perimeter and area

Year 6 Practice Book links:

- (page 104): Same area, different perimeter
- (page 105): All square
- (page 106): Areas of rooms

Calculating area

Prior learning

- Can calculate the area of scale drawings of rectangles using given measurements.
- Can convert between different units of length.

Learn

- Review methods that the children already know for calculating areas, from counting squares to using formulae, covering both rectangles and squares.
- Remind the children of the relationships between squared units, pointing out that $1m^2 = 10,000cm^2$.
- Preferably in separate sessions, introduce and explain the formulae for calculating the areas of triangles and parallelograms. For triangles, start with right-angled triangles – showing that they are half of a rectangle or a square helps the formula make sense. For irregular triangles, it is sufficient for children to simply apply the formula. (Counting squares can help with verification, but as well as whole squares, there will often be small parts of squares.)

- The formula for a parallelogram is easier to prove by cutting one end off and moving it to the other side to convert it to a rectangle.
- *100 Maths Lessons Year 6, Spring 1, Week 6, Lesson 2* and *Spring 2, Week 5, Lesson 5* provide ideas and resources for practising the calculation of areas of parallelograms and triangles.

Curriculum objectives

- To calculate the area of parallelograms and triangles.
- To recognise when it is possible to use formulae for area and volume of shapes.

Success criteria

- I can use formulae to calculate the areas of squares, rectangles, triangles and parallelograms.

Calculating area

Learn

Area is measured in **square units**. We can count squares for simple areas. This rectangle has an area of 6cm²

We can use formulae for many shapes. Formulae help us to find the areas of larger or more complex shapes. For rectangles we multiply the length by the width: $A = lw$
The formula for the area of a square is $A = s^2$

The formula for the area of a triangle can be found with the formula:
$A = \frac{1}{2}bh$
b = the length of the base
h = the *perpendicular* height
Finding h can be tricky.

It is easier for right-angled triangles!
$A = \frac{1}{2} \times 3 \times 4 = 6cm^2$

The areas of parallelograms are easy to find as long as you know the *perpendicular* height.
$A = hw$
Can you see why?
Imagine you had a pair of scissors and could move the dotted-line triangle.

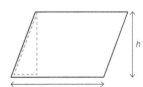

✓ Tips

- Think of a right-angled triangle as half of a rectangle. It makes the formula obvious!

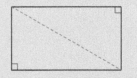

- The focus of the textbook activity is on using correct terms within each of the formulae for the areas of rectangles, squares, triangles or parallelograms. Encourage the children to start by drawing the shapes, and then move on to mental challenges.

- More confident learners might be challenged to calculate the areas of rectangles that have smaller shapes cut out of them.

Activities

- The *Year 6 Practice Book* provides a range of further areas to be found. Used alongside the textbook, this should provide ample material to assess children's understanding.

Problems

- The Brain-teaser can be simplified by altering the dimensions of the room, or extended to suggest the carpeting of a whole house. This can be extended to considering decorating costs for a whole home.

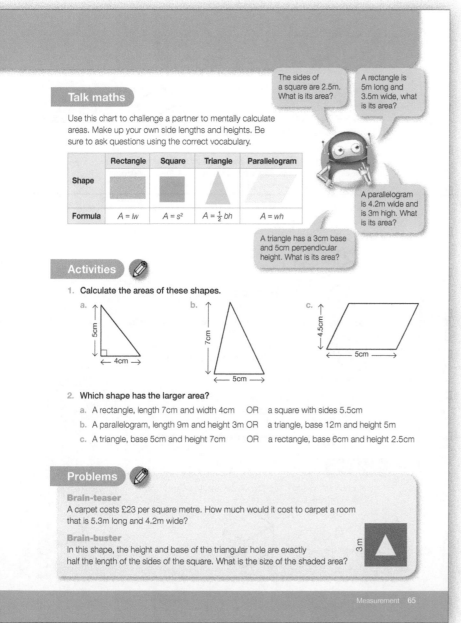

Talk maths

Use this chart to challenge a partner to mentally calculate areas. Make up your own side lengths and heights. Be sure to ask questions using the correct vocabulary.

	Rectangle	Square	Triangle	Parallelogram
Shape				
Formula	$A = lw$	$A = s^2$	$A = \frac{1}{2}bh$	$A = wh$

The sides of a square are 2.5m. What is its area?

A rectangle is 5m long and 3.5m wide, what is its area?

A parallelogram is 4.2m wide and is 3m high. What is its area?

A triangle has a 3cm base and 5cm perpendicular height. What is its area?

Activities

1. Calculate the areas of these shapes.

   a. 5cm, 4cm

   b. 7cm, 5cm

   c. 4.5cm, 5cm

2. Which shape has the larger area?

   a. A rectangle, length 7cm and width 4cm   OR   a square with sides 5.5cm
   b. A parallelogram, length 9m and height 3m OR   a triangle, base 12m and height 5m
   c. A triangle, base 5cm and height 7cm   OR   a rectangle, base 6cm and height 2.5cm

Problems

Brain-teaser
A carpet costs £23 per square metre. How much would it cost to carpet a room that is 5.3m long and 4.2m wide?

Brain-buster
In this shape, the height and base of the triangular hole are exactly half the length of the sides of the square. What is the size of the shaded area?

3m

Measurement   65

100 Maths Lessons Year 6 links:

- Spring 1, Week 6 (pages 118–122): calculate the area of parallelograms and triangles
- Spring 2, Week 5 (pages 152–156): calculate the area of parallelograms and triangles

Year 6 Practice Book links:

- (page 107): Areas of parallelograms and triangles

Calculating volume

Prior learning

- Can calculate the area of rectangles using given measurements.
- Can convert between different metric units of measure.

Learn

- Demonstrate to the children how to draw isometric cubes and cuboids. Allow the children to practise drawing a range of shapes (ideally on isometric paper). While doing so, model the key vocabulary and stress the possible units and the nature of cubed units.
- Using wooden or plastic 1cm cubes, consider the volume of single cubes and cubes and cuboids made up of several 1cm cubes. Then revisit square and cube numbers, saying single digits, and asking the children to give the squares and cubes of it. If desired, recap powers of 10 and practise reading numbers up to 10,000,000. (One cubic metre is one million cubic centimetres, and one billion cubic millimetres!)

- Bring a selection of different-sized cardboard boxes into school. If possible, write the length of each side on the boxes themselves, as well as the areas of the faces. Work with the children to calculate the volume of each box. If this is impractical, *100 Maths Lessons Year 6, Spring 1, Week 6, Lessons 4 and 5* provide alternative guidance.

- If desired, take the work a stage further by considering how many identical smaller boxes might fit in to a larger box. Ensure that children appreciate the importance of keeping units the same and for accurate calculation of cubed units.

Curriculum objectives

- To recognise when it is possible to use formulae for area and volume of shapes.
- To calculate, estimate and compare volume of cubes and cuboids using standard units, including cubic centimetres (cm³) and cubic metres (m³), and extending to other units.

Success criteria

- I can use formulae to calculate the volume of cubes and cuboids.

Calculating volume

Learn

3D shapes have faces, edges and vertices. A corner is a **vertex**. The plural is **vertices**.

edge
face
vertex

Sometimes *faces* are called *sides*.

Volume is the amount of space an object takes up. Volume isn't quite the same as capacity. We measure capacity in litres, centilitres or millilitres; we measure volume in cubic lengths: km³, m³, cm³, mm³.

A cubic centimetre is a cube that has length, width and height all equal to 1cm.

1cm
1cm   1cm

2cm
2cm   2cm

A cube that has sides of length 2cm has a volume of 8cm³. A cube is a 3D shape that has all sides the same length.

You need to be careful with units.
1cm³ = 10mm × 10mm × 10mm = 1000mm³
1m³ = 100cm × 100cm × 100cm = 1,000,000cm³

We can use formulae for calculating the volumes of cubes and cuboids.

s
s   s

Volume of cube = s³ (s = length of one side)
A cube with sides of 3cm has a volume of
3cm × 3cm × 3cm = 27cm³.

Volume of cuboid = *whl* (*w* = width, *h* = height, *l* = length)
A cuboid with width 4cm, height 2cm and length 5cm has a volume of 4cm × 2cm × 5cm = 40cm³.

h
w   l

A cuboid has rectangular faces, but they are not all the same size.

✓ Tips

- Drawing shapes to look 3D is called *isometric drawing*. The trick is to draw one end face, and then draw the edges as parallel lines.

Here's my advice for perfecting your 3D drawings...

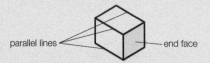

parallel lines ← ─── → end face

Talk maths

- The textbook activity is a combination of estimation and calculation skills. Working in pairs, children are asked to estimate the volume of larger objects, such as rooms. Ideally, they should stick to things that are cuboids (hence, rooms), although this can be simplified to looking at boxes that have not had dimensions marked on them.

- Children who find this too difficult might be given equipment such as interlocking cubes that they can use to make cubes and cuboids.

Activities

- For questions 1 and 2 in the textbook, the learning can be extended by asking children to draw all shapes and calculate all volumes. The *Year 6 Practice Book* provides extensive further practice in calculating volume.

- Be aware that some children can muddle volume and capacity. You may prefer to address this explicitly here, pointing out that one millilitre is equal to one cubic centimetre, but that they measure different quantities.

Problems

- Both problems can be extended by providing variations in different dimensions, and challenging children to provide answers in mm^3, cm^3 and m^3.

Talk maths

Work with a partner to discuss how you might estimate the volume of large objects. For example in a bathroom you could estimate that the room is 3m high, 4m long and 2m wide. So the volume of the bathroom could be estimated as $24m^3$.

What about the volume of a bath?

Or even the volume of your house?

Activities

1. **Use a pencil and ruler to draw each of these shapes.**
   a. A cube with side length 3cm   b. A cuboid, length 5cm, height 2cm, width 4cm

2. **Calculate the volume of these shapes.**
   a. Cube, side 6cm   b. Cuboid, l = 6m, w = 4m, h = 1.5m
   c. Cube, side 10m   d. Cuboid, l = 9cm, w = 5cm, h = 2cm
   e. Cube, side 12mm   f. Cuboid, l = 60mm, w = 30mm, h = 5mm

3. **How many cubic millimetres are there in $1m^3$?**

Problems

Brain-teaser
A cube-shaped packing crate is 0.5m long on each side. Calculate its volume.

Brain-buster
A wooden cuboid has a square-shaped hole cut right through its middle. What is the volume of the remaining wood?

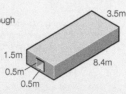

3.5m
1.5m
8.4m
0.5m
0.5m

---

100 Maths Lessons Year 6 links:

- Spring 1, Week 6 (pages 118–122): calculate the volume of cubes and cuboids

Year 6 Practice Book links:

- (page 108–109): Volumes of cubes and cuboids

Angles

Prior learning

- Can use a protractor.
- Can calculate angles.

Learn

- Recap key angles and terminology with the children. Using a teaching clock is a good way to reinforce angles as well as reminding the children that angle is a measure of turn.
- Using a real or digital protractor, remind children how to correctly measure angles. Model which scale to use, depending on which direction the angle is being read.

- Cover the key facts as shown in the textbook, covering angles up to 90° and 180°, vertically opposite and alternate angles.
- If appropriate, also cover angles in a complete rotation. Although 360° protractors have their uses, encourage children to only use 180° protractors and to measure reflex angles by using simple maths facts and knowledge of the number of degrees in a complete turn.
- *100 Maths Lessons Year 6, Autumn 1, Week 5, Lessons 2–4 provide further guidance and activities.*

Curriculum objectives

- To recognise angles where they meet at a point, are on a straight line, or are vertically opposite, and find missing angles.

Success criteria

- I can identify, measure, construct and use different angles.
- I can calculate missing angles.

Angles

Learn

We measure angles with a protractor.

A right angle is 90°. A straight line is 180°.	Acute angles are between 0° and 90°. Obtuse angles are between 90° and 180°.
90° 180°	obtuse 130° acute 50°

Angles greater than 180° are called *reflex* angles.	A complete turn is 360°.
200° reflex	360°

Angles that form a right angle add up to 90°.	Angles on a straight line add up to 180°.
65° 25°	118° 62°
Vertically opposite angles are equal.	Similar angles on parallel lines are equal.
30° 30°	120° 60° 60° 120° 120° 60° 60° 120°

✓ Tips

- Once you understand how angles work, identifying and constructing shapes is easy!
  - The three angles of a triangle add up to 180°.
  - Each angle of an equilateral triangle = 60°.
  - The four angles of a quadrilateral add up to 360°.
  - Each angle of a square and rectangle = 90°.

When drawing shapes, let's talk angles.

- As well as the presentation described in the textbook, the children could also prepare presentations about other pertinent angle topics, such as proving the angles of a triangle sum to 180° or add up 360° quadrilateral. In each case, cut off the corners, and then join them together to make either a straight line (triangle) or a complete turn (quadrilateral).

- While the children prepare their presentations, encourage them to use terminology correctly. As part of the presentation, they should provide a demonstration of how to use a protractor correctly, and what common errors to avoid when measuring angles.

Activities

- The questions can easily be extended by listing other angles for the children to measure and construct.

- *100 Maths Lessons Year 6, Summer 2, Week 4, Lesson 5* and the *Year 6 Practice Book* provide further practice materials. Be sure to check that all children can use rulers and protractors proficiently.

Problems

- Encourage the children to construct the requested lines and shape carefully and accurately.

- The solution to the Brain-buster activity is covered in 'Properties of 2D shapes' on pages 70–71 of the textbook, so do allow children the freedom to get stuck on this problem.

Talk maths

You will need a paper, a pencil, a ruler and a protractor.

Prepare a presentation that will explain the different types of angle from page 68.

Activities

1. Use a protractor to draw these angles, and then name them.

   a. 90°   b. 23°   c. 167°

2. Write down the value of each angle marked with a letter.

   a.

   b.

   c.

Problems

Brain-teaser
Two parallel lines are intersected by another line. There are eight different angles.

Copy and complete the diagram, adding the size of every angle.

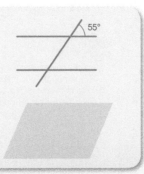

Brain-buster
This shape is a parallelogram – its opposite sides are parallel. How can you use it to prove that the four angles of a quadrilateral add up to 360°?

100 Maths Lessons Year 6 links:

- Autumn 1, Week 5 (pages 32–36): measure and calculate angles

- Summer 2, Week 4 (pages 228–233): estimate, measure and calculate angles

Year 6 Practice Book links:

- (page 112): Measuring and drawing angles

- (page 113): Angle facts

Properties of 2D shapes

Prior learning

- Can draw and measure angles using a protractor.
- Can recognise the properties of 2D shapes.

Learn

- In one or separate sessions as desired, recap the different types of triangles and quadrilaterals.
- If possible, provide a display showing images, names and properties of 2D shapes. Ideally, the names and properties could be on detachable labels that can be removed and children challenged regularly to match correctly. Creating this exercise using annotated pieces of paper is also useful.

- In addition, demonstrate to the children how quadrilaterals can be classified according to yes/no criteria in a decision tree. Prompts include: *Are all sides equal? Are opposite angles equal? Are opposite sides parallel?* If space permits, provide children with cut-out and labelled shapes and ask them to organise them into groups that share a certain property.

- Spend time practising identifying regular and irregular polygons, including accurate spelling of shape names and knowledge of the sum of the internal angles.
- Using drawn or digital shapes, investigate why the internal angles of both irregular and regular shapes with the same numbers of sides always total the same amount. (Squashing a rectangle to become a parallelogram to show this.)

Curriculum objectives

- To compare and classify geometric shapes based on their properties and sizes and find unknown angles in any triangles, quadrilaterals, and regular polygons.

Success criteria

- I can identify 2D shapes from their properties.

Properties of 2D shapes

Learn

There are the different types of triangles. Each has different properties.

Equilateral	Isosceles	Right-angled	Scalene
All sides equal All angles 60°	Two sides equal Two angles equal	One angle equals 90°	All sides different All angles different

Quadrilaterals also have different properties.

Square	Rectangle	Rhombus	Parallelogram	Kite	Trapezium
All sides equal. All angles 90°	Opposite sides equal All angles 90°	All sides equal Opposite angles equal	Opposite sides equal and parallel Opposite angles equal	Adjacent sides equal	Only one pair of parallel sides

We say that different 2D polygons have different properties. The sum of internal angles is the same for each shape, whether irregular or regular.

> Internal angles is a posh name for angles at the corners.

Triangle	Quadrilateral	Pentagon	Hexagon	Heptagon	Octagon
3 sides	4 sides	5 sides	6 sides	7 sides	8 sides
Angles add to 180°	Angles add to 360°	Angles add to 540°	Angles add to 720°	Angles add to 900°	Angles add to 1080°

✓ Tips

Think triangles!

- Take any regular shape and divide it into equal triangles. The total of the angles at the centre must be 360°, so we can work out each angle around the centre by dividing 360° by the number of triangles. The angles of a triangle all add to 180°, so we can work out the other angles of the triangle, and then the angles at each corner of the shape. Look at this regular pentagon. Can you see why each internal angle is 108°?

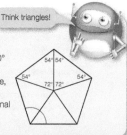

Talk maths

- *100 Maths Lessons Year 6, Autumn 2, Week 5, Lesson 1* provides a more detailed approach to this task.
- More confident learners could be encouraged to investigate the relationship between the number of sides of regular polygons and the size of each of their angles, linking this to work with algebra and formulae.

Activities

- Provide a selection of card or plastic templates of regular and irregular shapes to extend practice in naming and identifying properties.
- *100 Maths Lessons Year 6, Summer 2, Week 4* provides additional reinforcement work, and the *Year 6 Practice Book* has further shape construction work.

Problems

- Encourage children to examine, draw and cut up the shapes mentioned in the problems. Providing card or plastic templates to aid rapid construction will help.
- *100 Maths Lessons Year 6, Autumn 2, Week 5, Lesson 2* and *Summer 2, Week 4, Lesson 1* provide more detailed investigations of quadrilaterals and triangles.

Talk maths

You will need a protractor, a ruler, a pencil and paper.

Work with partner to investigate the angles inside the six regular shapes.

Read though the information and tips on the previous page, and discuss how you will approach your investigation.

$6 \times 60° = 360°$
Internal angle:
$60° + 60° = 120°$

Did you know?

A 12-sided shape is called a dodecagon!

Activities

1. What is the difference between a regular and an irregular polygon?

2. Write the names of these polygons, and say if each is regular or irregular.

a.

b.

c.

d.

e.

f.

Problems

Brain-teaser
How can you prove that a square is made of four identical right-angled triangles?

Brain-buster
Jade says that a regular hexagon is made of six equilateral triangles.
Explain whether she is right or wrong, and why.

Geometry 71

100 Maths Lessons Year 6 links:

- Autumn 2, Week 5 (pages 72–76): draw, identify, compare and classify 2D shapes
- Summer 2, Week 4 (pages 228–233): identify and use properties of shapes

Year 6 Practice Book links:

- (page 114): Identifying 2D shapes

Drawing 2D shapes

Prior learning

- Can identify various polygons and know some of their properties.

Learn

- Using drawn or digital shapes, review all the regular shapes covered so far, covering vocabulary and key properties of each shape. Next, draw or show a square, a regular hexagon and a regular octagon. Divide each shape into identical triangles that meet at the centre of each shape. Using knowledge of angles at a point and in an isosceles triangle, prove the size of the internal angles of each shape.

- Show also how any regular polygon can be inscribed (drawn) within a circle, with each angle touching the circumference providing its centre is also the centre of the circle.

- Demonstrate how to create a triangle from three given facts (two sides and one angle, or two angles and one side). Then work with the children to construct a range of such triangles. (If desired, demonstrate the link between geometry and algebra, naming the angles a, b and c.)

- Point out that, since all regular polygons are made up of a number of identical isosceles triangles, if we know the side length of any regular polygon, then we can draw it accurately. (If necessary, use the explanation above to demonstrate how to calculate the angles of each of the isosceles triangles in the regular polygon.)

Curriculum objectives

- To draw 2D shapes using given dimensions and angles.

Success criteria

- I can identify 2D shapes from their properties.

Drawing 2D shapes

Learn

A polygon is any straight-sided 2D shape. These are regular polygons. For each shape the internal angles are the same size and the sides are the same length.

Triangle	Quadrilateral	Pentagon	Hexagon	Heptagon	Octagon
3 sides	4 sides	5 sides	6 sides	7 sides	8 sides
Angles add to 180°	Angles add to 360°	Angles add to 540°	Angles add to 720°	Angles add to 900°	Angles add to 1080°

To draw any triangle you need to know two angle sizes and one side length. Or two side lengths and one angle.

To draw a square, rectangle, rhombus or parallelogram you only need to know one angle size and two lengths.

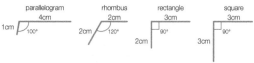

There is a link between geometry and algebra, because we can write formulae for different shapes. If the angles of a triangle are a, b and c, we can say $a + b + c = 180°$.

> Can you think of formulae for the angles in other regular polygons?

✓ Tips

- You need to know how to draw regular 2D shapes. Remember that all regular pentagons (five sides), hexagons (six sides), heptagons (seven sides) and octagons (eight sides) are all made of identical triangles.

- Also remember that all the angles at the centre add up to 360°.

- Encourage the children to work in pairs to draw and discuss a wide range of triangles, especially isosceles triangles. After plenty of practice, move on to how they can use their knowledge to construct regular polygons.

- To aid discussions, display a chart in the classroom showing the properties of all regular polygons. This should include the shape names, the number of sides and the size of the angles.

- If children have experience of drawing triangles, the first question will present little difficulty. The challenge can be easily extended by asking them to drawing other triangles and quadrilaterals, moving on to other polygons. The *Year 6 Practice Book* contains further questions.

- Those who struggle with these might consolidate their understanding of regular polygon facts through further practice at drawing them.

Talk maths

Play this game with a partner. You will need pencils, paper, a ruler and a protractor.

Take turns to challenge each other to draw shapes, giving verbal instructions.

Remember to give enough information, for example: *Draw an isosceles triangle with a base of 6cm and two angles of 65°.*

Draw a rhombus with sides of 5cm, and two angles of 125°.

Draw a regular hexagon with sides of 4cm.

Activities

1. Draw an equilateral triangle with each side 4cm.

2. Draw a rhombus, with sides 3cm and the larger angle = 120°.

3. Explain how you would construct a regular octagon.

Problems

Brain-teaser
The five internal angles of a regular pentagon add up to 540°. A ten-sided shape is called a decagon. What will the internal angles of a regular decagon add up to? Show your working out.

Brain-buster
Write a formula for calculating the size of each angle in a regular polygon, where a = the angle and n = the number of sides.

100 Maths Lessons Year 6 links:

- Autumn 2, Week 5 (pages 72–76): draw 2D shapes from dimensions
- Summer 2, Week 4 (pages 228–233): identify and use the properties of 2D shapes

Year 6 Practice Book links:

- (page 115): 2D shape problems

3D shapes

Prior learning

- Can recognise the properties of 2D shapes.
- Can recognise 3D shapes.

Learn

- If possible, display a large chart showing the common 3D shapes and their properties. Be sure to model terminology, and consider both common and different properties of the shapes. Point out the differences between the shapes that have all flat faces and those that have at least one curved face, for example cone, cylinder and sphere. If children can see how these shapes have fewer faces, edges and vertices, it can help secure their understanding of these terms.

- *100 Maths Lessons Year 6, Autumn 2, Week 5* has lessons and ideas for consolidating children's knowledge of 3D shapes.

- Discuss the occurrence of 3D shapes in real life and why they might occur naturally. What properties of certain shapes make them useful for certain real-life situations? For example, cuboid cereal boxes can be packed in a lorry without wasting space whereas a curved bowl means that cornflakes don't get stuck in a corner.

- With the chart still displayed, distribute plastic or wooden shapes and have children identify and discuss their features. (Keep the shapes in a feelie bag, ideally under a display of the shapes, for children to access at other times.)

- Introduce nets, using construction equipment. If this is not possible, make a selection of cubes and cuboids in advance so that the children can see how different nets can create the same shape.

- Move on to showing how to identify edges in a net that will join together. Demonstrate the use of tabs in making shapes. Point out how curved faces and edges make it difficult to draw nets for spheres and cones.

Curriculum objectives

- To recognise, describe and build simple 3D shapes, including making nets.

Success criteria

- I can identify and describe 3D shapes and make their nets.

3D shapes

Learn

3D shapes have different properties which identify them.

Shape	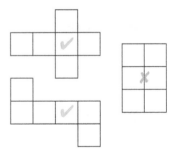						
Name	Cube	Cuboid	Cone	Sphere	Cylinder	Triangular prism	Square-based pyramid
Faces	6	6	2	1	3	5	5
Edges	12	12	1	0	2	9	8
Vertices	8	8	0	0	0	6	5

Some 3D shapes can be represented by **nets**. A net is a 2D drawing of the shape as if it has been taken apart, or unfolded. The skill is in thinking about which edges meet.

There is more than one way to make a net, and plenty of ways to get it wrong! Look at these cube nets.

You cannot make accurate nets for spheres or cones because they have curved faces. Try peeling an orange and laying it flat – it cannot be done accurately.

That is why maps of the world are tricky to make.

✓ Tips

- When looking at, or drawing, nets, use marks to help you see if the sides match up correctly. Use tabs to help you to join the faces together.

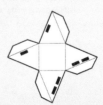

Mark it. Tab it. Net it!

Provide squared paper and drawing equipment. (It is okay to provide shapes for the children to draw around if that will help them to create nets.) Allow children time to explore a range of nets, focusing on cubes and cuboids and progressing to prisms and pyramids if desired. Children who need further support might use construction equipment to create nets.

- Ideally, children will create a set of 'rules' that they can explain to others to demonstrate how nets work.

Activities

- The textbook focuses on constructing nets. *100 Maths Lessons Year 6, Summer 2, Week 4, Lessons 3 and 4* provide further ideas and support for both identifying and creating shapes as does the *Year 6 Practice Book*.

Problems

- Support the children when completing the Brain-teaser by asking them to first create the net. The Brain-buster provides an opportunity for children to investigate the most efficient way to create a net.

Talk maths

You will need squared paper, a ruler and a pencil.
Work with a partner to construct three cuboids of different sizes, making nets for each one. When you have finished, discuss the steps you took to make a successful net, then explain these instructions to someone else and see if they can make a net using your advice.

Remember, you only need one tab to join two faces.

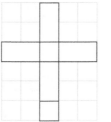

Activities

1. Redraw these nets, adding tabs so that the faces would join together.

a. Pyramid   **b.** Prism   **c.** Cuboid

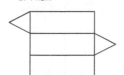

2. Draw a net for a cube with 2cm edges. Include tabs to join the faces together.

Problems

Brain-teaser
Write instructions for how to make a paper model of a square-based pyramid.

Brain-buster
Ryan has a sheet of paper 30cm long and 20cm wide.
a. What is the largest cuboid he can make from it?
b. How much paper will be wasted (in cm²)?
c. What will be the volume of the cuboid?

Geometry   75

100 Maths Lessons Year 6 links:

- Autumn 2, Week 5 (pages 72–76): identify, compare and classify 3D shapes
- Summer 2, Week 4 (pages 228–233): identify and use properties of shapes

Year 6 Practice Book links:

- (page 116): In the net
- (page 117): 3D shape sorting

Circles

Prior learning

- Can recognise the properties of 2D shapes.
- Can use a ruler to draw and measure lines.

Learn

- Display a selection of circles and discuss their features. Try to elicit that they have no angles, only one side, and a centre point that is the same distance from every point on the side.
- Demonstrate how a circle can be drawn around any regular polygon. The centre of the circle and the regular polygon are at the same point, and the vertices of the polygon are all on the circle's circumference.
- Introduce the children to the key circle vocabulary. Ask them to use pairs of compasses to draw three or four different circles and label the parts.

- Demonstrate how to draw a circle by using two pencils and a piece of string: tie the pencils at each end of the string, use one as a centre point and turn the other to draw a circle.
- *100 Maths Lessons Year 6, Autumn 1, Week 5, Lessons 1 and 5* provide further teaching guidance.

Talk maths

- Ask the children to work in pairs to create a chart like that in the textbook, investigating a range of circular objects to consolidate their familiarity with key vocabulary. If necessary, remind them of how string can be wrapped around the circumference and then measured against a ruler.

Curriculum objectives

- To illustrate and name parts of circles, including radius, diameter and circumference and know that the diameter is twice the radius.

Success criteria

- I can identify and draw the parts of a circle.

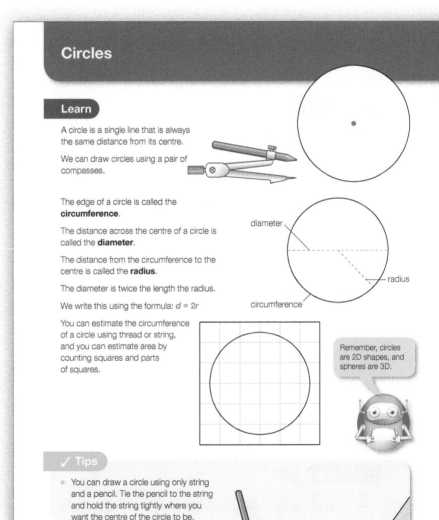

Circles

Learn

A circle is a single line that is always the same distance from its centre.

We can draw circles using a pair of compasses.

The edge of a circle is called the **circumference**.

The distance across the centre of a circle is called the **diameter**.

The distance from the circumference to the centre is called the **radius**.

The diameter is twice the length the radius.

We write this using the formula: $d = 2r$

You can estimate the circumference of a circle using thread or string, and you can estimate area by counting squares and parts of squares.

diameter

radius

circumference

Remember, circles are 2D shapes, and spheres are 3D.

✓ Tips

- You can draw a circle using only string and a pencil. Tie the pencil to the string and hold the string tightly where you want the centre of the circle to be.

Try drawing different-sized circles just using string.

76 Geometry

- More confident learners might start to consider a relationship between radius and circumference. A great activity for strengthening understanding is to use a trundle wheel. This has a wheel on a stick, which is pushed along to measure distances. The circumference of the wheel is exactly 1m. This can be used for various school-based measuring projects.

Activities

- The textbook checks understanding of the terms. In addition, encourage children to draw and label a range of circles.
- The *Year 6 Practice Book* provides additional practice, and moves children on to new terms such as chord, arc and segment. (Learn these if desired.)
- *100 Maths Lessons Year 6, Summer 2, Week 4, Lesson 2* focuses on symmetry, semicircles, sectors and segments.

Problems

- The textbook problems move children towards the relationships between circumference and diameter and area and radius.
- If appropriate, some children might investigate this further and move towards discovering the value of π (pi), as well as using algebraic expressions for calculating circumference and area.

Talk maths

You will need some string, a ruler, a compass and a pencil.

Working with a partner, find a selection of approximately ten circular objects. Using your equipment, find the radius, diameter and circumference for each one. Make sure you agree on each measurement before you add it to a table.

Object	Radius	Diameter	Circumference
10p	1.25cm	2.5cm	7.78cm
DVD	6cm	12cm	37.5cm
Bike wheel	25cm	50cm	157cm

Discuss the connection between the size of the circumference and the size of the diameter or the radius?

The string might help you measure the circumference.

Activities

1. Explain these terms.
   a. Radius   b. Diameter   c. Circumference
2. If a circle has a radius of 3.5m, what is its diameter?
3. A circular field has a diameter of 1.5km. What is its radius?

Problems

Brain-teaser
Aaron says that the circumference of any circle is just over five times its diameter.
Looking at this circle, would you say he is right?
Explain your answer

Brain-buster
Meena says that the area of any circle is approximately three times the radius squared, or 3r².
Looking at this circle, would you say she is right?
Explain your answer, using calculations if necessary.

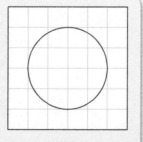

Geometry   77

100 Maths Lessons Year 6 links:

- Autumn 1, Week 5 (pages 32–36): draw and name parts of a circle
- Summer 2, Week 4 (pages 228–233): find relationships between parts of a circle

Year 6 Practice Book links:

- (page 110–111): Circles

Positive and negative coordinates

Prior learning

- Can use a 2D grid and coordinates in the first quadrant.
- Can reflect and translate shapes.

Learn

- Introduce the topic by drawing x- and y-axes with positive values only. Work with the children to plot a range of points, modelling correct practice and terminology. Remind them: along the hall and up the stairs for the correct order of x and y.

- Move on to draw a triangle and a square which is parallel to the axes. For the square, look at what the coordinates of the four corners have in common – they all share a coordinate with one other point.

- If appropriate, revise positive and negative numbers and number lines before introducing the children to a four-quadrant grid. Point out that the axes both work like the number lines they are already familiar with.

- Create a four-quadrant grid from −10 to +10 on both axes, and practise plotting a range of points in all four quadrants. Challenge the children to devise methods for knowing, just by looking at the coordinates, in which quadrant a point will be plotted.
- *100 Maths Lessons Year 6, Spring 1, Week 5, Lessons 1 and 2 provide structured guidance for teaching these concepts.*

Talk maths

- Working in pairs or groups, ideally provide children with a large four-quadrant grid that can be written on or wiped clean. (If this is not possible, rather than writing on an enlarged grid, ask them to challenge each other to place objects on the grid at different coordinates in all four quadrants.)
- If time permits, the children can play 'Animal Farm' in pairs. Each player has a four-quadrant grid on which they secretly mark

Curriculum objectives

- To describe positions on the full coordinate grid (all four quadrants).

Success criteria

- I can identify and plot coordinates in all four quadrants.

Positive and negative coordinates

Learn

We can plot points anywhere on a coordinate grid to make lines or to show the vertices of shapes.

The coordinates of B are (2, 6).

The triangle's coordinates are (3, 1), (5, 1) and (4, 3).

Remember: points on a grid are always shown with the x-coordinate first, and then the y-coordinate.

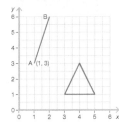

Grids can have negative axes too. They are just like number lines.

We say the coordinate grid has four **quadrants**.

Coordinates are positive and negative according to which quadrant they are in.

Remember, the point where the axes meet is called the origin. The coordinates of the origin are (0, 0).

Look at the points on the coordinate grids. Each one has its coordinates next to it. The coordinates of A are (3, 6).

The axes are like thermometers!

✓ Tips

- Each quadrant will always be positive or negative for x and y.
  1st quadrant: x and y positive
  2nd quadrant: x negative, y positive
  3rd quadrant: x and y negative
  4th quadrant: x positive, y negative
- Remember, for reading coordinates it's along first, then up.

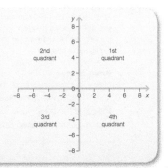

the positions of a range of farm animals: one dot (marked with a C) for a chicken, two dots next to each other for a sheep (marked with an S and joined with a line), and so on. Children must then take turns to find each others' animals by saying the coordinates for a point. Their partner has to tell them if they've found part of an animal or not.

Activities

- Note that 'Picture coordinates' in the *Year 6 Practice Book* provides an open-ended activity to increase children's familiarity with four-quadrant coordinates. It might be used prior to the textbook work, or as support.

- The textbook itself aims to provide practice while encouraging an appreciation of how to draw shapes on the coordinate grid. As such, these questions are easily adaptable, if desired, to cover new shapes in different parts of the grid.

Problems

- The problems are particularly tricky if children are not allowed to actually plot the points. Encourage more confident learners to discuss the problems and answer them verbally.

Talk maths

Draw a coordinate grid with four quadrants, with each axes going from –8 to +8, or use one of the grids on these pages. Working with a partner, challenge each other to identify points in particular quadrants.

Where is the point (–5, –8)?

Show me a point in the second quadrant. What are its coordinates?

Activities

1. **Copy the coordinates grid shown and accurately plot each point.**

   a. Write the coordinates of each point marked on the coordinate grid.

   b. What shape do they make?

   c. Write the coordinates of the centre of the shape.

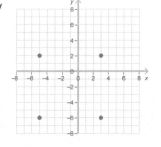

2. **Draw your own grid on squared paper.**

   a. mark these points on it.

   P (3, 5), Q (–1, 5), R (–4, –1), S (0, –1)

   b. What shape do they make?

Problems

Brain-teaser
What shape do these points make when joined together?
A (0, 6), B (–3, 4), C (0, –2), D (3, 4)

Brain-buster
A rectangle's centre is at the point (2, 1) and the coordinates of one vertex is at (7, 6).

Copy the chart and write the coordinates of the other three vertices and say which quadrant each is in.

	Quadrant	Coordinates
Vertex 1	1	(7, 6)
Vertex 2		
Vertex 3		
Vertex 4		

Geometry   79

100 Maths Lessons Year 6 links:

- Spring 1, Week 5 (pages 113–117): draw and label axes and place points in all four quadrants

Year 6 Practice Book links:

- (page 118): Picture coordinates

Reflecting and translating shapes

Prior learning

- Can use a four-quadrant grid.
- Can reflect and translate shapes.

Learn

- If possible, use a mirror to show how things change when reflected. (Displaying children's photographs next to a mirror and allowing them to look at both at once can help illustrate this.)

- Using a selection of capital letters on cards placed flat on a desktop and a mirror held vertically, demonstrate the differences between reflection and translation. For example, reflection reverses the letters but after a translation the letters are the same way round.

- Using a large four-quadrant grid (drawn or digital), work with the children to reflect and translate a selection of individual points. Start with reflection in the x- and y-axis. More confident learners could move on to reflection in any horizontal or vertical line.

- You may prefer to cover each concept separately: *100 Maths Lessons Year 6, Spring 1, Week 5, Lesson 3* covers reflection; *Lessons 4 and 5* cover translation.

- Using a new grid, move on to shapes, and examine with the children how shapes change when reflected and translated, and the rules for each operation. (The Tips in the textbook explain more about the changes too.)

Talk maths

- The textbook activity can be adapted for outdoor use. Using chalk, create a large grid on a suitable flat surface, and ask a child to stand on a point on the grid. Challenge the other children to reflect and translate the child's position as appropriate.

Curriculum objectives

- To draw and translate simple shapes on the coordinate plane, and reflect them in the axes.

Success criteria

- I can reflect and translate shapes with positive and negative coordinates.

Reflecting and translating shapes

Learn

When we translate points, we say how much the x and y coordinates change.
For example, A (2, 1) to A' (8, 4)
x has increased by +6
and y has increased by +3.

When we reflect points, the line of reflection acts like a mirror, and the coordinates of the reflected points change.
For example, B (3, 6) to B' (3, 8)

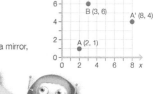

Why did only the y-coordinate change?

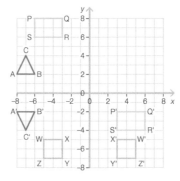

For four-quadrant grids, we can translate and reflect in the same way.

Rectangle PQRS has been **translated**. Each vertex of the rectangle moves by the same amount.
For P'Q'R'S', $x = +9$ $y = -10$

We can also reflect points and shapes in the x-axis and y-axis.

Notice how the triangle ABC has changed; it has been **reflected** in the x-axis.

WXYZ has been **reflected** in the y-axis. What has happened to each vertex of the square?

✓ Tips

- **Reflections**
  For reflections in the y-axis, only the x-coordinates change: they reverse their sign.
  For reflections in the x-axis, only the y-coordinates change: they reverse their sign.
- **Translations**
  We can write translations as, for example, $x - 8, y + 6$, or whatever the translation is.

  Remember, for shapes, every vertex will be translated by the same amount.

80   Geometry

- This activity is also a good way to show how shapes are reversed after reflection but not translation: challenge groups of three or four to arrange themselves with joined hands in a triangle or square, and then to reflect and translate the group's position. Can they do this without letting go of each other's hands? (Yes for translation. No for reflection.)

- The textbook refers to translated and reflected points by using a new form of notation: for example A translates to A^1. Although this is common in mathematics it may be a new concept for some children.

- Further practice at translating shapes can be provided with the advice in *100 Maths Lessons Year 6, Spring 1, Week 5, Lessons 4 and 5*.

- It may be beneficial to allow children to investigate the concepts beforehand using 'Translate and reflect' in the *Year 6 Practice Book*.

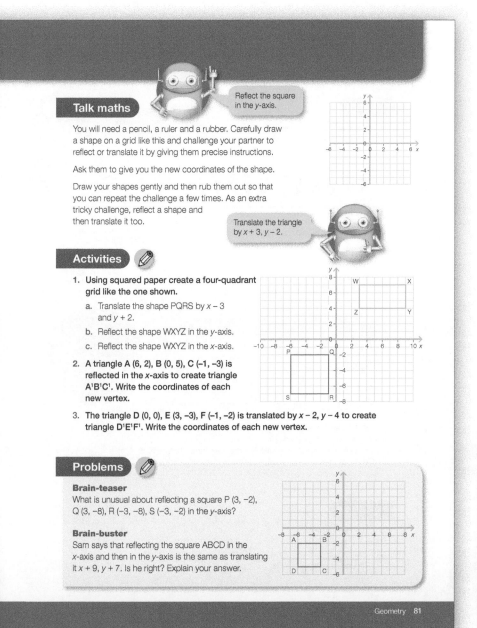

Talk maths

Reflect the square in the y-axis.

You will need a pencil, a ruler and a rubber. Carefully draw a shape on a grid like this and challenge your partner to reflect or translate it by giving them precise instructions.

Ask them to give you the new coordinates of the shape.

Draw your shapes gently and then rub them out so that you can repeat the challenge a few times. As an extra tricky challenge, reflect a shape and then translate it too.

Translate the triangle by $x + 3, y - 2$.

Activities

1. Using squared paper create a four-quadrant grid like the one shown.

   a. Translate the shape PQRS by $x - 3$ and $y + 2$.

   b. Reflect the shape WXYZ in the y-axis.

   c. Reflect the shape WXYZ in the x-axis.

2. A triangle A (6, 2), B (0, 5), C (–1, –3) is reflected in the x-axis to create triangle A^{1}B^{1}C^1. Write the coordinates of each new vertex.

3. The triangle D (0, 0), E (3, –3), F (–1, –2) is translated by $x - 2, y - 4$ to create triangle D^{1}E^{1}F^1. Write the coordinates of each new vertex.

Problems

Brain-teaser
What is unusual about reflecting a square P (3, –2), Q (3, –8), R (–3, –8), S (–3, –2) in the y-axis?

Brain-buster
Sam says that reflecting the square ABCD in the x-axis and then in the y-axis is the same as translating it $x + 9, y + 7$. Is he right? Explain your answer.

100 Maths Lessons Year 6 links:

- Spring 1, Week 5 (pages 113–117): reflect and translate shapes on coordinate axes

Year 6 Practice Book links:

- (page 119): Translate and reflect

Pie charts

Prior learning

- Can complete tables and bar charts from given information.
- Can solve problems using data presented in bar charts and tables.

Learn

- Discuss the different methods the children have encountered for representing data. Display and discuss samples of each type. (There is an interactive graphing tool on the CD-ROM for *100 Maths Lessons Year 6*.)
- Review the purpose behind representing data – it allows us to appreciate and understand quantities and 'phenomena' at a glance in a meaningful way, individually and in relation to each other.
- Spend time working with children to consider the relationships between the angles of different sectors of a circle and what fraction they are of a whole turn. Then look at the percentage equivalents of the fractions. (The Tips provide some key angles. Ideally, children will encounter the angles required to show $\frac{2}{10}$, $\frac{3}{10}$ and so on, while doing the

Talk maths activity.) Point out that to create a pie chart, the total number of whatever is being counted must be known. This is a difference between pie charts and bar charts, where the total does not have to be known.

- It is particularly important that children understand the proportional nature of pie charts – they show what fraction one aspect is of the whole. For example, if there are the same

number of boys and girls in a class, a pie chart would show that half the class were boys. However, just by looking at the pie chart, you would not be able to tell how many children were boys.

- *100 Maths Lessons Year 6, Autumn 2, Week 6* provides a comprehensive set of lessons and resources (including an interactive graphing tool on the CD-ROM) for teaching pie charts.

Curriculum objectives

- To interpret and construct pie charts and line graphs and use these to solve problems.

Success criteria

- I can interpret, construct and use pie charts.

Pie charts

Learn

We can represent information and data in different types of charts and graphs.

Different graphs are used for different situations and different types of data.

| Bar chart | Pictogram | Line graph | Pie chart |

Pie charts use fractions of circles to represent quantities. They are great for helping us to see proportions at a glance.

The pie chart below shows the different proportions of journeys to school made by all children in Britain.

Because a complete rotation is 360°, any fraction or percentage is shown as an angle, as a part of 360°.

Look at the same information in a chart.

Remember – a complete rotation has 360°

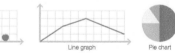

Transport	Walking	Car	Bike	Bus
Fraction	$\frac{1}{2}$	$\frac{1}{4}$	$\frac{1}{8}$	$\frac{1}{8}$
Percentage	50%	25%	12.5%	12.5%
Angle on pie chart	180°	90°	45°	45°

Although this pie chart doesn't show us the actual number of journeys, we can still work these out. If the total number of journeys to school each day in Britain was 10 million, we can use the pie chart to calculate numbers for each of the journey types. For example, 5 million children must walk, because 5 million is half of 10 million.

✓ Tips

- To understand pie charts you need to convert angles, fractions and percentages. Try to learn the main ones.

Angle	3.6°	18°	36°	45°	90°	180°	360°
Fraction	$\frac{1}{100}$	$\frac{1}{20}$	$\frac{1}{10}$	$\frac{1}{8}$	$\frac{1}{4}$	$\frac{1}{2}$	$\frac{1}{1}$
Percentage	1%	5%	10%	12.5%	25%	50%	100%

Talk maths

- The textbook activity can be developed further by introducing children to their 36-times tables. Although it is unrealistic to expect children to learn this by heart, recognising the key numbers for tenths of 360° will develop their abilities in interpreting pie charts.

Activities

- The questions in the textbook provide practice in interpreting and drawing pie charts. Note that the second question is considerably trickier, requiring children to total the amount of money the family have (£3.60), meaning that each penny represents one degree.

- *100 Maths Lessons Year 6, Summer 2, Week 6, Lessons 2 and 3* provide more supportive activities.

Problems

- If the problems prove too difficult, the *Year 6 Practice Book* provides closed and open activities for developing children's experience with pie charts.

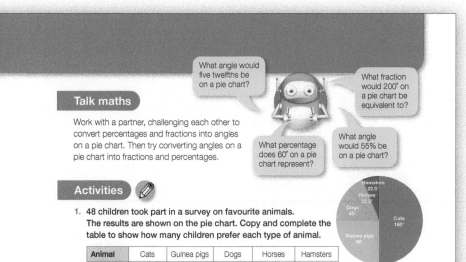

Talk maths

Work with a partner, challenging each other to convert percentages and fractions into angles on a pie chart. Then try converting angles on a pie chart into fractions and percentages.

What angle would five twelfths be on a pie chart?

What fraction would 200° on a pie chart be equivalent to?

What percentage does 60° on a pie chart represent?

What angle would 55% be on a pie chart?

Activities

1. 48 children took part in a survey on favourite animals. The results are shown on the pie chart. Copy and complete the table to show how many children prefer each type of animal.

Animal	Cats	Guinea pigs	Dogs	Horses	Hamsters
Angle	180°	90°	45°	22.5°	22.5°
Children					

2. You will need a protractor to do this activity.
A family of five are on holiday. They need to catch a taxi and they only have loose change in their pockets. Draw a pie chart to show the proportion each person contributes to the total amount.

Mum	Dad	Paul	Lizzie	Mary
£1.80	5p	45p	£1.20	10p

Problems

The pie chart shows the population of the world by continent.

■ Asia
■ Europe
■ North America
■ South America
■ Oceania
■ Africa

Brain-teaser
Without measuring, can you estimate the angle for Europe in the pie chart?

Brain-buster
Copy and complete the chart below. If the population of the world is 7 billion, estimate the population of each continent, to the nearest tenth of a billion.

Asia	Africa	Europe	Oceania	North America	South America
4.2 billion					

Statistics 83

100 Maths Lessons Year 6 links:

- Autumn 2, Week 6 (pages 77–81): read, interpret and construct pie charts
- Spring 2, Week 6 (pages 157–161): construct own pie charts and then interpret them
- Summer 2, Week 6 (pages 239–243): construct own pie charts to fractions and percentages

Year 6 Practice Book links:

- (page 120): Winning teams' pie chart
- (page 121): My day

Line graphs

Prior learning

- Can complete tables and bar charts from given information.
- Interpret and construct simple line graphs.

Learn

- Using *100 Maths Lessons Year 6, Spring 2, Week 6, Lessons 2 and 3*, work with the children to understand the basic elements of a simple distance–time graph (lesson 2) and a currency conversion graph (lesson 3). Use the interactive graphing tool on the CD-ROM to demonstrate each one.

- Use the line graph at the top of page 84 in the textbook to consider what the variations in the line in the distance–time graph show. In particular, what do the horizontal sections show was happening during the cycle ride? If the children can appreciate that this shows that the cyclist wasn't moving (because the distance they travelled didn't change), it will enhance their understanding of these graphs.

- Similarly, use the chart for converting pounds to dollars to practise accurate reading of a line graph.

- Ideally, recreate both graphs by using the interactive graphing tool on the CD-ROM accompanying *100 Maths Lessons Year 6*.

Curriculum objectives

- To interpret and construct pie charts and line graphs and use these to solve problems.

Success criteria

- I can interpret, construct and use line graphs.

Line graphs

Learn

Line graphs are useful for showing how things change over time, such as temperature, growth and speed. Normally time is shown along the horizontal *x*-axis.

Remember, to read a graph, you go along the *x*-axis and up the *y*-axis.

This graph shows the time taken for an 8km cycle ride.

Line graph for a bike ride

A flat line shows that the cyclist has stopped

The steeper the line, the faster the journey

Find these bits of information on the graph.

- The journey starts at 1pm.
- After 20 minutes the cyclist stops for five minutes.
- The cyclist travels fastest from 25 minutes to 40 minutes.
- The cyclist stops again after 40 minutes.
- The journey finishes at 8km.

Look carefully at the scale on each axis.

Line graphs can also be used for converting similar quantities that have different units, such as temperatures, distances and currencies.

This graph can be used for converting US dollars to pounds.

The direction of the line is affected by how many dollars there are for every pound. In this graph

£1 = $1.5   £5 = $7.5 $9 = £6   £10 = $15

How many pounds would you get for $9?

How many dollars would you get for £5?

✓ Tips

- Use a pencil and a ruler for accurate conversions. Remember that you need to read graphs carefully – use a ruler to help you read horizontal and vertical coordinates.

- If possible, display a range of 'conversion' line graphs, either digital or on paper. The most frequently encountered graphs are temperature (Celsius to Fahrenheit), distance (miles to kilometres) and currency. Displaying currency conversion rates for the British pound against a range of currencies will help illustrate how the rates affect the slope of the line, and the implications for conversion.

Activities

- Encourage the children to work very methodically in reading the graph. It may be helpful for them to copy the graph at a larger scale on squared paper.

- Note that the final question will potentially be too difficult for most children at this stage. The children are not required to know that speed equals distance divided by time, although some will be able to deduce this from the graph and/or from hearing that the units of speed can be kilometres per hour.

- *100 Maths Lessons Year 6, Summer 2, Week 6, Lesson 1* provides further support activities.

Problems

- The problems involve temperature conversion. If children find this too challenging, 'Converting miles to kilometres and vice versa' in the *Year 6 Practice Book* helps children to draw a line graph for converting between miles and kilometres. In addition, further support might be provided by returning to the currency conversion graph.

- In covering conversion line graphs, links to algebra can be made: all straight lines have a simple equation of the form $y = mx + c$, where c is the intersection of the line with the y-axis and m is the gradient (steepness) of the line.

Talk maths

Practise converting miles to kilometres, and kilometres to miles, using this line graph.

How many kilometres are there in 2 miles? How many miles are there in 5 kilometres? Can you use the graph to work out larger distances?

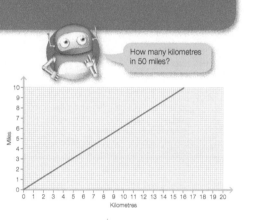

How many kilometres in 50 miles?

Activities

1. **The line graph shows the distance travelled on a charity walk.**

    a. Why is the line horizontal from 11am to 11.30am, and from 2pm to 3pm?

    b. How far did the walkers travel from 3pm to 5pm?

    c. The fastest part of the journey was from 9am to 11am. At what speed were the walkers travelling then?

    d. Another group of walkers started walking at 12 noon and walked at a constant speed and arrived at the end at exactly the same time as the other group. Draw their journey on a graph with a dotted line.

    e. What was the speed of the second set of walkers?

Problems

This is the formula for converting temperatures from Fahrenheit to Celsius: $C = \frac{5}{9} \times (F - 32)$ It can be used to create a line graph.

Draw a line graph on squared paper and then use it to solve these problems.

Brain-teaser
Water boils at 100°C. What is that in degrees Fahrenheit?

Brain-buster
Where does the line cross the y-axis? Where does the line cross the x-axis?

---

100 Maths Lessons Year 6 links:

- Spring 2, Week 6 (pages 157–161): construct and interpret line graphs

- Summer 2, Week 6 (pages 239–243): construct a line graph from given data

Year 6 Practice Book links:

- (page 103): Converting miles to kilometres and vice versa

- (page 122): Interpret a line graph

- (page 123): Construct a line graph

Averages

Prior learning

- Can solve problems involving mixed operations.
- Can interpret data shown in tables, bar charts, line graphs and pie charts.

Learn

- Review children's understanding of tables, bar charts, pictograms and tally charts. Remind the children that pie charts are different, where the sectors represent fractions of the whole.
- Using the bar chart in the textbook, and ideally some others (there is a graphing tool on the CD-ROM accompanying *100 Maths Lessons Year 6*), consider how the scale on the *y*-axis is important in representing and understanding the data being considered.
- The textbook provides definitions and examples for mean.
- Try to provide several differing scenarios, pointing out techniques for finding them as in the Tips section.

Curriculum objectives

- To calculate and interpret the mean as an average.

Success criteria

- I can calculate and interpret the mean of a data set.

Averages

Learn

We can collect data and represent it in tables, charts and graphs.

For example, this bar chart shows the number of vegetarian school lunches eaten each day for a week.
We call this collection of information a data set.

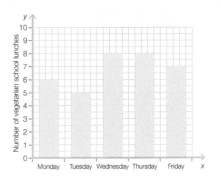

A mean is the average of the data set.

To find the mean, add together all of the numbers and then divide it by how many numbers there are.

Day	Monday	Tuesday	Wednesday	Thursday	Friday
Vegetarian lunches	6	5	8	8	7

Using the above definitions, we can find out the mean for this data set.
Mean = (6 + 5 + 8 + 8 + 7) ÷ 5
= 34 ÷ 5 = 6.8

We can say, on average, 6.8 vegetarian lunches are eaten each day.

✓ Tips

- Remember, the mean average is not always a whole number.
- Mean averages are useful for comparing things. For example, the number of people going on holiday in the summer, is higher than at other times. The mean average for holidays in a year would be very different to just the summer months.

Talk maths

- To support the textbook activity, provide the meaning and an example of a mean.
- If desired, move on to more complicated data sets and challenge the children to continue analysing these mentally and discuss their calculations accordingly.

Activities

- Both questions should be straightforward for most children. *100 Maths Lessons Year 6, Summer 2, Week 6, Lessons 4 and 5* and the *Year 6 Practice Book* provide further support in calculating various averages.
- If children require an extension, they could think about real-life uses of when they might need to find the mean.

Problems

- Both problems should be accessible to most of the children. Encourage children to take their learning further by researching or generating further data sets (school populations present lots of opportunities), perhaps tabulating and graphing them.

Talk maths

With a partner, discuss what the mean of this set of data will be.

Practise with different data sets. Roll a dice four or five times to generate a new set of numbers.

Can you find all of these without using a pencil and paper?

Activities

1. Seven children were asked how many pieces of fruit they eat each week. The results are shown here. Find the mean using the data. Show your working out.

   14 4 12
   12 6 8
   12 0

2. A park-keeper counts the number of flowers in each flowerbed.

Flowerbed 1	Flowerbed 2	Flowerbed 3	Flowerbed 4	Flowerbed 5	Flowerbed 6
23	25	20	23	26	28

   a. Find the total number of flowers in the park.
   b. Find the mean number of flowers per flowerbed.

Problems

Brain-teaser
Just before the summer holidays, ten Year 6 children each estimate (to the nearest five) how many books they have read in their time in the Juniors. Calculate the mean.

Aaron	Fahad	Beth	Jin	Eva	Scarlett	Mason	Sam	Jayden	Zac
45	50	75	35	50	90	40	50	45	80

Brain-buster
Gemma is reading a novel and wants to estimate how many words she has read. She counts the words on six different pages: 274 286 259 262 294 272

What is the average number of words per page?

If the book is 386 pages long, and 20 of the pages are only half full (because they start or end a chapter), estimate how many words in total are in the book.

Statistics 87

100 Maths Lessons Year 6 links:

- Summer 2, Week 6 (pages 239–243): calculate and interpret the mean of a set of data; write problems involving the mean

Year 6 Practice Book links:

- (page 124): Mean rainfall
- (page 125): Mean temperatures

Answers Year 5

NUMBER AND PLACE VALUE

Page 7

1   thirty-four thousand, eight hundred and five

2   237,120

3   forty thousand or four ten thousands

4   7; 12; 725; 25,612; 50,000; 225,421; 899,372; 1,000,000

5   3521 < 5630   15,204 > 9798   833,521 > 795,732

Brain-teaser: Winchcomb City
Brain-buster: Winchcomb City, Fintan United, Forest Rovers

Page 9

1   124; 224; 324; 424; 524; 624; 724

2   12,906; 11,906; 10,906; 9906; 8906; 7906; 6906

3   320,435; 420,435; 520,435; 620,435; 720,435; 820,435

4   243,000; 233,000; 223,000; 213,000; 203,000; 193,000; 183,000

Brain-teaser: 13 months
Brain-buster: 73,456

Page 11

1   a. 0   b. 0   c. −9   d. −4

2   −6, −4, −2, 0, 2, 4, 6

3   a. +   b. +   c. +   d. −

4   a. 4   b. 3   c. 9   d. 2

Brain-teaser: −2°C
Brain-buster: 36°C

Page 13

	nearest 10	nearest 100	nearest 1000	nearest 10,000	nearest 100,000
67	70	100	0	0	0
145	150	100	0	0	0
3320	3320	3300	3000	0	0
78,249	78,250	78,200	78,000	80,000	100,000
381,082	381,080	381,100	381,000	380,000	400,000
555, 555	555,560	555,600	556,000	560,000	600,000

Brain-teaser: 50,000
Brain-buster: Loss on a bad match: £46,000; Gain on a good match: £54,000

Page 14

1   a. 8   b. 22   c. 300   d. 95   e. 104   f. 140   g. 610
    h. 900

2   a. XXIII   b. XLI   c. LV   d. XCIII   e. CXII   f. CLX
    g. CCXII   h. CMLXV

Brain-buster:
Date the Romans left: CDX
Time spent in Britain: CDLXV

CALCULATIONS

Page 15

1   a. 96   b. 226   c. 5276   d. 9954   e. 130,320

2   a. 34   b. 95   c. 246   d. 1500   e. 265,675

Brain-teaser: 273
Brain-buster: £1097

Page 17

1   a. 3244   b. 12,309   c. 70,180   d. 621,229

2   a. 5966   b. 69,636   c. 213,925   d. 658,930

Brain-teaser: Yes
Brain-buster: No

Page 19

1   a. 139   b. 4163   c. 189,419

2   a. 119   b. 2273   c. 3968   d. 3861   e. 116,923

Brain-teaser: Bim and Bom
Brain-buster: 212,980

Page 21

1   1, 2, 3, 6

2   4, 8, 12, 16, 20, and so on.

3   a. 1 × 15 and 3 × 5
    b. 1 × 27 and 3 × 9
    c. 1 × 24, 2 × 12, 3 × 8 and 4 × 6
    d. 1 × 30, 2 × 15, 3 × 10 and 5 x 6

4   a. 1, 2 and 4   b. 1 and 5   c. 1, 2 and 4
    d. 1, 2, 5, 10, 25 and 50

Brain-teaser:

Children	1	2	3	4	6	8	12	24
Chocolates	24	12	8	6	4	3	2	1

Shared between 5 children there would be 4 chocolates left over.
Brain-buster: No, because 7 is not a factor of 365,
52 × 7 = 364

Page 23

1   A number that can only be divided by itself and 1.

2   2, 3, 5, 7, 11, 13, 17, 19

3   a. 25 is not a prime because 5 is a factor
    b. 71 is a prime because it can only be divided by itself and 1
    c. 87 is not a prime because 3 and 29 are factors

4   Many possible answers, such as 101, 103, 107, 109, 113

Brain-teaser: No, because it can be divided by 7 and 11.
Brain-buster: 27 is not a prime number because it can be divided by 3 and 9.

Page 25

1   a. 273   b. 552   c. 1395   d. 3528

2   a. 315   b. 832   c. 795   d. 1320

Brain-teaser: £6.45
Brain-buster: Yes, because 475 × £13 = £6175

Page 27

1   **a.** 19   **b.** 11 r2   **c.** 46 r4   **d.** 32 r2

2   **a.** 14   **b.** 25   **c.** 65 r2   **d.** 21 r3

Brain-teaser: 12 times
Brain-buster: 11 pieces per child. Teacher has 15 pieces.

Page 28

1   **a.** 200   **b.** 960   **c.** 8888   **d.** 30,000   **e.** 14,350

2   **a.** 50   **b.** 43   **c.** 1001   **d.** 902   **e.** 404

Brain-buster: £2050 each

Page 29

1	2	3	4	5	6	7	8	9	10
1^2	2^2	3^2	4^2	5^2	6^2	7^2	8^2	9^2	10^2
1×1	2×2	3×3	4×4	5×5	6×6	7×7	8×8	9×9	10×10
1	4	9	16	25	36	49	64	81	100
1^3	2^3	3^3	4^3	5^3	6^3	7^3	8^3	9^3	10^3
1×1 ×1	2×2 ×2	3×3 ×3	4×4 ×4	5×5 ×5	6×6 ×6	7×7 ×7	8×8 ×8	9×9 ×9	10×10 ×10
1	8	27	64	125	216	343	512	729	1000

Brain-teaser: 25 goals
Brain-buster: 9 × 9 × 9 = 729 apples

Page 31

	×10	×100	×1000
	3	30	300	3000
÷10	0.3	3	30	300
÷100	0.03	0.3	3	30
÷1000	0.003	0.03	0.3	3

	×10	×100	×1000
	27	270	2700	27000
÷10	2.7	27	270	2700
÷100	0.27	2.7	27	270
÷1000	0.027	0.27	2.7	27

	×10	×100	×1000
	48	480	4800	48000
÷10	4.8	48	480	4800
÷100	0.48	4.8	48	480
÷1000	0.048	0.48	4.8	48

	×10	×100	×1000
	317	3170	31700	317000
÷10	31.7	317	3170	31700
÷100	3.17	31.7	317	3170
÷1000	0.317	3.17	31.7	317

Brain-teaser: 32,000 feet
Brain-buster: 1.356kg

Page 33

1   **a.** 3 cakes   **b.** 5 adults   **c.** 22 animals   **d.** 75 children

2   Children's drawing of a rectangle 3 squares wide and 2 squares deep and 5 squares wide and 1.5 squares deep

3

Item	Room	Table	Chair	Cupboard	Basket
Real height	280cm	90cm	40cm	170cm	25cm
Model height	14cm	4.5cm	2cm	8.5cm	1.25cm

Brain-teaser: 3600 beats in an hour; 86,400 beats in a day
Brain-buster: Model scale: $\frac{1}{15}$

Page 35

1   **a.** 9   **b.** 12   **c.** 6   **d.** 0

2   **a.** correct   **b.** wrong (8)   **c.** correct   **d.** wrong (9)
   e. correct   **f.** wrong (5)

3   **a.** ÷   **b.** ÷ and −

Brain-teaser: £3.10
Brain-buster: £4.30

FRACTIONS, DECIMALS AND PERCENTAGES

Page 37

1   **a.** $\frac{4}{8}$ **b.** $\frac{2}{8}$ **c.** $\frac{6}{8}$ **d.** $\frac{8}{8}$

2   **a.** $\frac{6}{12}$ **b.** $\frac{3}{12}$ **c.** $\frac{8}{12}$ **d.** $\frac{10}{12}$

3   **a.** True   **b.** False   **c.** True   **d.** True   **e.** True   **f.** False
   g. True   **h.** False   **i.** False   **j.** True   **k.** True   **l.** False

4   **a.** $\frac{1}{10}, \frac{1}{6}, \frac{1}{5}, \frac{1}{4}, \frac{1}{3}, \frac{1}{2}$ **b.** $\frac{3}{5}, \frac{5}{8}, \frac{3}{4}$ **c.** $\frac{4}{7}, \frac{2}{3}, \frac{7}{9}$

Brain-teaser: $\frac{2}{5}$
Brain-buster: neutral ($\frac{5}{21}$) < red ($\frac{7}{21}$) < blue ($\frac{9}{21}$) **or**
neutral ($\frac{5}{21}$) < red ($\frac{1}{3}$) < blue ($\frac{3}{7}$)

Page 39

1   **a.** $\frac{7}{2}$ **b.** $\frac{9}{4}$ **c.** $\frac{21}{5}$ **d.** $\frac{4}{3}$ **e.** $\frac{8}{3}$ **f.** $\frac{11}{4}$ **g.** $\frac{19}{5}$ **h.** $\frac{17}{2}$

2   **a.** $1\frac{1}{2}$ **b.** $1\frac{1}{3}$ **c.** $1\frac{1}{4}$ **d.** $1\frac{1}{5}$ **e.** $3\frac{2}{3}$ **f.** $1\frac{3}{4}$ **g.** $7\frac{1}{2}$ **h.** $2\frac{3}{5}$

3   **a.** $\frac{3}{2} < 2\frac{1}{2}$ **b.** $\frac{4}{3} = 1\frac{1}{3}$ **c.** $\frac{7}{4} > 1\frac{1}{4}$ **d.** $\frac{13}{2} < 7\frac{1}{2}$
   e. $6\frac{1}{4} = \frac{25}{4}$ **f.** $3\frac{1}{2} < \frac{8}{2}$ **g.** $\frac{10}{3} > 2\frac{2}{3}$ **h.** $3\frac{1}{5} > \frac{12}{5}$

Brain-teaser: Ali
Brain-buster: $\frac{3}{4}$ a pizza

Page 41

1   **a.** $\frac{3}{5}$ **b.** $\frac{5}{7}$ **c.** $\frac{4}{4}$ or 1   **d.** $1\frac{1}{5}$ or $\frac{6}{5}$

2   **a.** $\frac{1}{6}$ **b.** $\frac{3}{8}$ **c.** $\frac{2}{4} = \frac{1}{2}$ **d.** $\frac{6}{20} = \frac{3}{10}$

3   **a.** $\frac{3}{4}$ **b.** $\frac{5}{8}$ **c.** $\frac{3}{6} = \frac{1}{2}$ **d.** $\frac{9}{10}$

4   **a.** $\frac{1}{4}$ **b.** $\frac{3}{8}$ **c.** $\frac{1}{6}$ **d.** $\frac{3}{10}$

Brain-teaser: $\frac{3}{6}$ or $\frac{1}{2}$ a pizza
Brain-buster: $\frac{5}{12}$

Page 43

1   **a.** 5   **b.** 2   **c.** 6   **d.** 10

2   **a.** $2\frac{1}{2}$ or $2\frac{2}{4}$ **b.** $1\frac{1}{2}$ **c.** $1\frac{5}{7}$ **d.** $3\frac{1}{3}$

3   **a.** 7   **b.** $4\frac{1}{2}$ **c.** $10\frac{5}{6}$ **d.** $26\frac{2}{3}$

Brain-teaser: $19\frac{1}{2}$ logs
Brain-buster: 8 laps

Page 45

1   **a.**

Fraction	$\frac{1}{10}$	$\frac{2}{10}$	$\frac{3}{10}$	$\frac{4}{10}$	$\frac{5}{10}$	$\frac{6}{10}$	$\frac{7}{10}$	$\frac{8}{10}$	$\frac{9}{10}$	$\frac{10}{10}$
Decimal	0.1	0.2	0.3	0.4	0.5	0.6	0.7	0.8	0.9	1.0

b.

Fraction	$\frac{1}{5}$	$\frac{2}{5}$	$\frac{3}{5}$	$\frac{4}{5}$	$\frac{5}{5}$
Decimal	0.2	0.4	0.6	0.8	1 or 1.0

2   **a.** 0.5   **b.** 0.75   **c.** 0.1

3   **a.** $\frac{1}{4}$ **b.** $\frac{7}{10}$ **c.** $\frac{4}{10}$ or $\frac{2}{5}$

Brain-teaser: $\frac{3}{4}$
Brain-buster: No, one quarter = 0.25

Fraction name	Decimal Fraction	Decimal	Decimal name
five tenths	$\frac{5}{10}$	0.5	zero point five
twenty-three hundredths	$\frac{23}{100}$	0.23	zero point two three
Three tenths	$\frac{3}{10}$	0.3	zero point three
Eighty-six hundredths	$\frac{86}{100}$	0.86	zero point eight six
Five hundred and seven thousandths	$\frac{507}{1000}$	0.507	zero point five zero seven
Eight tenths	$\frac{8}{10}$	0.8	zero point eight
One hundred and thirty-two thousandths	$\frac{132}{1000}$	0.132	zero point one three two
Thirty-nine hundredths	$\frac{39}{100}$	0.39	zero point three nine
One hundred and four thousandths	$\frac{104}{1000}$	0.104	zero point one zero four

Brain-teaser: $\frac{87}{100}$, 0.87

Brain-buster: $\frac{765}{1000}$, 0.765

Page 49

1. **a.** 0.465   **b.** 0.204

2. **a.** 0.6   **b.** 0.12   **c.** 0.325

3. **a.** zero point three nine five   **b.** zero point six zero two
    c. zero point zero zero five

4. **a.** 0.002, 0.084, 0.146, 0.327, 0.5, 0.75, 0.807, 0.999
    b. Check numbers are positioned correctly on the number line.

Brain-teaser: Bugs B and C
Brain-buster: Bug C: 0.009cm, Bug B: 0.029cm, Bug D: 0.031cm, Bug A: 0.101cm

Page 51

1. **a.** 1   **b.** 2   **c.** 5   **d.** 0   **e.** 1   **f.** 7   **g.** 12   **h.** 7

2. **a.** 0.8   **b.** 0.8   **c.** 0.5   **d.** 0.8   **e.** 5.6   **f.** 4.1
    g. 12.8   **h.** 7.0

3. Rounding decimals makes it easier to calculate amounts, but the answers will not be accurate.

Brain-teaser:

Day	Monday	Tuesday	Wednesday	Thursday	Friday	Saturday
Money	£52.14	£45.61	£60.13	£46.50	£72.24	£35.51
Rounded	£52	£46	£60	£47	£72	£36

Brain-buster: More, because he rounds up more than he rounds down (rounded to £313; exact amount £312.13).

Page 53

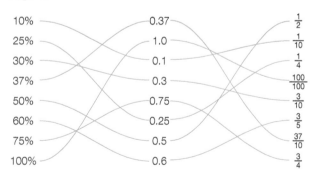

Brain-teaser: 15 have dinners, 10% have sandwiches
Brain-buster: 12 children go home for lunch. This is 40% of the class.

MEASUREMENT

Page 55

1. **a.**

mm	cm
10	1
25	2.5
52	5.2
100	10
300	30
170	17
60	6
2	0.2

b.

cm	m
100	1
35	0.35
450	4.5
1000	10
8000	80
900	9
90	0.9
27	0.27

c.

m	km
1000	1
250	0.25
5350	5.35
10,000	10
6000	6
4500	4.5
1350	1.35
4	0.004

2.

Imperial	Metric
1 inch	2.54cm
5 inches	12.7cm

Imperial	Metric
10 inches	25.4cm
1 mile	1.61km

Imperial	metric
100 miles	161km
300 miles	483km

Brain-teaser: 4.8m
Brain-buster: 5.35km

Page 57

1. **a.** 10cm   **b.** 8cm   **c.** 12cm

2. **a.** 24cm   **b.** 24cm

3.

shape	formula	length	width	perimeter
rectangle	$P = 2(l + w)$	6mm	3mm	18mm
square	$P = 4s$	2.5mm	2.5mm	10mm (1cm)

4. **a.** w = 1cm   **b.** w = 8m

Brain-teaser: 3m
Brain-buster: 7m

Page 59

1. **a.** approx 15cm^2 **b.** approx 8cm^2 **c.** approx 13cm^2

2. **a.** 108cm^2 **b.** 49m^2 **c.** 300m^2

3. **a.** a rectangle, length 5cm and width 1cm
    b. a square of side 5cm
    c. a square of side 6m
    d. a rectangle, length 17km and width 9km

Brain-teaser: 14m^2
Brain-buster: 81,000 potatoes

Page 61

1.

object	grams	kilograms
child	50,000g	50kg
dog	12,000g	12kg
pencil	75g	0.075kg
book	408g	0.408kg

2.

object	millilitres	litres
teapot	1250ml	1.25l
sink	8500ml	8.5l
mug	125ml	0.125l
thimble	12ml	0.012l

3. 483g or 0.483kg

4. 137ml or 0.137l

5. 50.408kg or 50,408g

6. 1.262l or 1262ml

Brain-teaser: 20kg
Brain-buster: 851ml or 0.851l

Page 63

12-hour	midnight	2:10am	9:15am	noon	3:30pm	9pm	11:59pm
24-hour	00:00	02:10	09:15	12:00	15:30	21:00	23:59

2   **a.** 180 minutes **b.** 48 hours **c.** 84 days
      d. 1460 days (or +1 if leap year included)
      e. 1 hour 40 minutes **f.** 4 days 4 hours
      g. 3 hours 45 minutes **h.** 1 year 135 days

3   **a.** 11 hours and 55 minutes
      b. 4 days 12 hours and 41 minutes
      c. 9 days 2 hours and 58 minutes

Brain-teaser: 8:37am
Brain-buster: 604,800 seconds

Page 65

1

Pence	200p	135p	6325p	9p	10,903p
Pounds	£2	£1.35	£63.25	£0.09	£109.03

2

Pounds	£4	£2.56	£0.12	£82	£403.20
Pence	400p	256p	12p	8200p	40,320p

3   **a.** £7.77 **b.** £22.15 **c.** £1.70 **d.** £41.73 **e.** £6.70
      f. £70.40 **g.** £12.50 **h.** £7.70

Brain-teaser: £15.75
Brain-buster: £600

GEOMETRY

Page 67

1   **a.** 90° right-angle **b.** 130° obtuse angle **c.** 65° acute angle

2   **a.**   **b.**   **c.**

     right-angle   reflex angle   acute angle

Brain-teaser: Aaron can place his ruler alongside the line to decide if it is more or less than 180°. Over 180° is reflex, less than 180° is acute or obtuse. If he rests his pencil at right angles to his ruler this will give him a right angle. Angles less than this will be acute; more than this but less than 180° will be obtuse.
Brain-buster: Because the angles on a straight line add up to 180°.

Page 69

1   **a.**   **b.**   **c.**

     d.   **e.**

2   **a.** 90° **b.** 270° **c.** 360°

3   **a.** 270° **b.** 90° **c.** 360°

Brain-teaser: 3, 270°
Brain-buster: 180° clockwise or anticlockwise

Page 71

1   **a.** regular triangle **b.** regular hexagon
      c. irregular quadrilateral **d.** irregular pentagon

2   Because the sides are not all the same length.

3   **a.** square **b.** parallelogram **c.** kite **d.** rectangle
      e. trapezium **f.** rhombus

Brain-teaser: Both long sides should be labelled 6cm, both short sides should be labelled 4cm. All four angles should be labelled 90°.

Page 73

1

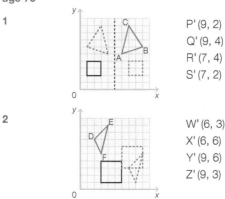

| triangular prism | cylinder | cube | cuboid |

2   **a.** sphere **b.** cube **c.** cone **d.** cylinder
      e. triangular prism **f.** cuboid

Brain-teaser: cuboid
Brain-buster: The cylinder would hold more water than the cone because it is the same width all the way along, but the cone gets narrower.

Page 75

1

P' (9, 2)
Q' (9, 4)
R' (7, 4)
S' (7, 2)

2

W' (6, 3)
X' (6, 6)
Y' (9, 6)
Z' (9, 3)

Brain-buster: If the mirror line is horizontal the point moves up or down, so the y-coordinate changes. If it is vertical they move left or right, so the x-coordinate changes. Find the distance the point is from the mirror line, then move the x or y coordinate by double the amount.

STATISTICS

Page 77

1   **a.**

     b. 3 weeks **c.** 8 weeks **d.** 6 weeks

Brain-teaser: Highest temperature: 18°C at 8am
Brain-buster: Find the difference between the highest and lowest temperatures: 16°C

Page 79

1   **a.** Earth **b.** Mars **c.** Mercury **d.** Earth and Mars

2   **a.** number 7 bus **b.** every half hour **c.** 3 minutes
      d. The train station could be further away than the supermarket, or the number 6 bus may have to wait at the train station for a set amount of time.

Brain-teaser: The number 7 at 10:15
Brain-buster: 14:45

Answers Year 6

NUMBER AND PLACE VALUE

Page 7

1. **a.** 350 **b.** 190 **c.** 3500 **d.** 1666
2. **a.** four hundred or 400 **b.** thirty thousand or 30,000
   c. four million or 4,000,000 **d.** six hundred thousand or 600,000

Brain-teaser: 1,000,001
Brain-buster: 9,999,999
Nine million, nine hundred and ninety-nine thousand, nine hundred and ninety-nine

Page 9

1. Eight hundred and forty-five thousand, two hundred and eighty-three
2. 604,190
3. Six hundred thousand or 600,000
4. 97,612 500,000 825,421 6,899,372 10,000,000
5. 3521 < 5630   15,204 > 9798   833,521 > 795,732

Brain-teaser: Madrid
Brain-buster: Paris, Rome, Madrid

Page 11

1. **a.** 5000 **b.** 23,000 **c.** 45,000 **d.** 79,000
2. **a.** 100,000 **b.** 500,000 **c.** 1,400,000 **d.** 8,000,000
3. **a.** 6,000,000 **b.** 1,000,000 **c.** 4,000,000 **d.** 10,000,000
4. **a.** 0; 100,000; 200,000; 300,000; 400,000; 500,000
   b. 370,000; 380,000; 390,000; 400,000; 410,000
   c. 7,500,000; 8,500,000; 9,500,000; 10,500,000; 11,500,000

Brain-teaser:

City	Rome	Paris	Madrid
Population	3,000,000	2,000,000	3,000,000

Brain-buster: 8,000,000. This is lower than the actual total because there has been more rounding down than rounding up.

Page 13

1. **a.** −2 **b.** −4 **c.** 3 **d.** 0
2. −20 −16 −12 −8 −4 0 4 8 12 16 20
3. **a.** − **b.** + **c.** − **d.** −
4. **a.** 14 **b.** 19 **c.** 7 **d.** −9

Brain-teaser: 8°C
Brain-buster: 69.4°C

CALCULATIONS

Page 15

1. **a.** 792 **b.** 5526 **c.** 479,369
2. **a.** 540 **b.** 117,450 **c.** 2355
3. **a.** 548,704 **b.** 962,825 **c.** 5,167,467
4. **a.** 79,740 **b.** 635,231 **c.** 2,482,597

Brain-teaser: 982,136
Brain-buster: 8,312,272

Page 17

1. **a.** 4800 **b.** 62,000 **c.** 1600 **d.** 50,000 **e.** 430,000
   f. 1,000,000
2. **a.** 2000 **b.** 25 **c.** 25,000 **d.** 90,000 **e.** 80,001
   f. 25,000
3. **a.** 27,072 **b.** 723

Brain-teaser: £160,000
Brain-buster: 3000 tickets

Page 19

1. **a.** 868 **b.** 7150 **c.** 13,770 **d.** 329,576
2. **a.** 8925 **b.** 38,010 **c.** 79,890 **d.** 567,840

Brain-teaser: 24,984
Brain-buster: £729,723

Page 21

1. **a.** 23 **b.** 24 r3 **c.** 434 r1 **d.** 313 r2
2. **a.** 12 r2 **b.** 64 r2 **c.** 460 r5 **d.** 1132 r4

Brain-teaser: 13 each with 2 stickers left over
Brain-buster: 1248 tickets
You can check your answer by multiplying the number of tickets by the ticket price.

Page 23

1. **a.** 13 r4 **b.** 23 **c.** 210 r14 **d.** 254 r8
2. **a.** 22 r8 **b.** 211 r7 **c.** 353 r4 **d.** 228 r22

Brain-teaser: 134 rows
Brain-buster: £2341.75

Page 25

1. **a.** 0 **b.** 6 **c.** 27
2. **a.** 2 **b.** 12 **c.** 5
3. **a.** correct **b.** correct **c.** incorrect (−7) **d.** correct
4. **a.** $8 \times (5 + 2) - 3 = 53$ **b.** $14 \div 7 + 2 \times (11 - 6) = 12$
   c. $64 - (12 + 5 \times 3) = 37$

Brain-teaser: Yes. $(34 + 17 + 43) \times 2 - 20 = 168$
Could also be expressed as $(34 \times 2) + (17 \times 2) + (43 \times 2) - 20 = 168$
Brain-buster: $12,000 \times 2 + (7000 - 2500) \times 3 = £37,500$
2 new cars and 3 second hand cars.

Page 27

1. 1, 2 and 4
2. 1, 2, 5 and 10
3. 15, 30, 45, 60, 75, 90, and so on.
4. $2 \times 5 \times 7 = 70$
5. 2, 3 and 5
6. 94: 2×47

Brain-teaser: 38 has prime factors, but it is not a prime number. Prime numbers only have themselves and 1 as factors.
Brain-buster: 6

FRACTIONS, DECIMALS AND PERCENTAGES

Page 29

1. **a.** 2 **b.** 3 **c.** 1 **d.** 20 **e.** 30 **f.** 11
2. **a.** True **b.** True **c.** False **d.** True
3. **a.** $\frac{3}{4}$ **b.** $\frac{3}{4}$ **c.** $\frac{3}{4}$ **d.** $\frac{3}{4}$ **e.** $\frac{9}{20}$ **f.** $\frac{5}{8}$ **g.** $\frac{32}{75}$ **h.** $\frac{8}{25}$

Brain-teaser: $\frac{8}{25}$
Brain-buster: $\frac{17}{25}$

Page 31

1. **a.** $\frac{15}{30}$ **b.** $\frac{20}{30}$ **c.** $\frac{18}{30}$ **d.** $\frac{25}{30}$
2. **a.** = **b.** > **c.** > **d.** <
3. **a.** True **b.** True **c.** False
4. **a.** $\frac{5}{8} < \frac{2}{3} < \frac{3}{4}$ **b.** $\frac{1}{3} < \frac{3}{7} < \frac{4}{9}$ **c.** $\frac{13}{24} < \frac{5}{9} < \frac{7}{12}$

Brain-teaser: $\frac{3}{8}$ ($\frac{3}{8} = \frac{15}{40}$ and $\frac{7}{20} = \frac{14}{40}$)

Brain-buster: cats ($\frac{21}{84}$) or $\frac{3}{12}$) < dogs ($\frac{24}{84}$ or $\frac{2}{7}$) < no pets ($\frac{39}{84}$ or $\frac{13}{28}$)

Page 33

1 **a.** $\frac{5}{6}$ **b.** $\frac{7}{10}$ **c.** $\frac{7}{8}$

2 **a.** $\frac{1}{8}$ **b.** $\frac{4}{9}$ **c.** $\frac{11}{60}$

3 **a.** + **b.** − **c.** + **d.** − **e.** − **f.** +

4 **a.** $4\frac{1}{4}$ **b.** $1\frac{1}{4}$ **c.** $1\frac{2}{15}$ **d.** $4\frac{7}{15}$

Brain-teaser: $\frac{1}{6}$

Brain-buster: $\frac{16}{77}$

Page 35

1 **a.** 10 **b.** 6 **c.** 18 **d.** 10 **e.** 25 **f.** 26

2 **a.** $3\frac{1}{2}$ **b.** $12\frac{1}{2}$ **c.** $13\frac{1}{3}$ **d.** 6 **e.** $7\frac{1}{5}$ **f.** $16\frac{2}{3}$

3 **a.** $\frac{1}{6}$ **b.** $\frac{6}{20}$ or $\frac{3}{10}$ **c.** $\frac{24}{72}$ or $\frac{1}{3}$ **d.** $\frac{20}{30}$ or $\frac{2}{3}$ **e.** $\frac{10}{24}$ or $\frac{5}{12}$
   f. $\frac{40}{35}$ or $1\frac{1}{7}$

Brain-teaser: $5\frac{1}{4}$ minutes (or 5 minutes 15 seconds)

Brain-buster: $\frac{1}{3600}$

Page 37

1 **a.** right **b.** right **c.** wrong **d.** right **e.** wrong **f.** right

2 **a.** $\frac{1}{4}$ **b.** $\frac{1}{12}$ **c.** $\frac{1}{15}$ **d.** $\frac{1}{6}$ **e.** $\frac{3}{16}$ **f.** $\frac{1}{30}$

Brain-teaser: $\frac{1}{14}$ of the whole cake

Brain-buster: $\frac{1}{80}$ of the sheet; 3 stickers per child.

Page 39

1 **a.** 0.4 **b.** 0.6 **c.** 0.375

2

Fraction	$\frac{1}{8}$	$\frac{2}{8}$	$\frac{3}{8}$	$\frac{4}{8}$	$\frac{5}{8}$	$\frac{6}{8}$	$\frac{7}{8}$	$\frac{8}{8}$
Decimal	0.125	0.25	0.375	0.5	0.625	0.75	0.875	1 or 1.0

3 $\frac{3}{4} = 0.75$, $\frac{5}{8} = 0.625$, $\frac{4}{5} = 0.8$, $\frac{1}{3} = 0.333$

4 $0.166 = \frac{1}{6}$, $0.4 = \frac{2}{5}$, $0.7 = \frac{7}{10}$, $0.125 = \frac{1}{8}$

Brain-teaser: $\frac{5}{6}$ (= 0.833)

Brain-buster: He is wrong. $\frac{1}{12} = 0.083$ and $\frac{1}{10} = 0.1$

Page 41

1 **a.** 0.375: 5 thousandths, 7 hundredths, 3 tenths
   b. 0.903: 3 thousandths, 0 hundredths, 9 tenths

2

Fraction	Decimal	3dps	2dps	1dps
$\frac{2}{7}$	0.285714	0.286	0.29	0.3
$\frac{3}{13}$	0.230769	0.231	0.23	0.2
$\frac{4}{11}$	0.363636	0.364	0.36	0.4
$\frac{2}{3}$	0.666666	0.667	0.67	0.7
$\frac{8}{9}$	0.888888	0.889	0.89	0.9

Brain-teaser: Jared is wrong. It would be rounded down to zero point zero.

Brain-teaser: It is a recurring number because 3 ÷ 11 is 0.272727. Rounded to 3dp it is 0.273.

Page 43

1 **a.** 0.6 **b.** 6.6 **c.** 0.92 **d.** 2.04
   e. 3.68 **f.** 13 **g.** 2.64 **h.** 1.14

2 **a.** 4.83 **b.** 6.75 **c.** 6.25 **d.** 109.89

Brain-teaser: £9.20
Brain-buster: £15.20

Page 44

1 **a.** 0.13 **b.** 0.27 **c.** 0.04

2 **a.** 0.04 **b.** 0.22 **c.** 0.15 **d.** 5.16

Brain-teaser: £3.48

Page 45

Percentage	Decimal	Fraction
33.3%	0.333	$\frac{1}{3}$
12.5%	0.125	$\frac{1}{8}$
40%	0.4	$\frac{2}{5}$
85%	0.85	$\frac{85}{100}$
87.5%	0.875	$\frac{7}{8}$

Brain-teaser: 40%

RATIO AND PROPORTION

Page 47

1 **a.** 4 in 9 or $\frac{4}{9}$ **b.** 1 in 2 or $\frac{1}{2}$ **c.** 1 in 5 or $\frac{1}{5}$

2 **a.** 1:2 **b.** 1:2 **c.** 3:4

Brain-teaser: **a.** 1 in 5 can speak two languages
b. dual to single = 1:4
Brain-buster: **a.** 20 blueberries
b. The proportion of blueberries will be 4 in 7

Page 49

1 **a.** 25% **b.** 70% **c.** 40% **d.** 37.5%

2 **a.** 1 in 4 **b.** 2 in 5 **c.** 13 in 50 **d.** 7 in 8

3 **a.** 50 **b.** 0.5 **c.** 62.4 **d.** 285 **e.** 14.4 **f.** 54

4 **a.** Percentage: parts out of 100
   b. Proportion: the fraction of an amount
   c. Ratio: the comparison of quantities

Brain-teaser: 55 cars
Brain-buster: 7,560,000 dogs

Page 51

1 **a.** 8cm **b.** 20cm **c.** 40cm

2

Scale	Side length	Area
5:1	5cm	25cm²
10:1	10cm	100cm²
25:1	25cm	625cm²

3 **a.** 50cm **b.** 20cm **c.** 5cm

Brain-teaser: 5.5m or 550cm
Brain-buster: 7.5:1 or 15:2

ALGEBRA

Page 53

1

Length	Width	P	A
5cm	2cm	14cm	10cm²
5m	4m	18m	20m²
7km	1.5km	17km	10.5km²
3.2m	2.3m	11m	7.36m²

2

h	11	14	20	35	308
i	1	2	4	9	100

Brain-teaser: $334
Brain-buster:

Fahrenheit	32°	104°	212°
Celsius	0°	40°	100°

Page 55

1   **a.** 8   **b.** 18   **c.** 25   **d.** –2   **e.** 6   **f.** 7   **g.** 4   **h.** 33

2   **a.** 62   **b.** 6   **c.** 10   **d.** –3

Brain-teaser: $n = £42.50 – (25 × £1.50)$
$n = £5$
Brain-buster: $n = (190.40 ÷ 2) ÷ 5.60$
$n = 17$ children

Page 57

1   **a.**

x	0	1	2	3	4	5	–1	–2	–3
y	2	3	4	5	6	7	1	0	–1

b.

s	0	2	5	6	7	8	9	10	–1
t	8	6	3	2	1	0	–1	–2	9

c.

q	0	1	1.5	2	5	10	100	–1	–10
p	–3	–1	0	1	7	17	197	–5	–23

Brain-teaser: **a.** 60   **b.** 85
Brain-buster: x = 6, y = 2 or x = 9, y = 7

MEASUREMENT

Page 59

1   **a.** 300 minutes   **b.** 7200 seconds
    c. $8\frac{1}{2}$ minutes or 8.5 minutes   **d.** 86,400 seconds

2   **a.** 23,000mm   **b.** 2400m   **c.** 100,000cm   **d.** 0.685m

3   **a.** 0.75kg   **b.** 32,500g   **c.** 0.001kg   **d.** 350g

4   **a.** 2500ml   **b.** 0.75l   **c.** 63.425l   **d.** 250ml

Brain-teaser: 242 metres 63 centimetres and 7 millimetres
Brain-buster: 31,622,400 seconds

Page 61

Brain-teaser: 18.75 seconds   0.79kg or 790g   233g
Brain-buster: Height = 1m 49.86cm Weight = 39.498kg
29,220 days   701,280 hours   42,076,800 minutes

Page 63

1   **a.** P = 13cm A = 9cm²   **b.** P = 6cm A = 2.25cm²

2   **a.** P = 50m A = 87.5m²   **b.** P = 24m A = 13.75m²

Brain-teaser: 15m²
Brain-buster: 180 tiles

Page 65

1   **a.** 10cm²   **b.** 17.5cm²   **c.** 22.5cm²

2   **a.** square   **b.** triangle   **c.** triangle

Brain-teaser: £511.98
Brain-buster: 7.875m²

Page 67

1   **a.** and **b.** Check that children's drawings are accurate.

2   **a.** 216cm³   **b.** 36m³   **c.** 1000m³   **d.** 90cm³
    e. 1728mm³   **f.** 9000mm³

3   1,000,000,000 (one billion)

Brain-teaser: 0.125m³, 125,000cm³
Brain-buster: 42m³

GEOMETRY

Page 69

1   **a.** right angle   **b.** acute angle   **c.** obtuse angle

2   **a.** 90°   **b.** 143°   **c.** 25°

Brain-teaser: All acute angles should be 55°;
all obtuse angles 125°
Brain-buster: Look for understanding that parallel lines have similar angles when intersected and that angles on a straight line add up to 180. The formula might be along the lines of $2a + 2b = 360°$

Page 71

1   A regular polygon has all sides and angles equal.

2   **a.** equilateral triangle – regular
    b. rhombus (quadrilateral) – irregular
    c. pentagon – irregular   **d.** square – regular
    e. hexagon – regular   **f.** heptagon – irregular

Brain-teaser: The distance from the centre to each corner is identical, and the four angles at the centre are all 90°.
Brain-buster: She is right. The angle at the centre must be 60° for each triangle, and the side lengths from the centre must be identical, therefore the other angles must also be 60°, and the other side an identical length.

Page 73

1   Check that all sides and angles are the same.

2   Check that angle is 120° and all sides are 3cm.

3   Construct an isosceles triangle with single angle = 360 ÷ 8 = 45°; repeat this 8 times, with the 45° angles forming a complete turn in the centre of the octagon.

Brain-teaser: 1440°
Brain-buster: a = (n × 180 – 360) ÷ n

Page 75

1   Check that all sides are connected by one tab.

2   Check that net would fold and glue correctly.

Brain-teaser: Check that instructions show understanding of faces joining and dimensions of sides being correct.
Brain-buster: **a.** 5cm × 5cm × 20cm   **b.** 150cm² wasted
c. 500cm³

Page 77

1   **a.** radius: the distance from the centre of a circle to the circumference
    b. diameter: the distance across the widest part of a circle, twice the radius
    c. circumference: the distance around the edge of a circle.

2   7m

3   0.75km or 750m

Brain-teaser: No. The circumference of a circle is in fact 3.14d, in this case = 12.56cm

Brain-buster: Yes. The area of a circle is in fact $3.14r^2$, which in this case = $12.56cm^2$

Page 79

1   **a.** A (3, 2), B (−5, 2), C (−5, −6), D (3, −6) **b.** Square
    c. (−1, −2)

2   **a.** P (3, 5), Q (−1, 5), R (−4, −1), S (0, −1) **b.** Parallelogram

Brain-teaser: A kite

Brain-buster: In no particular order, (−3, 6), 2nd quadrant; (−3, −4), 3rd quadrant; (7, −4), 4th quadrant.

Page 81

1   **a.** P¹ (−9, 0), Q¹ (−4, 0), R¹ (−4, −5), S¹ (−9, −5)
    b. W¹ (−3, 7), X¹ (−9, 7), Y¹ (−9, 4), Z¹ (−3, 4)
    c. W¹ (3, −7), X¹ (9, −7), Y¹ (9, −4), Z¹ (3, −4)

2   A¹ (6, −2), B¹ (0, −5), C¹ (−1, 3)

3   D¹ (−2, −4), E¹ (1, −7), F¹ (−3, −6)

Brain-teaser: The reflected square sits on top of the original square, with the coordinates for P and S swapped, and Q and R swapped.

Brain-buster: Sort of. The square will end up in the same place by reflection or translation, but the vertices will have changed positions.

STATISTICS

Page 83

1

Cats	Guinea pigs	Dogs	Horses	Hamsters
24	12	6	3	3

2   Use a protractor to check the angles on the pie chart.
    (1p = 1°)

Mum	Dad	Paul	Lizzie	Mary
180°	5°	45°	120°	10°

Brain-teaser: Around 40°

Brain-buster: Accept answers + or − 0.3 billion.

Asia	Africa	Europe	Oceania	North America	South America
4.2 billion	1.1 billion	0.6 billion	0.1 billion	0.6 billion	0.4 billion

Page 85

1   **a.** The walkers are not moving. **b.** 5km **c.** 7.5km/h
    d.

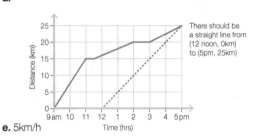

There should be a straight line from (12 noon, 0km) to (5pm, 25km)

    e. 5km/h

Brain-teaser: 212°F

Brain-buster: x-axis: 32°F, y-axis: −18°C (answers may not be exact due to the scale of the graph.)

Page 87

1   8

2   **a.** 145 **b.** 24.17

Brain-teaser: 56

Brain-buster: **a.** average = 274.5 words per page **b.** 103,212

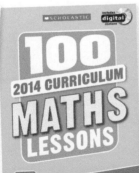